AQA MEDICINE & HEALTH THROUGH TIME

Ian Dawson
Dale Banham

DYNAMIC LEARNING

HODDER EDUCATION
AN HACHETTE UK COMPANY

The Schools History Project

Set up in 1972 to bring new life to history for students aged 13–16, the Schools History Project continues to play an innovatory role in secondary history education. From the start, SHP aimed to show how good history has an important contribution to make to the education of a young person. It does this by creating courses and materials which both respect the importance of up-to-date, well-researched history and provide enjoyable learning experiences for students.

Since 1978 the Project has been based at Trinity and All Saints University College Leeds. It continues to support, inspire and challenge teachers through the annual conference, regional courses and website: http://www.schoolshistoryproject.org.uk. The Project is also closely involved with government bodies and awarding bodies in the planning of courses for Key Stage 3, GCSE and A level.

Note: The wording and sentence structure of some written sources have been adapted and simplified to make them accessible to all students, while faithfully preserving the sense of the original.

Memory maps on pages 15 and 200 courtesy of Hannah Mitcheson.

Although every effort has been made to ensure that website addresses are correct at time of going to press, Hodder Education cannot be held responsible for the content of any website mentioned in this book. It is sometimes possible to find a relocated web page by typing in the address of the home page for a website in the URL window of your browser.

Hachette Livre UK's policy is to use papers that are natural, renewable and recyclable products and made from wood grown in sustainable forests. The logging and manufacturing processes are expected to conform to the environmental regulations of the country of origin.

Orders: please contact Bookpoint Ltd, 130 Milton Park, Abingdon, Oxon OX14 4SB. Telephone: (44) 01235 827720. Fax: (44) 01235 400454. Lines are open 9.00–5.00, Monday to Saturday, with a 24-hour message answering service. Visit our website at www.hoddereducation.co.uk

First published in 2009 by
Hodder Education,
An Hachette UK Company
338 Euston Road
London NW1 3BH

Impression number 5 4 3 2 1
Year 2013 2012 2011 2010 2009

Cover photo © Bettman/Corbis
Illustrations by Dylan Gibson, Ian Foulis, Barking Dog, Janek Matysiak, Pat Murray, Peter Lubach, Richard Duszczak, Steve Smith, Tony Randell
Typeset in Palatino Light by Ian Foulis and Mark Walker
Printed in Italy

A catalogue record for this title is available from the British Library

ISBN: 978 0340 98671 4

Contents

Acknowledgments

Photo credits

The Publishers would like to thank the following for permission to reproduce copyright illustrations:

p.18 akg-images/ullstein bild; **p.19** *t* Private Collection/Peter Newark American Pictures/The Bridgeman Art Library, *m* Wellcome Library, London, *b* Werner Forman Archive/Centennial Museum, Vancouver, British Columbia, Canada; **p.22** © Sandro Vannini/Corbis; **p.23** The Art Archive/Dagli Orti; **p.24** *b* The Art Archive/Graeco-Roman Museum, Alexandria/Nicholas J. Saunders; **p.30** The Art Archive/National Archaeological Museum Athens/Dagli Orti; **p.31** akg-images/Erich Lessing; **p.32** *l* Photograph: Rohrer, DAI Athen, Neg.D-DAI-ATH-Thera 110, *r* © The Trustees of the British Museum; **p.33** *t* © The Trustees of the British Museum, *b* The Art Archive/Museo Nazionale Romano Rome/Dagli Orti; **p.34** Wellcome Library, London; **p.35** Museo della Civilta Romana, Rome, Italy/Giraudon/The Bridgeman Art Library; **p.36** The Art Archive/Anagni Cathedral Italy/Dagli Orti (A); **p.37** © Peter Smith; **p.42** *l* © Chris Warren/Loop Images/Corbis, *r* The Oxford Archaeological Unit ltd; **p.43** *t* © English Heritage Photo Library, *b* © Canterbury City Council Museums; **p.55** *t* By permission of the British Library (MS Egerton, 1070, f53), *bl* Topfoto/AP, *br* Rischgitz/Hulton Archive/Getty Images; **p.56** *l* Bodleian Library MS Rawlings B124f 197v Oxford, *r* Hulton Archive/Getty Images; **p.57** *t* akg-images, *m* Musee Conde, Chantilly, France/The Bridgeman Art Library; **p.60** © geogphotos/Alamy; **p.66** Mary Evans Picture Library; **p.67** The Art Archive/Victoria and Albert Museum London/Eileen Tweedy; **p.69** The Art Archive/Bibliothèque Universitaire de Médecine, Montpellier/Dagli Orti; **p.70** *l* The Art Archive/University Library Prague/Dagli Orti, *r* The Art Archive/Bodleian Library Oxford/The Bodleian Library; **p.71** akg-images/British Library; **p.72** English Heritage Photo Library; **p.73** *l* The Art Archive/Bibliothèque Universitaire de Médecine, Montpellier/Dagli Orti, *r* Wellcome Library, London; **p.75** Trinity College, Cambridge, UK/The Bridgeman Art Library; **p.78** *l* Wellcome Library, London, *r* www.topfoto.co.uk; **p.79** *l* Fitzwilliam Museum, University of Cambridge, UK/The Bridgeman Art Library, *r* www.topfoto.co.uk; **p.86** Ann Ronan Picture Library/HIP/TopFoto; **p.88** Mary Evans Picture Library; **p.89** www.topfoto.co.uk; **p.90** *m* The Art Archive/Marc Charmet, *b* Wellcome Library, London; **p.92** The Art Archive/Musée des Beaux Arts Orléans/Dagli Orti (A); **p.93** Imagno/Getty Images; **p.94** *t* Wellcome Library, London, *b* © Charles Walker/TopFoto; **pp.95 & 96** Wellcome Library, London; **p.97** City of London/HIP/TopFoto; **p.108** Wellcome Library, London; **p.118** *l&r* Paul Nadar/Getty Images, *m* Hulton Archive/Getty Images; **p.119** *Ehrlich* Ann Ronan Picture Library/HIP/TopFoto, *Fleming, Florey & Chain* AP/Press Association, *Watson & Crick* © Bettmann/Corbis; **p.120** Wellcome Library, London; **p.121** Science Museum; **p.123** © Bettmann/Corbis; **pp.124 & 125** Hulton Archive/Getty Images; **p.126** *l* Chris Ware/Keystone Features/Getty Images, *r* © Bettmann/Corbis; **p.127** *t* World History Archive/TopFoto, *b* © Hulton-Deutsch Collection/Corbis; **p.130** *l* Warner Bros/DC Comics/The Kobal Collection, *r* Eric Draper/AP Photo/Press Association Images; **p.134** Kurt Hutton/Picture Post/Getty Images; **p.140** akg-images/British Library; **p.142** British Museum, London, UK/The Bridgeman Art Library; **p.143** *t* The Art Archive/Science Museum London/Eileen Tweedy, *b* Museum of London/HIP/TopFoto; **p.149** Hulton Archive/Getty Images; **p.151** *t* Wellcome Library, London, *b* The Granger Collection/TopFoto; **p.152** © Punch Limited/TopFoto; **p.153** HIP/TopFoto; **p.154** Rischgitz/Getty Images; **p.156** *tl* Courtesy of Newham Heritage and Archives Service, *tr* © Hulton-Deutsch Collection/Corbis, *bl* Science Museum, *br* © Mary Evans Picture Library/Alamy; **p.157** *t* Popperfoto/Getty Images, *b* © Bettmann/Corbis; **p.158** The Art Archive/Private Collection MD; **p.159** *l* Wellcome Library, London, *r* Topical Press Agency/Getty Images; **p.161** Mirrorpix; **p.162** Reg Speller/Fox Photos/Getty Images; **p.166** Royal College of Surgeons, London, UK/The Bridgeman Art Library; **p.169** *t & b* © Peter Smith; **p.171** Wellcome Library, London; **p.172** © Mary Evans Picture Library; **p.173** *r* © Hulton-Deutsch Collection/Corbis; **p.174** Hulton Archive/Getty Images; **p.180** *t* Imperial War Museum, *b* Popperfoto/Getty Images; **p.181** *t* Fritz Goro/Time Life Pictures/Getty Images, *b* © Corbis; **p.182** *tl* Imperial War Museum, image no: CH 18730, *tr* National Library of Medicine/Science Photo Library, *b* Charles H. Phillips/Time Life Pictures/Getty Images; **p.183** Mark Harmel/Stone/Getty Images; **p.190** *t* Hulton Archive/Getty Images, *b* Greater London Council, UK/The Bridgeman Art Library; **p.193** *l* Museum of the City of New York/Getty Images, *r* Hulton Archive/Getty Images; **p.194** National Portrait Gallery/Getty Images; **p.204** © Peter Smith.

Text Acknowledgements

The Publishers would also like to thank the following:

Account of a cure for a diseased eye from the Ebers Papyrus (c.1500BC); instructions on how to treat a broken nose from a papyrus (c.1600BC); extract from an Egyptian medical document (between 1900 and 1500BC); extract from *On the Treatment of Acute Diseases*, the Hippocratic collection; extract from *A Programme for Health*, the Hippocratic collection; Celsus: extracts from *On Medicine*; Galen: *On Anatomy* (c.AD190); Lindsay Allason-Jones, extract from *Women in Roman Britain* (Council for British Archaeology, 1989); Brother John Clynn: extract from his account of the plague; Petrarch: letter to a friend (1350); Swedish bishop: extract from his writings on the plague; Prior of Christchurch Abbey, Canterbury: extract from a letter to the Bishop of London (September 1348); John of Burgundy: extract from his writings on the plague (1365); John of Burgundy: extract from his advice on the plague (1365); King Edward III: letter to the Mayor of London (1349); extract from the rules of the hospital of St John, Bridgwater (1219); Geoffrey Chaucer: extract from *The Canterbury Tales: The General Prologue* (c.1380s); Paré: description of his breakthrough in treating gunshot wounds in the middle of a battle (c.1535–40); James Woodforde: extracts from his diary (1778, 1779, 1791); suggestions on how to help plague sufferers (1660s); extract from *The New London Dispensary* (1682); Ian Mortimer, *The Time Traveller's Guide to Medieval England* (The Bodley Head, 2008); Lord Mayor of London: extract from Orders issued after the outbreak of plague (1665); Dr Jenner: extract from his casebook (1798); Lt Colonel Pulvertaft: account of the first use of penicillin in the British army (1943); Louis Pasteur: extract from a lecture on the prevention of rabies (1885); description of the first use of penicillin (1940s); a traveller's description of Leeds, *The Morning Chronicle* (1848); James Smith; extract from 'Report on the Condition of the Town of Leeds' (1844); extracts from a letter on cholera, *The Times* (1 August 1854); John Snow: extract from 'On the Model of Communication of Cholera' (1854); letter about public health, *The Times* (1 August 1854); extract from an article in *The Times* on plans to provide free school meals for the poorest children (2 January 1905); extract from an interview with Kathleen Davys on home cures; extract from a speech by Aneurin Bevan introducing the National Health Service to Parliament (1946); Fanny Burney: account of her mastectomy operation (1811); Professor James Syme: account of amputating a leg at the hip joint (early 1800s); John Leeson: account of surgery in St Thomas's Hospital, London (1871); John Collins Warren: account of an operation to remove a neck tumour using ether as an anaesthetic (1846); Margaret Matthewson: account of her shoulder operation (1877); James Simpson: extract from a speech to a meeting of doctors in Edinburgh (1847); Joseph Lister: description of how the idea of using carbolic developed; Joseph Lister: *On the New Method of Treating Compound Fracture* (1867); memorials put up to women healers (1629, 1643, 1689); Thomas Huxley: extract from his writings on women (1851); W. M. Thackeray: 'An ideal woman' (1850s); statement by students at the Middlesex Hospital, London, protesting against Elizabeth Garrett attending lectures (1861); Charles Dickens: extract from *Martin Chuzzlewit* (1844); Mary Seacole: extract from *The Wonderful Adventures of Mrs Seacole in Many Lands* (1857); William Howard Russell: article in *The Times* (September 1855); Dr Reid: extract from a letter written to his family (1855); extract from a poem in *Punch* (1856); extract from an article on the Crimean War, *The Times* reprinted by permission of News International, © 2000 (4 September 2000).

Every effort has been made to trace all copyright holders, but if any have been inadvertently overlooked the Publishers will be pleased to make the necessary arrangements at the first opportunity.

Key features of Smarter History
Medicine through time

Before you start using this book here is a guide to help you get the most out of it.

Enquiries

The book is structured around a series of Enquiries, each one focussing on a key aspect of your GCSE course. Each Enquiry helps you understand a particular event, person or breakthrough and then links it to the broader history of medicine.

Banners introduce each Enquiry so you know exactly what you are focussing on from the start.

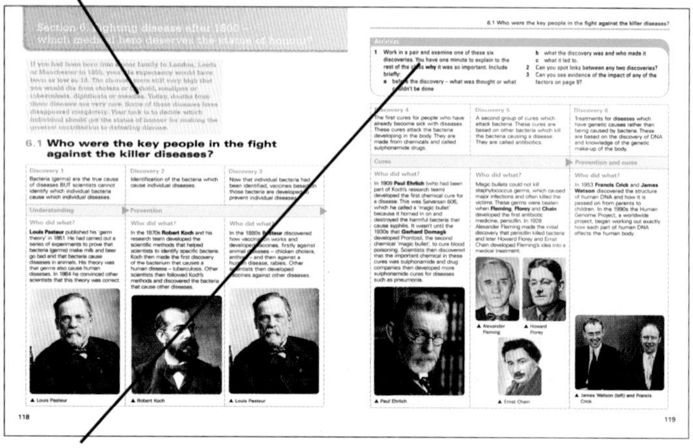

Activities guide you through the material so you build up your knowledge and understanding of the key content of your GCSE course. They also link into the on-going Smarter Revision activities.

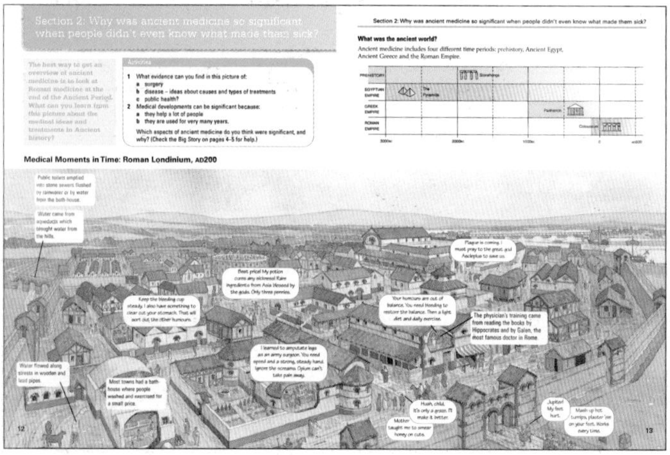

Medical Moments in Time

These pages give you an overview of the key features of medicine at five important points in history – AD200, 1347, 1665, 1848 and 1935.

Smarter Revision

These pages help you prepare effectively for your examinations, showing you a variety of ways to build up your knowledge and understanding of the history of medicine. You will be building up your revision material from the very beginning of your course – not waiting until you have completed it. See page 11 for more details on Smarter Revision pages.

Smarter Revision sections give you clear advice on how to use each Smarter Revision strategy.

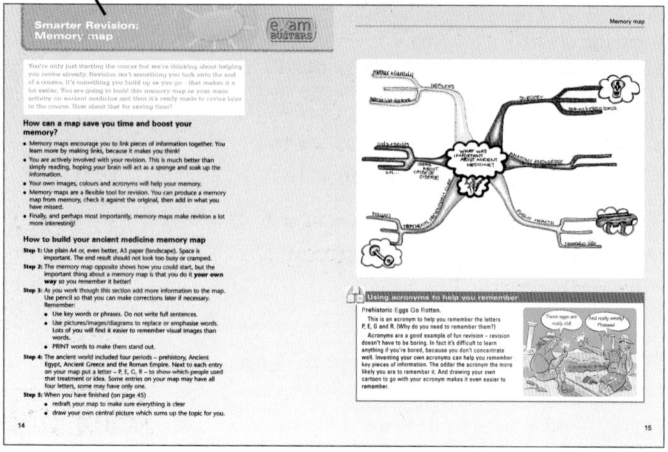

Meet the Examiner

These pages explain how to win high marks in your exams. They show you how to:

- answer each type of question in your examinations
- identify exactly what a question is asking
- structure answers and develop the vocabulary to make full use of what you know.

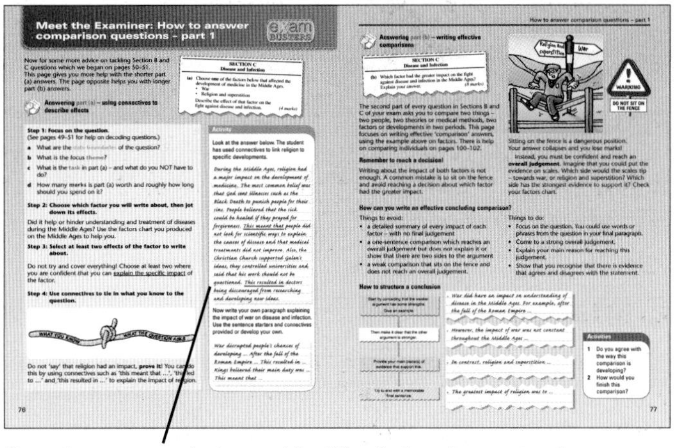

Sample answers help you identify what makes a good answer.

AQA themes

Summary pages help you bring together the key developments in the three AQA themes:

- Disease and infection
- Surgery and anatomy
- Public health

References to the three AQA themes are colour coded, especially in summary charts at the start of sections, and use icons, as above.

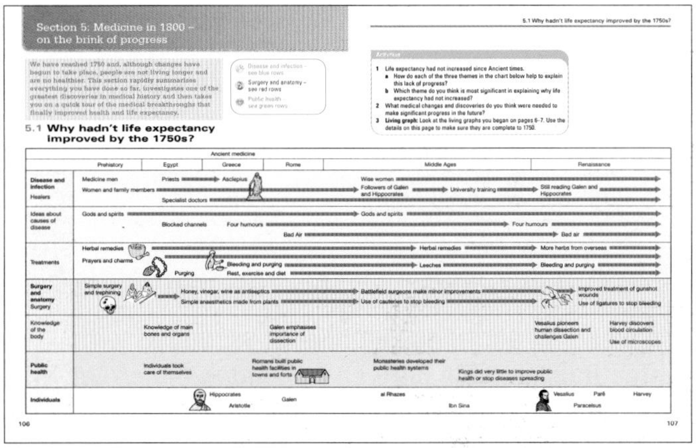

Dynamic Learning digital resources

Dynamic Learning resources provide an extensive range of supporting resources. They feature:

- enquiries developing your knowledge and understanding of key topics within each period
- thematic investigations helping you understand the development of major themes across time
- exambuster activities helping you revise and prepare effectively for examinations.

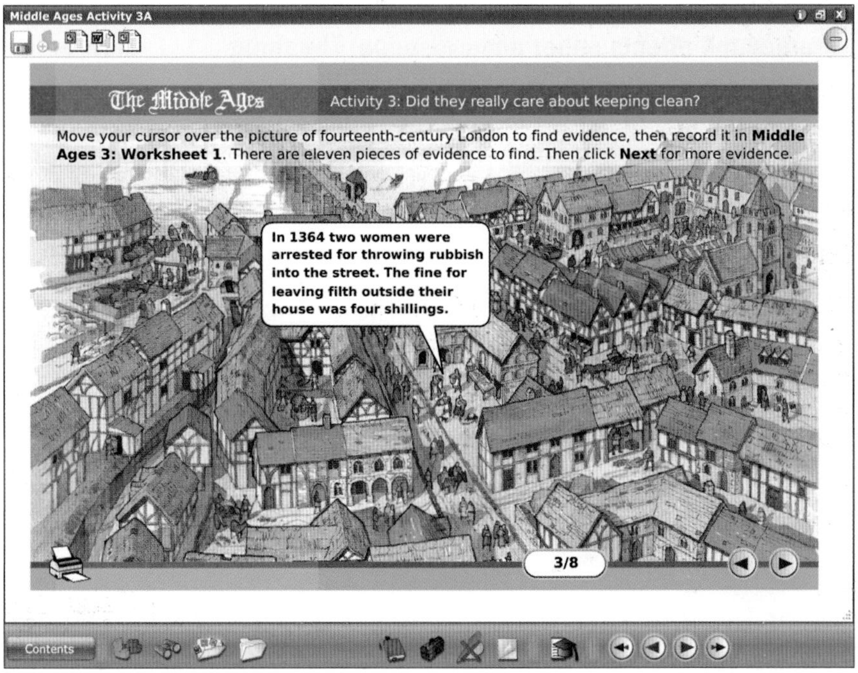

Section 1: The Big Story of medicine and health through time – what do you think happened when?

This section helps you build up an outline picture of the history of medicine in your mind and on paper. We'll start by getting you to think! Which period of history do you think each of the clues comes from?

Activity

The history of medicine can be surprising. Sometimes what seems to be a modern idea turns out to be thousands of years old. Sometimes a treatment we take for granted only began quite recently.
Read clues A–J. Think about what each one tells you about medical ideas or treatments. Then draw your own version of the timeline at the foot of these pages and pencil in each clue heading where you think it belongs on the timeline.

Clue A Treatments – Penicillin, the first antibiotic

'We had an enormous number of wounded with infections, terrible burn cases among the crews of armoured cars. The usual medicines had absolutely no effect. The last thing I tried was penicillin. The first man was a young man called Newton. He had been in bed for six months with fractures of both legs. His sheets were soaked with pus. Normally he would have died in a short time. I gave three injections of penicillin a day and studied the effects under a microscope. The thing seemed like a miracle. In ten days' time the leg was cured and in a month's time the young fellow was back on his feet. I had enough penicillin for ten cases. Nine were complete cures.'

Clue B Treatments – herbal medicine

'Medicine for dimness of the eyes: take the juice of the celandine plant, mix with bumblebees' honey, put in a brass container then warm until it is cooked and apply to the eyes.'

Clue C Explaining disease – the four humours

Hippocrates wrote: 'Man's body contains Four Humours – blood, phlegm, yellow bile and melancholy (black) bile. When all these humours are truly balanced, he feels the most perfect health. Illness occurs when there is too much or too little of one of these Humours or one is entirely thrown out of the body.'

Clue D Explaining disease – God sends diseases

'Terrible is God towards men. He sends plagues of disease and uses them to terrify and torment men and drive out their sins. That is why the realm of England is struck by plagues – because of the sins of the people.'

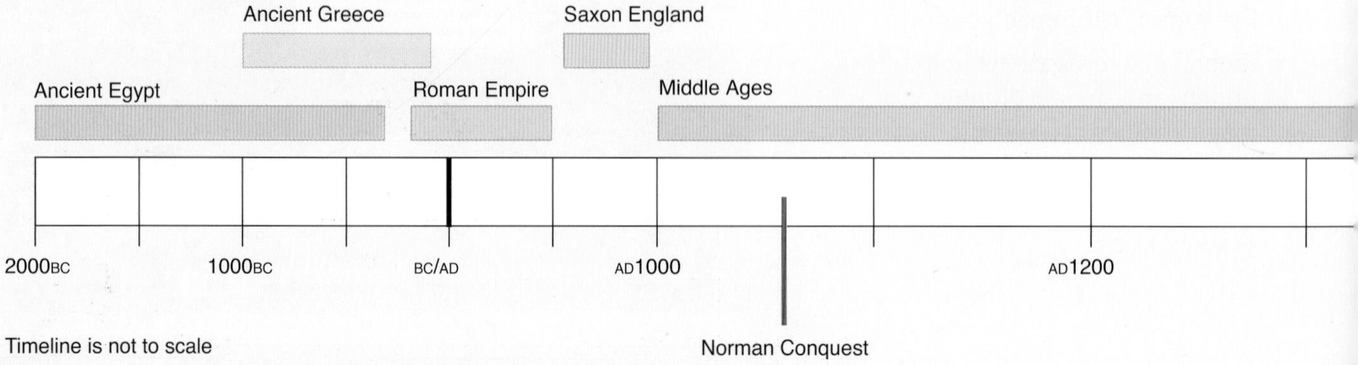

Clue E Public health – the NHS begins

'On the first day of free treatment on the NHS, Mother went and got tested for new glasses. Then she went further down the road to the chiropodist and had her feet done. Then she went back to the doctor's because she'd been having trouble with her ears and the doctor said he would fix her up with a hearing aid.'

Clue F Explaining disease – Pasteur and germ theory

Louis Pasteur, a French scientist, published his 'germ theory' suggesting that bacteria or 'germs' were the true cause of diseases. His germ theory replaced all previous ideas about the causes of disease.

Clue G Treatments – the black cat remedy

'The stye on my right eyelid was still swollen and inflamed very much. It is commonly said that rubbing the eyelid with the tail of a black cat will do it much good so, having a black cat, a little before dinner I tried it and very soon after dinner the swelling on my eyelid was much reduced and almost free of pain.'

Clue H Treatments – wash, exercise, diet

'Every day wash face and eyes with the purest water and clean the teeth using fine peppermint powder. Begin the day with a walk. Long walks before meals clear out the body, prepare it for receiving food and give it more power for digesting.'

Clue I Surgery – without anaesthetics

Robert Liston, a famous London surgeon, once amputated a man's leg in two and a half minutes but worked so fast he accidentally cut off his patient's testicles as well. During another high-speed operation Liston amputated the fingers of his assistant and slashed the coat of a spectator who, fearing he had been stabbed, dropped dead with fright. Both the assistant and the patient then died of infection caught during the operation or on the hospital ward. Liston worked really fast because there were no anaesthetics.

Clue J Public health – fresh water, baths and sewers

Sextus Julius Frontinus wrote: 'There was a great increase in the number of reservoirs, fountains and water-basins. As a result the air is purer. Water is now carried through the city to latrines, baths and houses.'

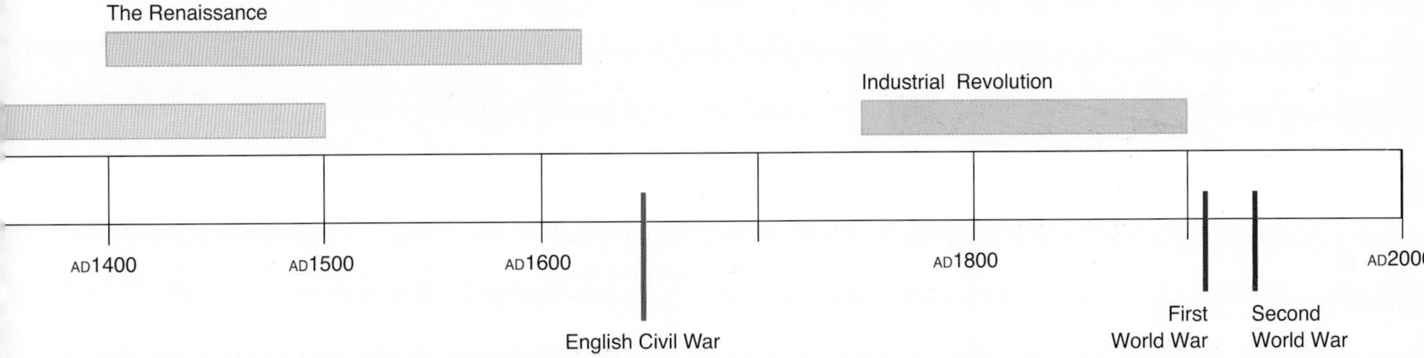

The Big Story of medicine and health through time

Activities

1 Work in a group of three. You have one minute to tell the outline story of medicine. Your story needs to answer the question: 'Why do people today have better health and live longer lives than people in the past?'

Spend ten minutes preparing your story. Include each of these words:

- continuity
- change
- turning point
- progress.

2 One of the most important skills in History is asking questions.

a What questions do you want to ask about this outline to help you understand it better?

b Look at the blue and red lines on the graph. What questions do you want to ask about the shapes of these lines?

Information

Life expectancy

These graphs show the life expectancy of men and women throughout history. The life expectancy age is the average age that people lived to.

Until the 1900s around 20 per cent of babies died before their first birthday and this therefore reduced the average life expectancy.

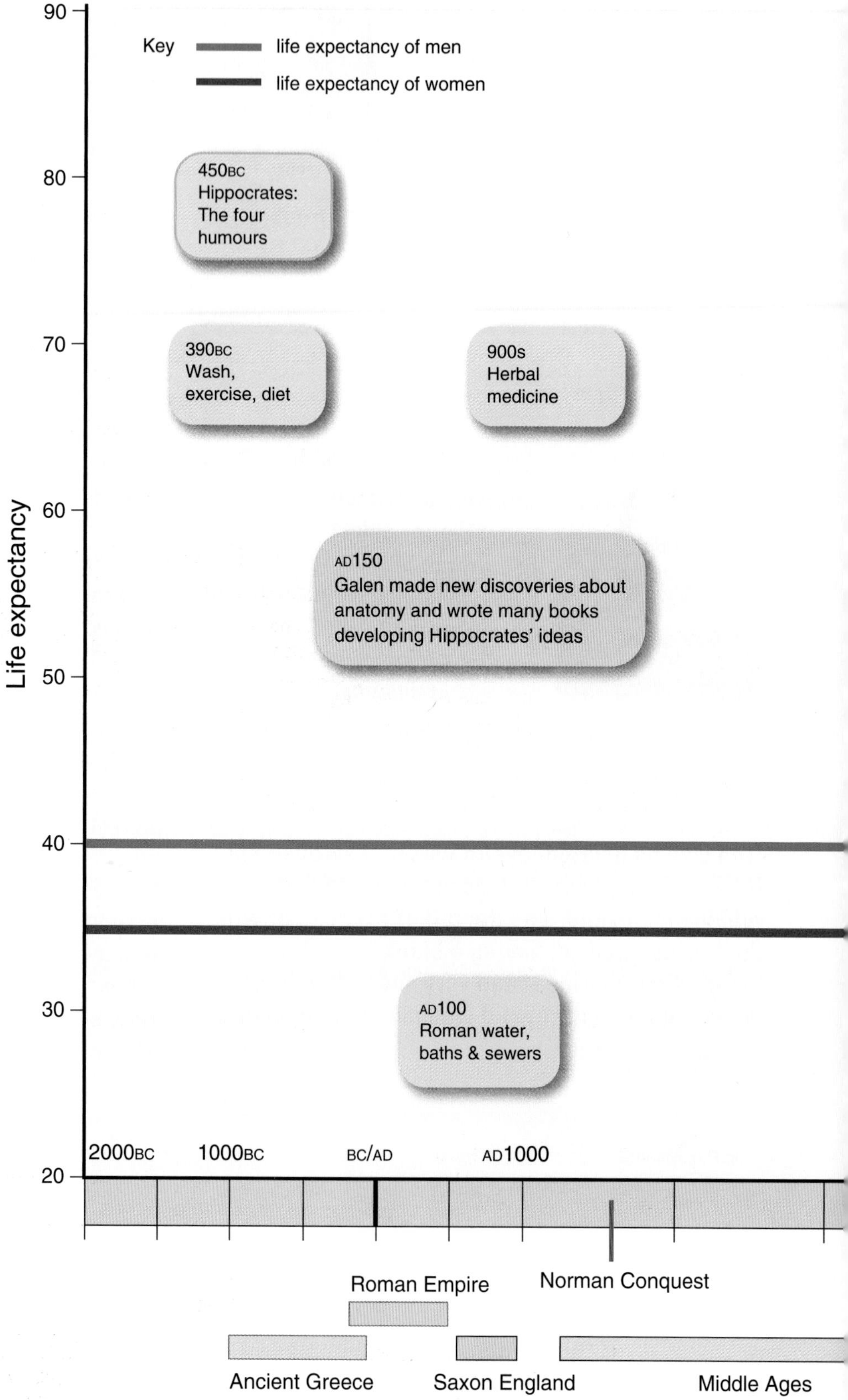

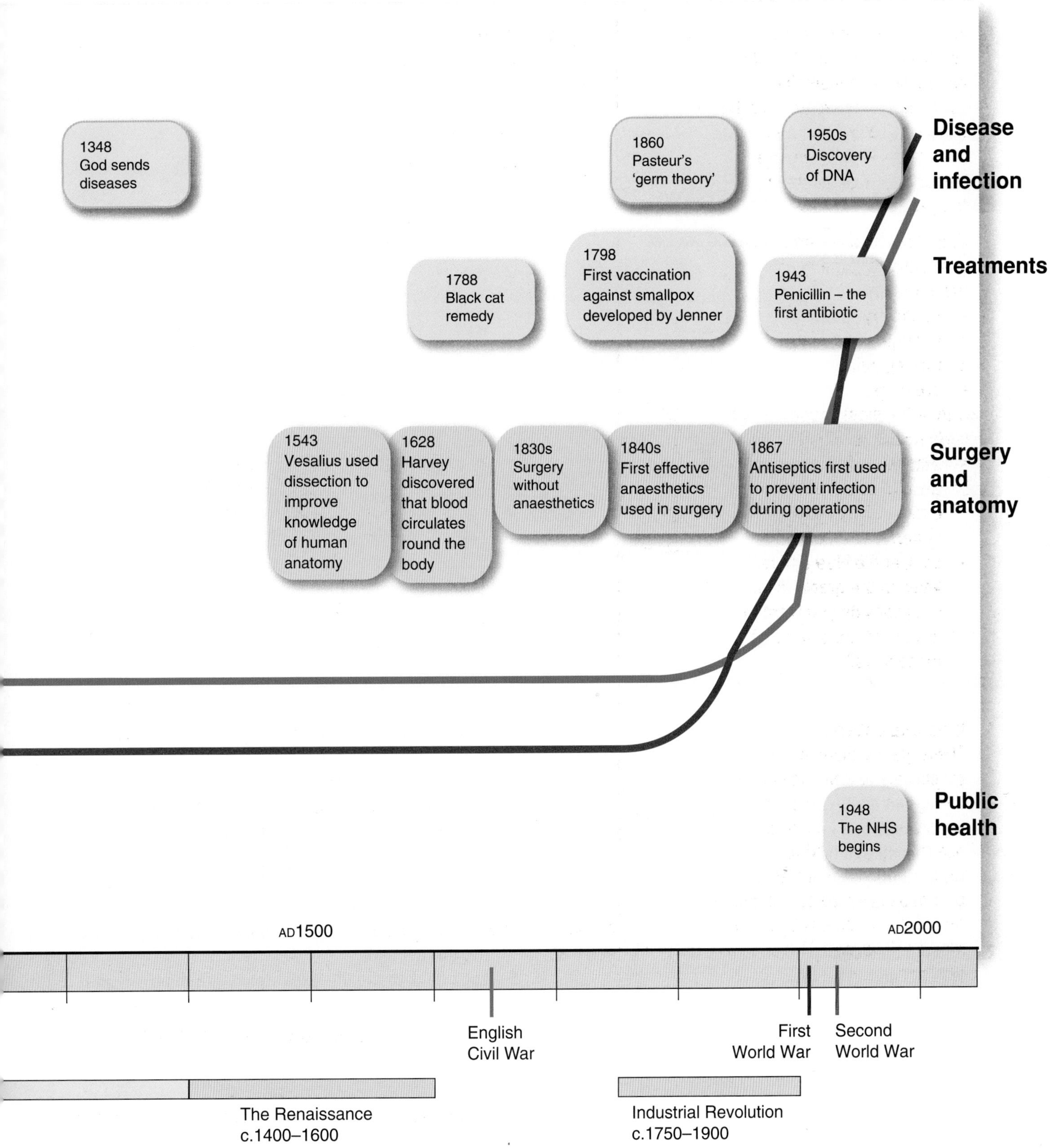
1348
God sends diseases
1860
Pasteur's 'germ theory'
1950s
Discovery of DNA
Disease and infection
1788
Black cat remedy
1798
First vaccination against smallpox developed by Jenner
1943
Penicillin – the first antibiotic
Treatments
1543
Vesalius used dissection to improve knowledge of human anatomy
1628
Harvey discovered that blood circulates round the body
1830s
Surgery without anaesthetics
1840s
First effective anaesthetics used in surgery
1867
Antiseptics first used to prevent infection during operations
Surgery and anatomy
1948
The NHS begins
Public health
AD1500
AD2000
English Civil War
First World War
Second World War
The Renaissance c.1400–1600
Industrial Revolution c.1750–1900

Smarter Revision: Living graph

On the last two pages you saw the story of life expectancy right across time – all in one graph. Graphs are really helpful for following the story of medicine across time so it's important to start early – NOW!

Activities

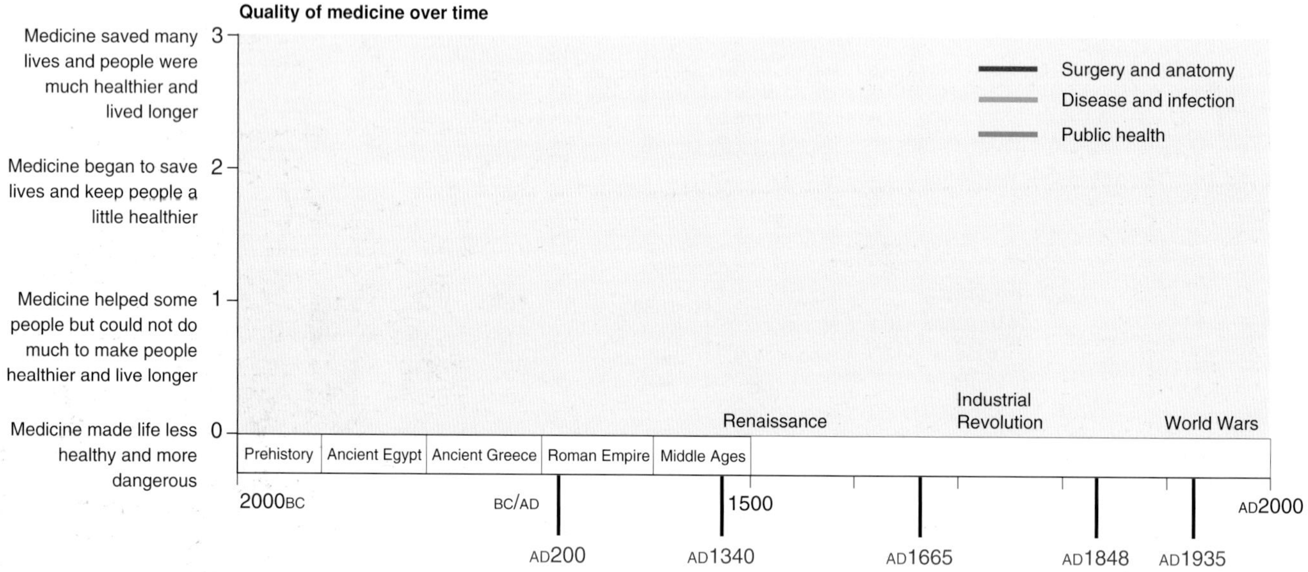

You are going on an evidence hunt through the book to create three lines on your graph.

1 Work in a small group. Choose one theme:
- **a** Surgery and anatomy (the effectiveness of surgery and how much people know about the human body)
- **b** Disease and infection (ideas about what causes disease and how effectively diseases have been treated)
- **c** Public health (how people and governments try to prevent illnesses)

2 Use the medical moments pages 12–13, 52–53, 84–85, 112–113 and 114–115.
- **a** Pick out from each picture the evidence about your theme. Decide for each date where to place your theme on the graph.
(For example, if you think surgery in AD200 made life less healthy and more dangerous, put a cross at level 0 above AD200.)
- **b** Use sticky notes to list the evidence for your choice of level. Stick these on your graph.

3 When your outline graph is complete you have one minute to explain it aloud to your class. You must include each of these words:
- change
- continuity
- progress
- turning point.

4 Compare the lines for each theme. What similarities and differences can you see between the shapes of the three lines?

5 Look back to the life-expectancy graph on pages 4–5. What have you learned from your new graphs that helps to explain the shape of the life-expectancy graph?

Why is this page really important?

To be successful in your examination you need to have an overview of the history of medicine in your mind. You will remember this outline better if you build it up from the beginning, filling in the detail as you go through the course. The best way to build up this outline knowledge is to see it as a graph. You can do this in different ways:

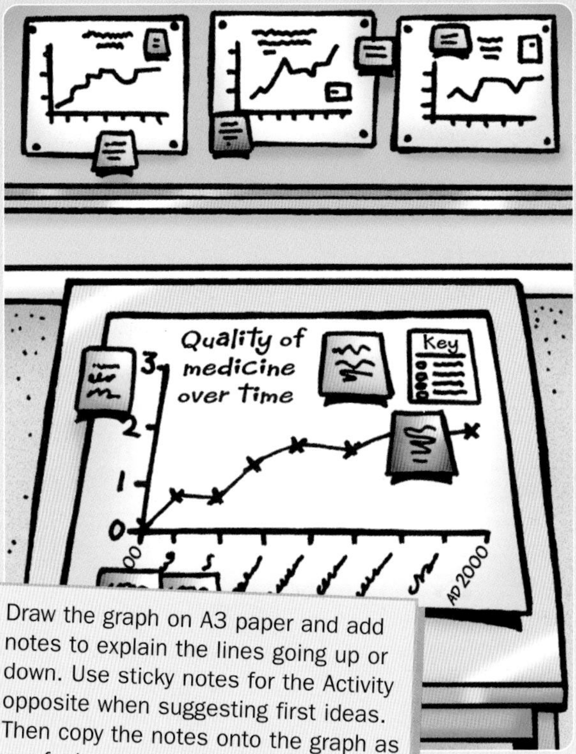

1 Draw the graph on A3 paper and add notes to explain the lines going up or down. Use sticky notes for the Activity opposite when suggesting first ideas. Then copy the notes onto the graph as you feel more certain about the patterns of changes and continuities.

2 Use your IT skills to create a spreadsheet to record the shape of the graph and the details explaining the shape of the graph.

3 Turn the graphs into living graphs with a group of friends. Create a graph on the floor, then choose a theme such as understanding of the causes of disease. Each person is a period in history and has to decide where on the graph to stand. Then each person has 30 seconds to explain why they are in that place on the graph. Turning your ideas into more precise spoken words and sentences is an effective way of revising. Doing this physically is an excellent way of remembering the patterns of changes and continuities.

Why are you studying the history of medicine?

Your course will stretch back over 4000 years, all the way to prehistoric times. Why are we going so far back? Why are you studying the history of medicine? Pages 8–11 will help you understand how your History course links together and where the history of medicine fits in.

This course isn't trying to turn you into doctors. It's aiming to help you get better at History and enjoy finding out about the people who lived in the past. Here are three things that you are going to become a lot better at.

1 Having a sense of chronology

You will increase your knowledge of some of the most important events in history, understand better how they fit together and why each period was important.

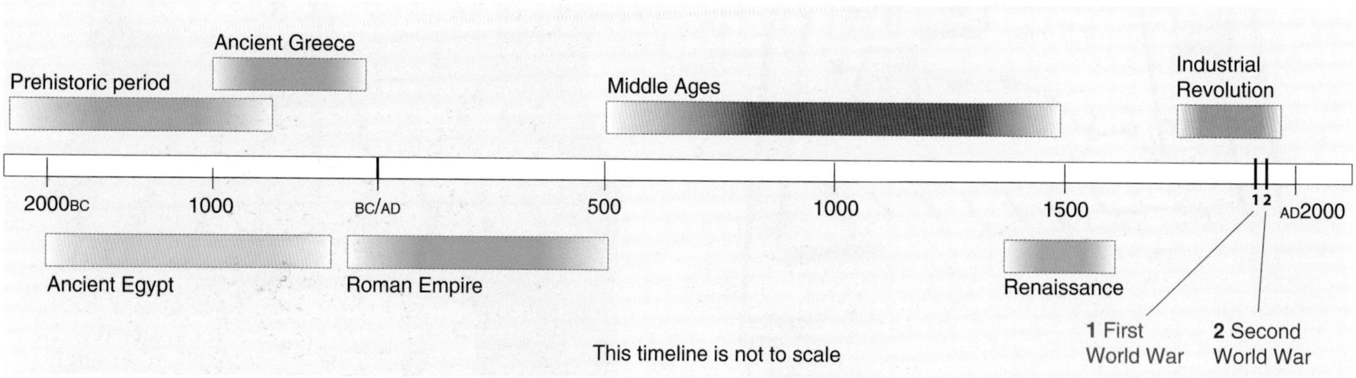

2 Understanding how people's lives developed over this long period of time – especially their health and medicine

Your core question is 'Why are we healthier and why do we live longer lives than people in the past?' but by the end of the course, you will be able to answer this question and many more!

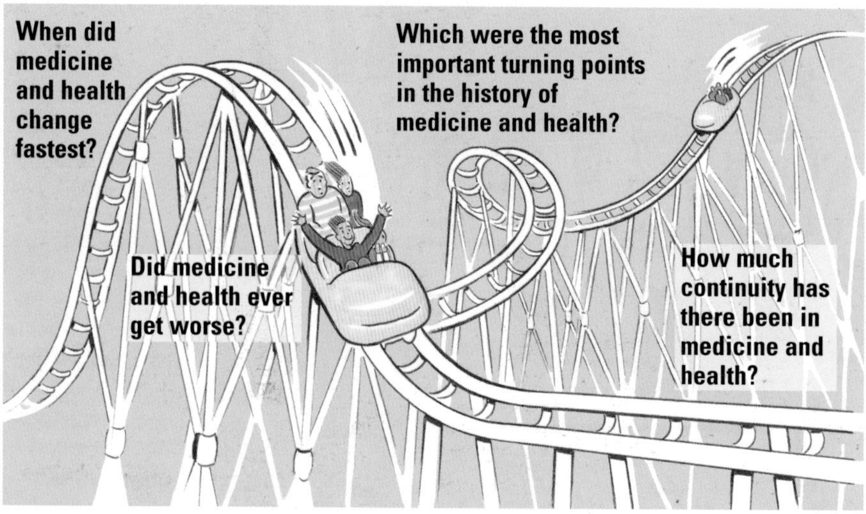

Activities

1 Think back to your KS3 History and what you learned about different periods.
   - a Do you think the Middle Ages was a time of many improvements in medicine?
   - b How might the Industrial Revolution have affected people's health?
   - c When do you think changes in medicine have been fastest?

2 Now use your answers to question 1 to suggest answers to the questions on the rollercoaster.

3 Explaining why changes happened – and why they didn't happen

You are going to describe the continuities and changes in medicine and why they happened. The people shown below will help you a lot with your explanations. They are the reasons, the factors, which explain the changes and continuities in medicine.

Activities

3 Can you suggest how any of the factors shown in the cartoon below improved medicine and so helped to save lives?

4 How might any of the factors have hindered (stopped or slowed down) the development of medicine?

(Don't worry if you can't suggest any ideas right now. You will be able to give really good answers at the end of the course.)

How does your GCSE History course all fit together?

**Your GCSE History course is special.
Here are three good reasons why.**

Reason 1: Different types, topics and periods

Your course may look like a random set of topics, but it's not like that at all. This course was designed to let you investigate different types, topics and periods of history. This is much more varied and interesting than sticking to just one period throughout your course.

Reason 2: Concepts and processes

It's not just about topics such as the history of medicine. It is developing your ability to use all the concepts and processes you used in KS3. The people, topics and periods we study change but we always use the same concepts and processes to study that content.

Interpretations
Diversity
Sources and evidence
Chronological understanding
Significance
Cause and consequence
Enquiry
Change and continuity

Reason 3: Understand events today

It will help you see how understanding and knowledge of history helps us understand events today. It's really satisfying to understand how past events and people have led to the items in the news – and knowing that events are complicated stops us leaping to simple conclusions.

HISTORY AROUND US (25%)

This investigation of a historical site in your locality lets you use different kinds of sources and contrasts with the national and international history in the other units.

STUDY IN DEVELOPMENT (35%)

Medicine through time shows the value of developing a long overview of the development of a topic.

ENQUIRY IN DEPTH (40%)

This investigation of a short period of time allows you to understand the ideas and attitudes of a period and contrasts with the much longer Development Study.

Activities

1. Which topics are you studying and where do they fit into this diagram?
2. Can you suggest how any part of your History course helps you understand the world today?

What are the best ways to prepare for your GCSE exams?

Good revision and planning will help you do well at GCSE. We will help you using the two important features below.

smarter revision

The Smarter Revision Toolkit

The toolkit helps you prepare your revision notes thoroughly and intelligently. Each tool helps you with a different aspect of your revision.

SMARTER REVISION TOOLKIT

- **Factors Chart** – helps you record how difficult factors affected the development of Medicine. See page 46.
- **Concept Map** – helps you to link factors to improve your explanation. See page 98.
- **Living Graph** – helps you see the pattern of change and continuity in each medical theme. See page 6.
- **Using a digital camera to help revision** – find out more on page 37.
- **Memory Map** – helps you remember the key medical developments in each period. See page 14.
- **'Role of the individual' chart** – helps you record the impact of key people. See page 27.

meet the examiner

These pages will:

- advise you how to write good answers *and* how to avoid writing bad answers
- show you sample answers and ask you to mark and improve them
- set you sample questions to improve your skills at writing good answers.

They will also explain how to answer the main types of exam questions, e.g.:

- Using Sources questions
- Using Sources and your own knowledge questions
- Describe … questions
- Compare … questions such as:
  - Who contributed most to …
  - When was there most …
  - Which factors …

Section 2: Why was ancient medicine so significant when people didn't even know what made them sick?

The best way to get an overview of ancient medicine is to look at Roman medicine at the end of the Ancient Period. What can you learn from this picture about the medical ideas and treatments in Ancient history?

Activities

1 What evidence can you find in this picture of:
   a surgery
   b disease – ideas about causes and types of treatments
   c public health?
2 Medical developments can be significant because:
   a they help a lot of people
   b they are used for very many years.

   Which aspects of ancient medicine do you think were significant, and why? (Check the Big Story on pages 4–5 for help.)

Medical Moments in Time: Roman Londinium, AD200

What was the ancient world?

Ancient medicine includes four different time periods: prehistory, Ancient Egypt, Ancient Greece and the Roman Empire.

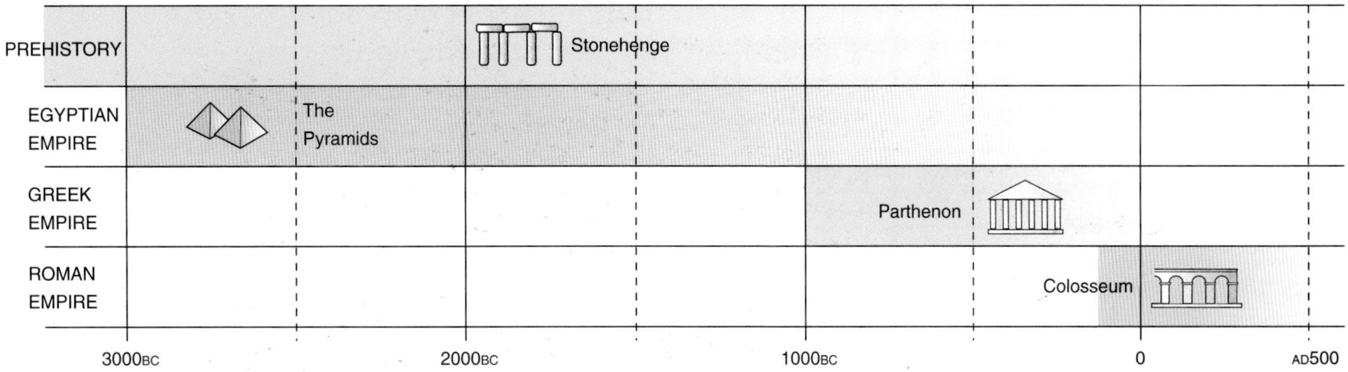

Smarter Revision: Memory map

You're only just starting the course but we're thinking about helping you revise already. Revision isn't something you tack onto the end of a course. It's something you build up as you go – that makes it a lot easier. You are going to build this memory map as your main activity on ancient medicine and then it's ready made to revise later in the course. How about that for saving time?

How can a map save you time and boost your memory?

- Memory maps encourage you to link pieces of information together. You learn more by making links, because it makes you think!
- You are actively involved with your revision. This is much better than simply reading, hoping your brain will act as a sponge and soak up the information.
- Your own images, colours and acronyms will help your memory.
- Memory maps are a flexible tool for revision. You can produce a memory map from memory, check it against the original, then add in what you have missed.
- Finally, and perhaps most importantly, memory maps make revision a lot more interesting!

How to build your ancient medicine memory map

Step 1: Use plain A4 or, even better, A3 paper (landscape). Space is important. The end result should not look too busy or cramped.

Step 2: The memory map opposite shows how you could start, but the important thing about a memory map is that you do it **your own way** so you remember it better!

Step 3: As you work though this section add more information to the map. Use pencil so that you can make corrections later if necessary. Remember:

- Use key words or phrases. Do not write full sentences.
- Use pictures/images/diagrams to replace or emphasise words. Lots of you will find it easier to remember visual images than words.
- PRINT words to make them stand out.

Step 4: The ancient world included four periods – prehistory, Ancient Egypt, Ancient Greece and the Roman Empire. Next to each entry on your map put a letter – P, E, G, R – to show which people used that treatment or idea. Some entries on your map may have all four letters, some may have only one.

Step 5: When you have finished (on page 45)

- redraft your map to make sure everything is clear
- draw your own central picture which sums up the topic for you.

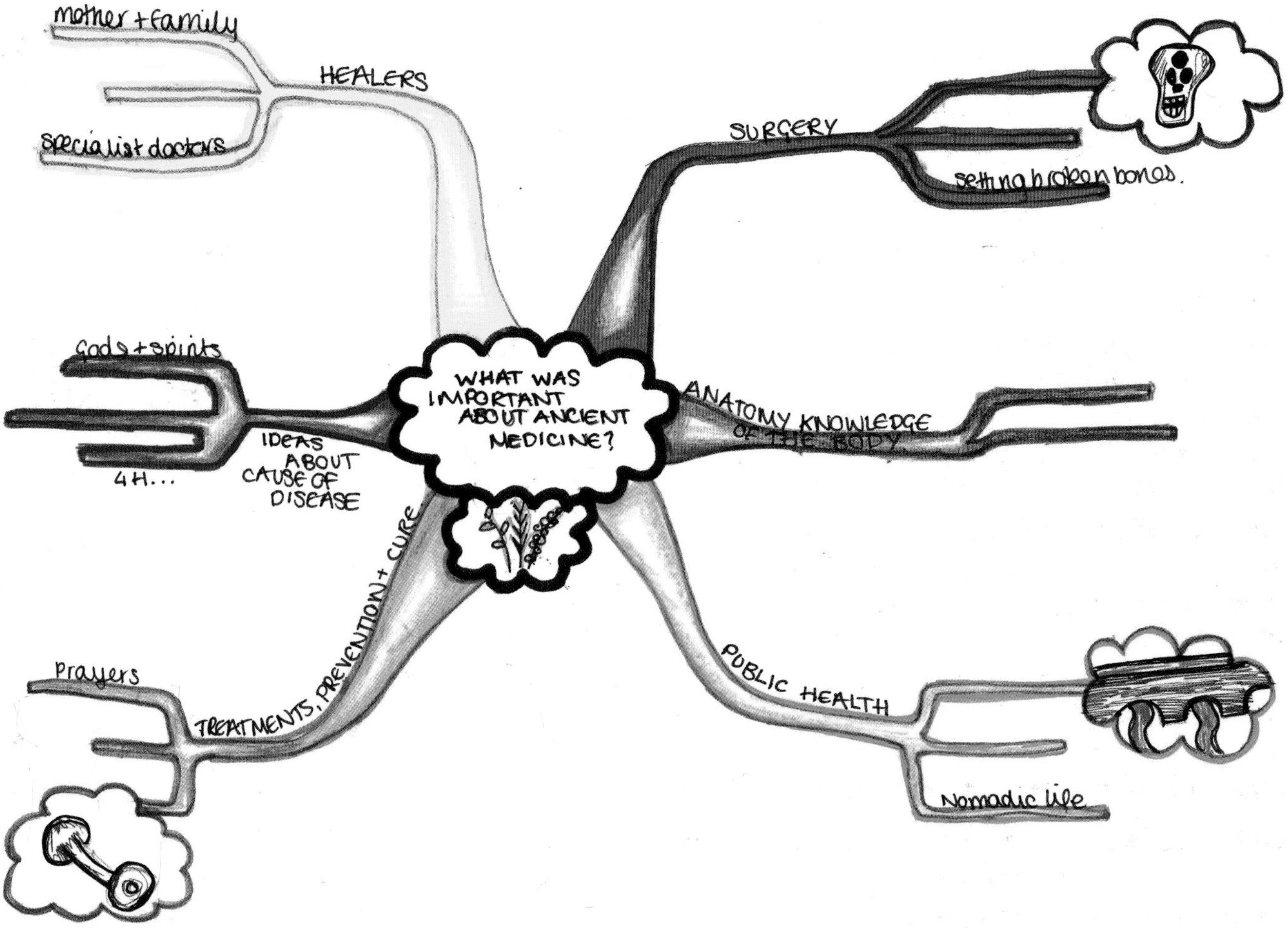

Using acronyms to help you remember

Prehistoric **E**ggs **G**o **R**otten.

This is an acronym to help you remember the letters P, E, G and R. (Why do you need to remember them?)

Acronyms are a good example of fun revision – revision doesn't have to be boring. In fact it's difficult to learn anything if you're bored, because you don't concentrate well. Inventing your own acronyms can help you remember key pieces of information. The odder the acronym the more likely you are to remember it. And drawing your own cartoon to go with your acronym makes it even easier to remember.

2.1 What kinds of medicine were prehistoric peoples good at – and not so good at?

Now let's go back to the beginning of ancient medicine, right back to the Prehistoric Period. In prehistoric times people lived in two different ways, as shown on these pages. What can you work out from the pictures and information about prehistoric medicine?

Activities

Use both reconstruction drawings.

1. How did their different ways of life:
   - **a** help avoid health problems
   - **b** cause health problems?
2. Who treated the sick?
3. What kinds of surgery did they use?
4. What did they think caused illnesses?
5. What kinds of treatments did they use for illnesses?

Hunter-gatherers (life expectancy around 19–25)

Until about 10,000BC people lived by hunting animals and gathering fruits and nuts as they travelled. They were nomads, living 'on the move'.

Information

What does prehistoric mean?
The word 'prehistory' means 'before writing'. Therefore the Prehistoric Period was the time before writing began, so 'prehistory' means different times in different places. For example, the Ancient Egyptians developed writing c.3000BC and so that is when the Prehistoric Period ended in Egypt. In Britain, the Prehistoric Period lasted three thousand years longer, until the Romans brought writing when they conquered Britain in AD43. Peoples such as the Aboriginals of Australia or the Azande in Sudan, Africa, did not develop writing until the nineteenth century so their Prehistoric Periods lasted until then.

Farmers (life expectancy around 20–27)

Around 10,000BC people developed a different lifestyle, settling in one place to farm the land, grow crops and keep herds of animals. This drawing shows prehistoric farmers 5000 years ago.

Explaining and treating illnesses – the natural and the supernatural

Activities

1 Work in a small group. Explain to the rest of the class how prehistoric people would have treated someone with one of these problems:
   a a broken arm
   b a pain in the stomach
   c a headache that won't go away.
   Include details about the healer, the kind of treatment and what you think caused the problem.

2 a How do people such as the Australian Aboriginals help us to understand prehistoric medicine?
   b Why aren't we completely certain about the details of prehistoric medicine?

3 **Memory map:** Use the information on pages 16–19 to add to the memory map you began on page 14.

4 Look back to pages 12–13. Which aspects of Roman medicine had been first developed thousands of years earlier in the Prehistoric Period?

Illnesses and injuries that had NATURAL causes

Examples

Accidents, hunting or war wounds, hunger, common ailments such as fever.

Who would you go to for help?

Family, probably the women who had learned remedies from their own mothers.

How did they treat wounds and illnesses?

Common remedies were made from herbs, plants, minerals and animal parts. Although prehistoric people did not understand why, some of these cures did work because the ingredients included chemicals which acted as antiseptics to combat infection or as anaesthetics.

Cuts and wounds were also helped by the use of plants. Aboriginals covered cuts with sphagnum moss, which is now an ingredient in hospital dressings and field dressings in war zones. Broken bones as well as cuts were covered with mud, clay or animal fat and then bound up with feathers, animal skin or tree bark.

Fevers, pain and swellings, chest and lung complaints were all treated with steam. Sweat lodges were used all over North America. In 1805 a member of a European exploration group in America became so crippled with stiffness and back pain that he could not ride or walk but after using a steam lodge and drinking a local herbal tea he was able to walk freely for the first time in four months.

Source 1

▲ A cure developed by the Aboriginals of Australia was based on tea-tree leaves. People with colds and coughs breathed in the vapour from crushed tea-tree leaves boiled in water. People with fevers were bathed in the same tea-tree liquid. Today tea-tree oil is used to treat colds and other ailments and as an antiseptic. American Indians used the bark of the cherry tree, which we now know contains chemicals that reduce coughing.

These natural and supernatural methods were not two different systems but all part of one overall system of medicine.

Natural

Information

How do we know about prehistoric medicine?
There are no written records of prehistoric medicine but there are two important sources of evidence that tell us a lot.

1 Archaeological evidence from skeletons tells us about simple surgery or about the height of people and the age at which they died.
2 Peoples who continued to live into modern times in the same ways as their ancestors. Hunter-gatherers and farmers in Australia, Africa and America did not need to change their ways of life because they were well-suited to their environments and had plentiful supplies of food.

Source 2

▲ A medicine man c.1834 from the Mandan tribe, which lived in North America.

Illnesses and injuries that had SUPERNATURAL causes

Examples

Anything caused by gods, the spirits of the dead, enemies, witches, for example the Aboriginal belief that illness could be caused by an enemy who made evil spirits enter the victim's body by using a pointing bone and chanting a curse. The bone could also cause illness by taking someone's spirit out of their body.

Who would you go to for help?

The medicine man who had been trained to communicate with the gods and spirits. The training of North American medicine men (as in Source 2) took several years of constant work.

How did they treat wounds and illnesses?

Medicine men gave people charms to protect them from evil spirits but if this didn't work they used a range of methods, including the same kinds of herbal remedies and practical remedies as other people. However, medicine men also used special prayers and chants, and some were skilled in surgery such as trephining. The skull shown in Source 4 had been cut open, probably to let out evil spirits that were causing pain.

Source 3

▲ A bone used as an amulet (a charm worn as protection against evil spirits).

Source 4

▲ Trephined skulls have been found all over the world. On many the bone grew back, showing that the patient lived after the operation.

Medicine men used herbs; mothers used chants and charms.
There were strong connections between the two approaches.

Supernatural

2.2 Did the Egyptians develop any important new medical ideas?

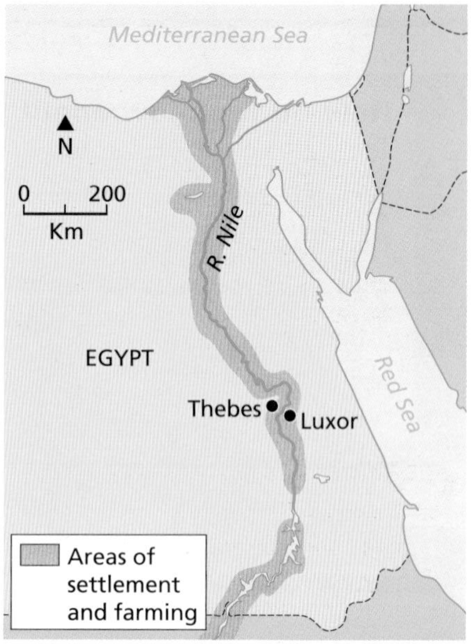

Now it's time to find out about medicine in Ancient Egypt, the land of Pyramids and Pharaohs.

Activities

Look carefully at the details in the picture below.

1. What evidence can you see of similarities with prehistoric medicine?
2. What evidence can you see of differences from prehistoric medicine?
3. What evidence can you see of:
   a religion **b** communications **c** technology?
4. How might each factor have affected medicine in Egypt?

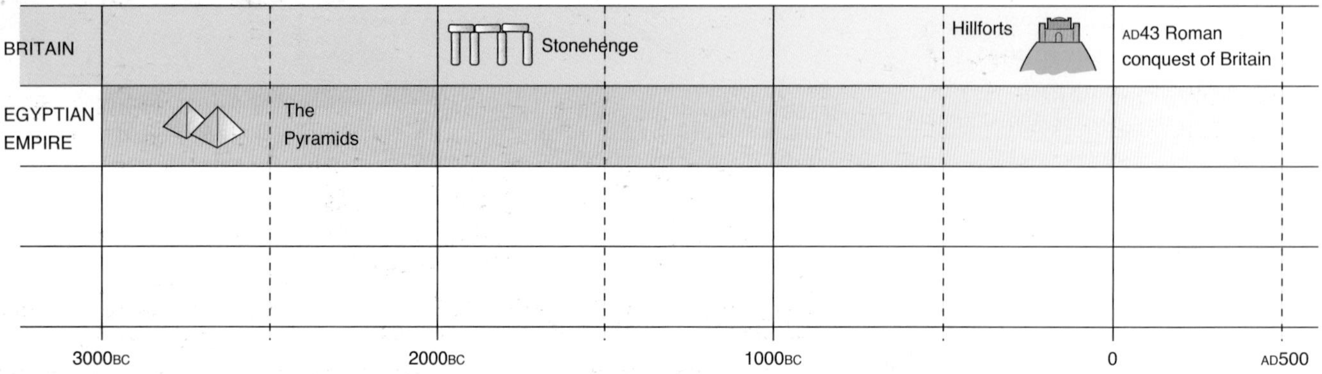

Activities

5 Read Sources 1–3. How are they similar to prehistoric treatments?
6 Why do you think each of them continued to be used? (Source 4 will help you with one of the remedies.)
7 How does the evidence about Egyptian medicine differ from the evidence about prehistoric medicine?

Source 1

A cure for a diseased eye from the Ebers Papyrus from c.1500BC:

'To clear up the pus: honey, balm from Mecca and gum ammoniac. To treat its discharge: red ochre, malachite, honey.'

(Gum ammoniac is the resin from the Dorena ammoniac plant.)

Source 2

From an Egyptian medical document dating from between 1900 and 1500BC:

'I have made a charm for my child which will protect him against you, oh evil spirits! This charm is made from evil smelling herbs and from garlic which is harmful to you; from honey which is sweet for men and horrible for spirits, from a fishtail and a rag and a backbone of a perch.'

Source 3

How to treat a broken nose – instructions from a papyrus dating from c.1600BC. The document contains descriptions of the diagnosis and treatment of 48 surgical cases.

EXAMINATION

If you examine a man whose nose is disfigured, part of it being squashed in, while the other part is swollen and both nostrils are bleeding.

DIAGNOSIS

Then you should say 'You have a broken nose and I can treat this ailment.'

TREATMENT

You should clean his nose with two plugs of linen and then insert two plugs soaked in grease into his nostrils. You should make him rest until the swelling has gone down. Bandage his nose with stiff rolls of linen and treat him with lint every day until he recovers.

Source 4

Scientists have analysed and tested some Ancient Egyptian remedies. Honey was used in 30 per cent of remedies recorded in one document. Malachite was another common ingredient. Malachite is a kind of stone that contains copper. It was also used by American Indians as a medicine.

Why did Egyptian medicine change?

One important skill that helps you learn more effectively is skim-reading. You read quickly to get an overall idea of what the key points are on a page. Then you go back and read more carefully, picking out the detail that supports those key points. Pages 22–25 help you develop your skim-reading skills with a game of Egyptian bingo!

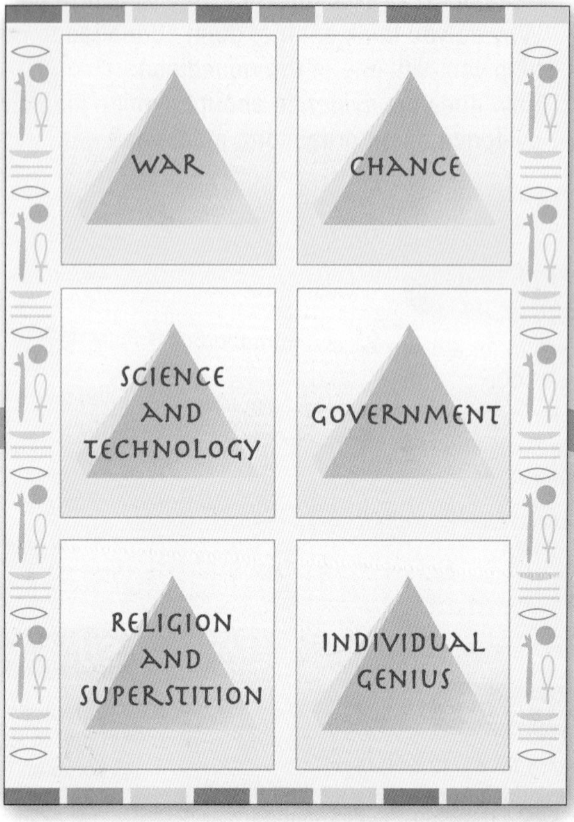

Activities

1 Organise yourselves into pairs. Each pair has to skim-read pages 23–25 looking for examples of how the factors shown on the bingo card on the right affected Egyptian medicine.
2 The winners are the first pair to find one example of each factor in one of the rows. As soon as you have completed a row, shout out 'Pyramid' and ask your teacher to check that your examples are correct.
3 When you have finished, turn to page 25 and complete the more detailed activity.

Information

The importance of writing

The Egyptians were one of the first peoples to develop writing and they also learned to make a kind of paper from a plant called papyrus.

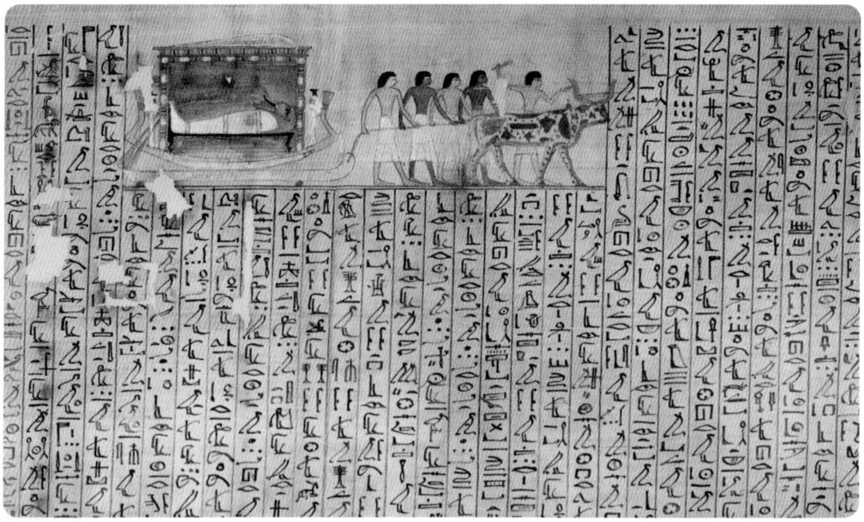

On papyrus, Egyptian doctors recorded their medical cases, detailing symptoms, how to examine a patient and treatments. This is why we know a lot more about Egyptian medicine than about prehistoric medicine.

Writing was also important because doctors could pass on their knowledge more easily to new generations of Egyptian doctors. Unfortunately, the two different kinds of Egyptian writing – hieroglyphs and hieratic writing – were not understood by people from other countries who had their own kinds of writing so doctors from other countries, such as Greece, did not learn much about Egyptian medicine.

Specialist doctors

Egyptian doctors were a mixture of doctor and priest. They were carefully trained, studying the medical papyri recording cases and treatments. Some were general doctors, but others were specialists. The Pharaoh's physician Ir-en-akhty, for example, specialised in eye diseases and problems in the stomach and rectum. One thing they all had in common was using a variety of treatments – herbal remedies, simple surgery, charms, prayers and chants.

Specialist doctors developed because the Pharaoh and his lords were very rich and could afford to employ their own doctors – so the doctors themselves were wealthy enough to spend their time improving their medical knowledge by studying the medical papyri and discussing cases.

Specialists

Causes of illness

Egyptians continued to believe that illnesses were caused by the gods and evil spirits, but they also developed a new natural theory. This theory said that illness was caused when the channels in the body became blocked. This idea came from farming. Egypt was rich because of its farming, a vital part of Egyptian life. People made sure their crops got plenty of water by digging irrigation channels from the river Nile to their fields. If those channels kept running then the crops grew well but, if the irrigation channels became blocked, the crops did not get enough water and died.

Egyptian doctors thought that crops and people had a lot in common. People stayed healthy so long as blood, air and water flowed through the channels around the body, but if the channels became blocked people fell sick. For example, undigested food rotting in the bowels could cause blockages in the channels and so make people ill.

Disease and infection

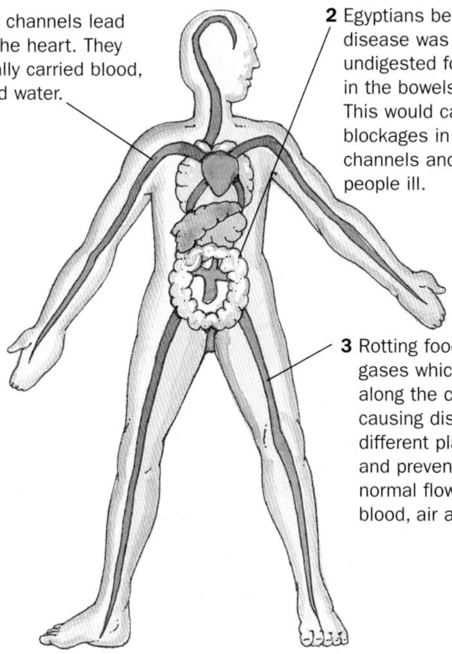

▲ The Egyptian theory of channels in the body.

▲ This is a statue of Sekhmet, the lion-headed goddess of war and plagues. Egyptians believed she could cause and cure plagues of disease. Each medical specialisation had its own god. For example, Dauw was the god of eye diseases, Taweret the goddess of childbirth. Gods protected individual parts of the body; for example, Isis protected the liver and Neith the heart.

Disease and infection

Treatments

Doctors, priests and mothers used many treatments made from herbs, plants, minerals and animal parts. Most ingredients, such as honey, were local but others were brought by traders from abroad. Cinnamon and pepper came from India and China, and malachite from North Africa.

Doctors developed new treatments to unblock blocked channels. These included bleeding the patients (taking blood out of their veins) or making the patients vomit or empty their bowels.

▲ This hieroglyph says swnw (pronounced sewnew) meaning physician. It consists of a man, a pot of medicine and a lancet (knife). Sometimes the physician was drawn leaning on a stick to show he was experienced and well-respected.

The body

Surgery and anatomy

Doctors knew about many parts of the body's anatomy – the heart, lungs, liver and brain, and about veins, arteries, muscles and many bones – although they often did not know exactly what each part did. For example, they did not know that the heart pumps blood around the body.

They did not learn about the body by dissection (careful cutting and analysis of dead bodies) because their religion said the body was needed in the after-life. The most likely method was by examining wounded soldiers or workers injured on building projects. They may have learned about anatomy from embalming, removing and preserving the body's organs after death. However, at times in Egyptian history embalmers were regarded as 'unclean' and were cut off from contact with other people so they could not have passed on knowledge of the body. On the other hand, some doctors were also embalmers and one embalmer was the grandfather of a doctor. So, embalming may have increased knowledge of anatomy but we cannot be certain about this.

Doctors also carried out simple surgery on the outside of the body, cutting out swellings or sewing up wounds. They carried out trephining, cutting holes in the skull, to ease pain or swellings. Doctors had stronger, sharper bronze surgical instruments thanks to improved metal-working skills, developed making weapons, fine jewellery and tools for builders.

The Pharaoh and his government did not do anything to protect the people from illnesses. However, Egyptians took great care to keep clean, probably as part of their religion, to stay at peace with the gods. People washed twice a day and every night and before meals. They used soda, scented oil and ointments as soap. Ladies shaved their bodies with bronze razors and used eye make-up that included powdered emerald-green copper ore which may have reduced eye infections.

Excavations show that richer homes contained a room for washing but did not have plumbing to bring water in and out. People bathed by having a servant pour water over them from a jug. The waste water ran away through a hole in the wall or into a sunken vase in the floor.

Toilets for the poor were wooden stools with a hole above a cup half-filled with sand. Richer families had a limestone seat over a bowl standing in a pit – but all toilets had to be emptied by hand.

Public health

Activities

Your skim-reading identified the factors affecting Egyptian medicine. Now build your detailed knowledge.

1 Working in your pair, complete one of the rows of this table by:
   a summarising each development in column A. Write a sentence or two describing the development below each heading
   b completing columns B and C, using the factors in the box below
   c assessing how great a change each development was. Make sure you explain the reasons for your decision.
2 Your class will now have completed the table. Decide:
   a which factor did most to help Egyptian medicine develop
   b which factor did most to hinder the development of medicine.
3 **Memory map:** Use the information on pages 20–25 to add to your memory map.

Science and technology

War

Superstition and religion

Chance

Government

A. What were the developments?	B. Which factors helped this development take place?	C. Did any factors hinder this development?	D. How great a change? 4 = huge 1 = small
1 Disease and infection			
a Specialist doctors			
b Ideas about the causes of illness			
c Treatments			
2 Public health			
3 Surgery and anatomy			
a Knowledge of the body			
b Surgery			

2.3 Did the Greek doctor Hippocrates completely change medicine?

In the Big Story section you discovered that the Greek doctor Hippocrates was one of the most important people in the history of medicine. Doctors were still following his ideas 2000 years after he died. It's easy to think that someone so important changed medicine completely – but did he?

What was special about the Greeks?

Like the Egyptians, many Greeks became rich from farming and trade while the hard work in the fields and towns was done by slaves and the poor. This allowed the wealthy classes to spend their time being educated. Most continued to believe that the gods controlled everything, but a small number of educated Greeks became interested in finding more logical, natural explanations for all kinds of aspects of the world around them. One example was Anaximander, who argued that thunder was not the sound of the god Zeus being angry but was a natural event, caused by air being trapped in a cloud and bursting out with great force. Men like Socrates, Plato and Aristotle became famous philosophers (meaning 'lovers of knowledge'), investigating mathematics, science, astronomy, politics and other subjects.

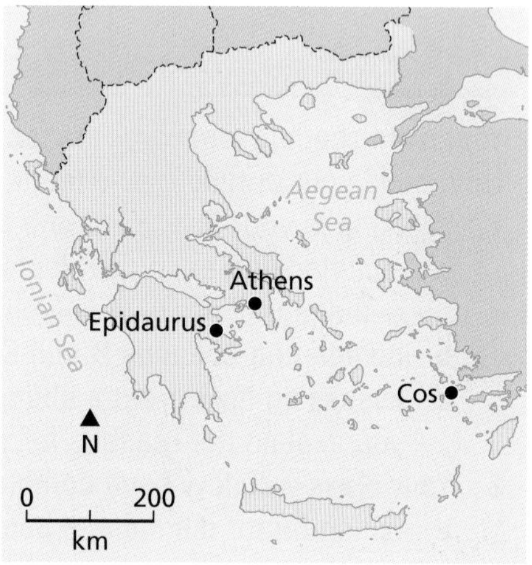

▲ The Greek Empire

Activities

1. Why were the Greeks likely to have new ideas about medicine?
2. Which aspect of medicine were the Greeks most likely to change?
3. The chart opposite helps you investigate Hippocrates. We have begun to fill it in for you but your task is to copy the chart and complete the rest. Take pages 28–31 in turn and answer the questions there, then return to this chart and add in what you have discovered **in pencil**.
4. When you have completed your draft, look over the chart and finalise your thoughts. Add small drawings or use colours to pick out the most important developments.

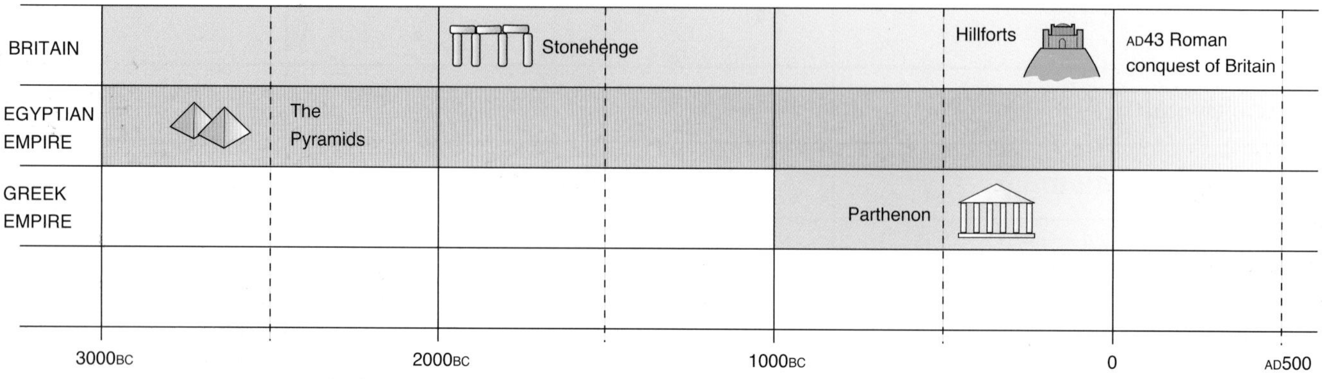

Smarter Revision: 'Role of the individual' chart

During your course you will need to record the achievements of a number of key individuals – Hippocrates, Galen, Vesalius, Pasteur and others. It will be much easier to work out why each person was important (and, later, to revise their achievements) if you use the same kind of chart for each of them. That way you will be able to recall the pattern of the chart in your mind if you need it in an examination.

'Role of the individual' chart

Hippocrates

Hippocrates was born around 460BC and died around 370BC. He was a teacher and doctor on the island of Cos.

BEFORE

What did the Egyptians think caused disease?

Ideas about causes

People believed that gods and spirits caused illnesses. Some Egyptians had begun to think about...

How did people try to treat or prevent illness?

Preventing and treating illnesses

Treatments often involved...

FACTORS

How did enquiry help him?

✓ that HELPED

Attitudes...

Can you suggest other factors that helped Hippocrates?

How did religion hinder the spread of ideas?

that HINDERED ✗

Religion...

Can you suggest another factor that hindered Hippocrates?

AFTER

POSITIVE SHORT-TERM IMPACT

Can you complete this acronym?

- *H = Hippocratic Oath. That meant ...*
- *H= ... ... books which resulted in ...*
- *4H = ...*
- *O = ...*
- *T = ...*

POSITIVE LONG-TERM IMPACT

Suggest two or three ways in which Hippocrates' work had a long-term impact.

LIMITATIONS

What aspects of medicine were not changed?

What did Hippocrates do that was so important?

Activities

1. **'Role of the individual' chart:** Use pages 28–29 to fill in the 'Impact' boxes on your chart (see page 27).
2. Work in a small group and devise a way of explaining the theory of the four humours to people who do not understand it. You could use props, physical movement, labels or tabards to help you.

Hippocrates was born c.460BC on the island of Cos where he worked as a doctor and teacher of doctors. Very little else is known about him. He died c.370BC.

H The Hippocratic Oath

This oath was created by Hippocrates to give people confidence in doctors. It makes clear that doctors are not magicians. They have to keep high standards of treatment and behaviour, and work for the benefit of their patients, not to make themselves wealthy.

'I will swear by Apollo, Asclepius and by all the gods that I will carry out this oath. I will use treatment to help the sick according to my ability and judgement but never with a view to injury or wrongdoing. I will not give poison to anybody. Whatever I see or hear professionally will be kept secret.'

H The Hippocratic Collection of books

Hippocrates probably wrote some of the books known as the Hippocratic Collection but many were written by other doctors. This collection is important because it is the first detailed list of symptoms and treatments. Doctors continued to use the theories and methods in these books for many centuries.

O Observing and recording

Hippocrates showed that it was very important to observe and record carefully the symptoms and development of diseases. This had two advantages. Doctors were more likely to choose the right cure if they took care to find the cause of the problem. These notes could then be used to help with diagnosis and treatment of future patients.

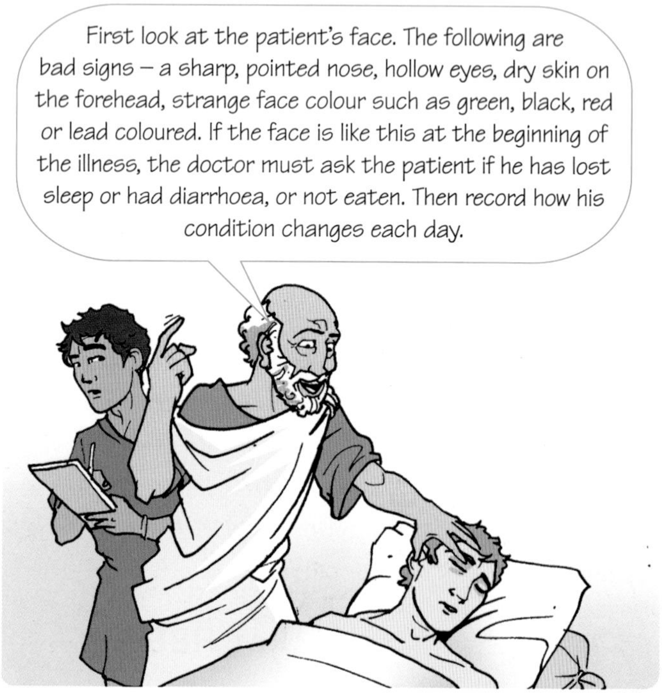

T Natural treatments

Hippocrates encouraged doctors to look for natural treatments for illnesses rather than praying to the gods for help.

4H The causes of disease

▲ Blood ▲ Yellow bile ▲ Black bile ▲ Phlegm

Did Hippocrates end the belief that gods caused illnesses?

Hippocrates thought that doctors should always look for natural causes for sickness and use natural treatments, but not everybody agreed with him. The best evidence comes from the Asclepeia. An Asclepion was a temple dedicated to Asclepius, the Greek god of healing.

The Greeks continued to believe that the gods affected every part of their lives. If there was a good harvest they said the gods were pleased. If there was an earthquake they said the gods were angry. Asclepius, the son of the great god Apollo, was the Greeks' chief god of healing. By 200BC Asclepeia had been built in every Greek town. Each Asclepion had its own priests who were experienced and skilled healers.

Some Asclepeia were very large, like modern health resorts. The priests encouraged patients, depending on their illness, to take exercise and cleanse themselves in the baths. Patients built up their strength by eating regular meals and had plenty of rest, including time for prayer. The priests also carried out simple surgery, probably while the patient was in a drugged sleep. One recorded example is the removal of fragments of a spearhead from the sufferer's cheek.

Activities

1. Who was Asclepius and how was he supposed to help the sick?
2. Why did many visitors to Asclepeia feel better?
3. Which treatments at the Asclepeia would Hippocrates have approved of?
4. What evidence is there that people believed that visiting Asclepeia helped them?

Source 1

▲ A carving of the god Asclepius treating a patient while another patient lies down. The god was helped by his daughters, Panacea and Hygieia, and by his snake, which could cure blindness by licking the patient's eyelids. Asclepius is usually shown with his snake twined around his staff. Snakes were symbols of health because they could shed their skins and so appear younger and healthier. Harmless snakes were left in the abaton overnight while patients slept.

Source 2

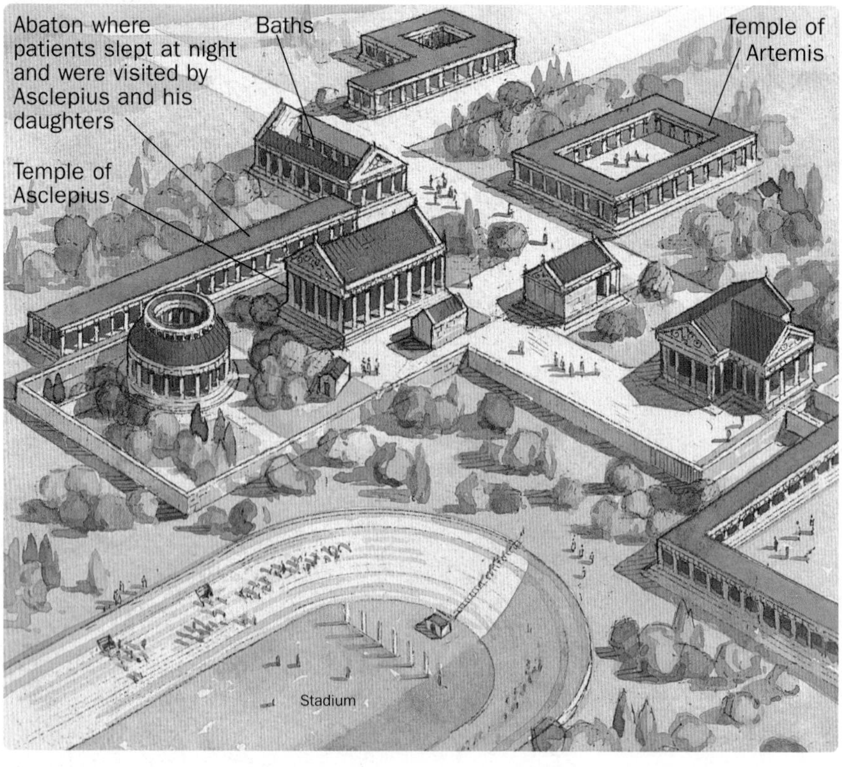

▲ Some Asclepeia were very simple temples but others were much larger. The Asclepion at Epidaurus contained baths, a gymnasium, an athletics stadium, and a theatre seating 14,000 people.

Source 3

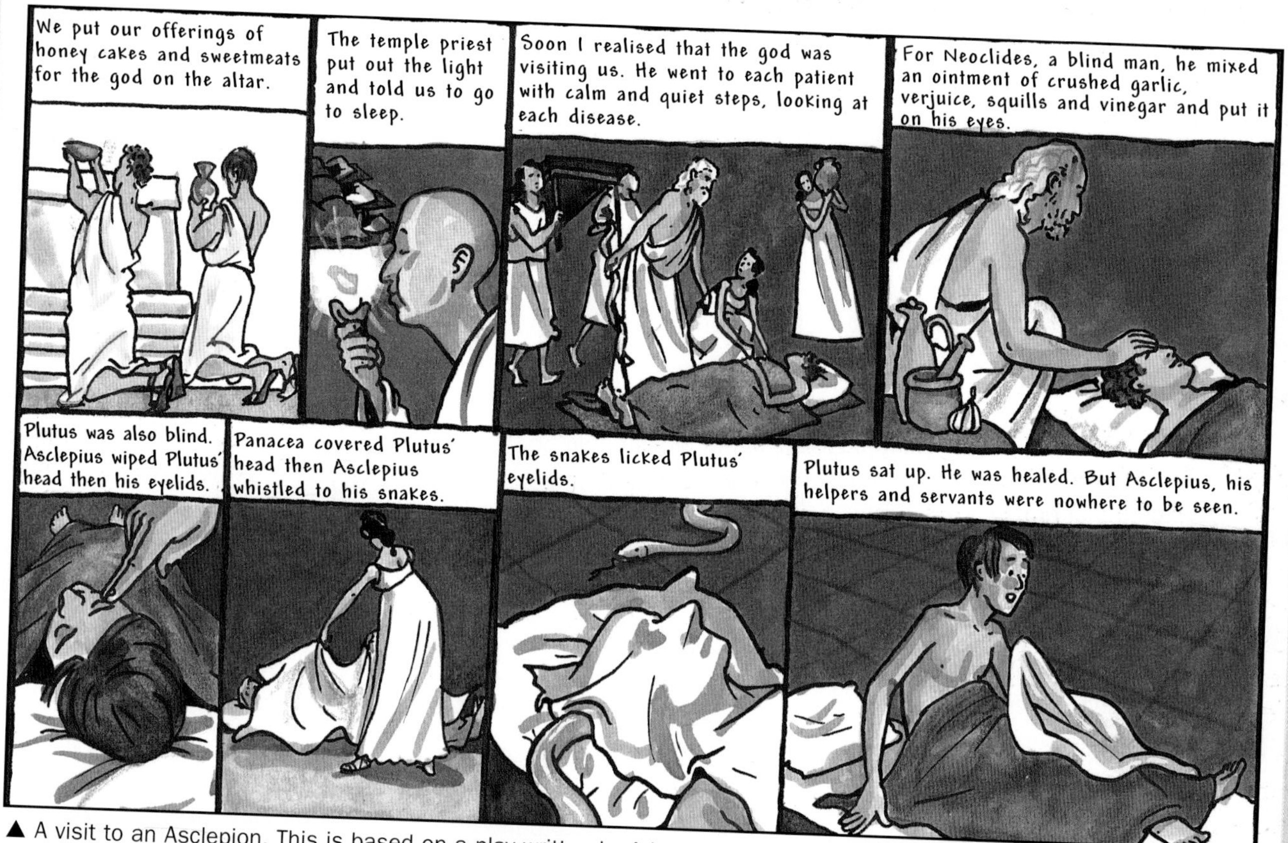

▲ A visit to an Asclepion. This is based on a play written by Aristophanes, a Greek writer, around 400BC.

Did Greek cures work?

Many Greeks believed that the god Asclepius could heal them but the evidence also shows that the god and his priests were very practical healers. The ointment mixed by Asclepius in picture 4 of Source 3 might well have helped if the 'blindness' was caused by an infection which made the eyes close up. We now know that garlic acts like an antibiotic to kill infections, while vinegar cleans wounds like an antiseptic. Verjuice is the juice of unripe fruit such as green apples and squill is a plant used in a wide range of cures.

Source 4

◀ Archaeologists have discovered votive stones like this. They were thanksgiving offerings to the god Asclepius, paid for by people grateful for their recoveries. Some were carved in the shape of the affected part of the body. Others have inscriptions, describing the ailment and the cure and giving thanks to Asclepius. The inscription here reads 'Tyche to Asklepios and Hygieia as a thank offering'. Some votive stones record recoveries from serious problems such as a stomach abscess and even complete paralysis.

How much of Greek medicine was really changed by Hippocrates?

Activities

These activities sum up how much Hippocrates changed medicine.
Use pages 28–33 to help you.
Read the statements below about Greek medicine.

1 List the correct ones and explain which evidence supports each correct statement.
2 Re-write the incorrect statements so they are correct and include evidence to show why your version is correct.

Disease and infection

a Hippocrates completely changed ideas about why people became ill.
b Hippocrates taught doctors to observe and record patients' symptoms carefully.
c Treatments and cures did not change. People still relied on herbal remedies and prayers.

Public health

d Greek rulers followed Hippocrates' ideas and took great care to protect people's health.

Surgery and anatomy

e Greek surgeons made some minor improvements in surgery.
f Greek doctors made important new discoveries about anatomy.

Disease and infection – treatment and cures

Source 1

From *On the Treatment of Acute Diseases*, a book in the Hippocratic Collection:

'If the pain is under the diaphragm, clear the bowels with a medicine made from black hellebore, cumin or other fragrant herbs. A bath will help pneumonia as it soothes pain and brings up phlegm.'

Source 2

▲ A bleeding cup from a set of Greek medical instruments. The warm cup was placed over a small cut and, as the cup cooled, it caused blood to flow out and fill the cup.

Source 4

From *A Programme for Health*, a book in the Hippocratic Collection:

'In winter, people should eat as much as possible and drink as little as possible – unwatered wine, bread, roast meat and few vegetables. This will keep the body hot and dry. In summer they should drink more and eat less – watered wine, barley cakes and boiled meat so that the body will stay cold and moist. Walking should be fast in winter and slow in summer.'

Public health

Source 3

◀ A public lavatory in the Greek city of Corinth. Running water under the seats took the waste away.

However, public lavatories were rare. City governments left people to keep clean and prevent illnesses in their own ways. The rich could afford their own baths and lavatories but most people lived in small dirty houses with only basins to wash in. The streets were filthy but the city governments did not organise any cleaning.

Surgery and anatomy

Source 5

▲ A set of surgical instruments. Greek surgeons were good at setting broken bones and could amputate limbs, although they did not have effective anaesthetics. They learned how to drain the lungs of people who had pneumonia, but very few operations were done inside the body. Greek doctors were much more interested in understanding the causes of illness and in remedies based on the four humours than in surgery – probably because it was so dangerous.

The work of Aristotle (384–322BC)

Aristotle was one of the greatest Greek philosophers. His interest in biology led him to dissect animals and plants with great care. Like Hippocrates he believed that careful, methodical observation was the basis of all learning. This scientific method was copied by others for many centuries. William Harvey, who discovered the circulation of the blood in the 1600s, was one scientist who admired Aristotle's approach.

Although he did not dissect human bodies Aristotle's studies led him to suggest that the heart and brain are the most important organs in the body. He suggested that the heart provides the body's heat and the brain cools it down, the two working together to control the body.

Activities

3 Now for an overall conclusion about Greek medicine. Do you agree with the statement below? What evidence would you use to support your view?
'Greek medicine was a mixture of natural and supernatural methods, just like prehistoric and Egyptian medicine.'

4 **'Role of the individual' chart:** Complete your chart on Hippocrates from page 27.

5 **Memory map:** Update your memory map on page 15.

Source 6

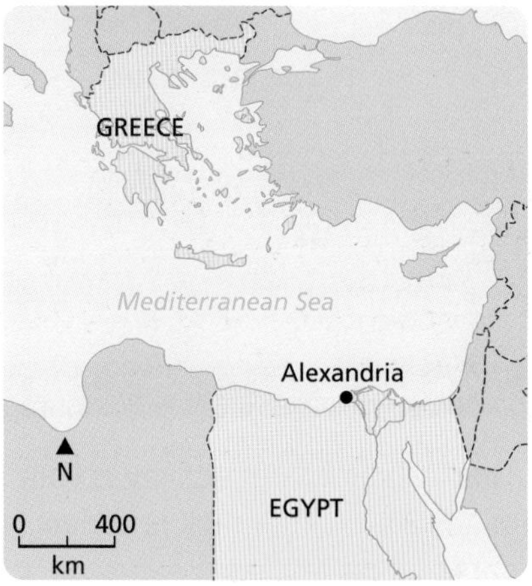

Around 330BC Alexander the Great conquered Egypt and made it part of the Greek Empire. He founded the city of **Alexandria** and made it the capital of Egypt. At Alexandria, the Greeks built a university and library that collected medical books from India, China and Mesopotamia as well as those by Hippocrates and other Greek writers. It became the greatest centre of medical learning in the ancient world.

Dissection of bodies was illegal in Greece so doctors had not developed detailed knowledge of anatomy and physiology. However, human dissection was allowed for a time in Alexandria. This led to important discoveries. Herophilus, who lived around 350BC, discovered that the brain, not the heart, controls the workings of the body. He also identified parts of the stomach. Erasistratus dissected the brain and began to understand that the brain sends messages to the rest of the body through the nerves. He also dissected hearts and wondered whether the heart was a pump, pumping air and blood around the body. It wasn't until the 1600s that William Harvey, an English scientist, proved that the heart pumps blood around the body.

2.4 Did the Romans just steal the Greeks' ideas ... or did they have any good medical ideas of their own?

Greek ideas were important because they were still being used over a thousand years later. The Romans copied Greek ideas but did they have any good medical ideas of their own? Your task is to create a 'washing line' to record your answer.

Activities

This 'washing line' activity is your main activity for pages 36–41. Your task is to decide where the five cards go on the line.

Causes of disease

Treatments

Surgery

Knowledge of anatomy

Public health

1 Sources 1–4 provide evidence to support four of the scenes on pages 12–13. Which four scenes are they?
2 Now use pages 12–13 to start thinking about the 'washing line'. Pencil on your 'washing line' your first thoughts on which topics were continuities from the Greeks and which were changes.
3 As you work through pages 34–43 position the cards on the line and jot down next to each card the evidence that supports its position.

Source 1

◀ Roman altars found in Britain include inscriptions like this: 'To the holy god Asclepius and to Hygieia, Julius Saturninus set this [altar] up.'

Source 2

◀ Dioscorides, a Greek surgeon in the Roman army, wrote a book c.AD64 describing many herbal remedies. Modern tests show that at least 20 per cent of the remedies contained ingredients, such as honey or garlic, that would have helped patients by killing infections.

Continuities borrowed from Greece

Minor changes but closely linked to Greek methods

Changes the

Source 3

From *On Medicine*, a book by Celsus, a wealthy Roman who wrote books on many aspects of medicine:

'A surgeon should be youthful or at any rate nearer youth than age; with a strong and steady hand which never trembles, and ready to use the left hand as well as the right; with vision sharp and clear, and spirit undaunted; filled with pity; so that he wishes to cure the patient, yet is not moved by his cries, to go too fast, or cut less than is necessary; but he does everything just as if the cries of pain cause him no emotion.'

Source 4

◀ This wall sculpture shows a Roman doctor inspecting the eye of a patient. What are the two objects shown hanging on the wall upside down?

Activities

4 Which clues on the map suggest that the Romans borrowed a lot of Greek ideas?

5 **a** Which clues suggest that the Romans might have come up with new ideas and methods of their own?

b Which clues can you link to any new ideas you found on pages 14–15?

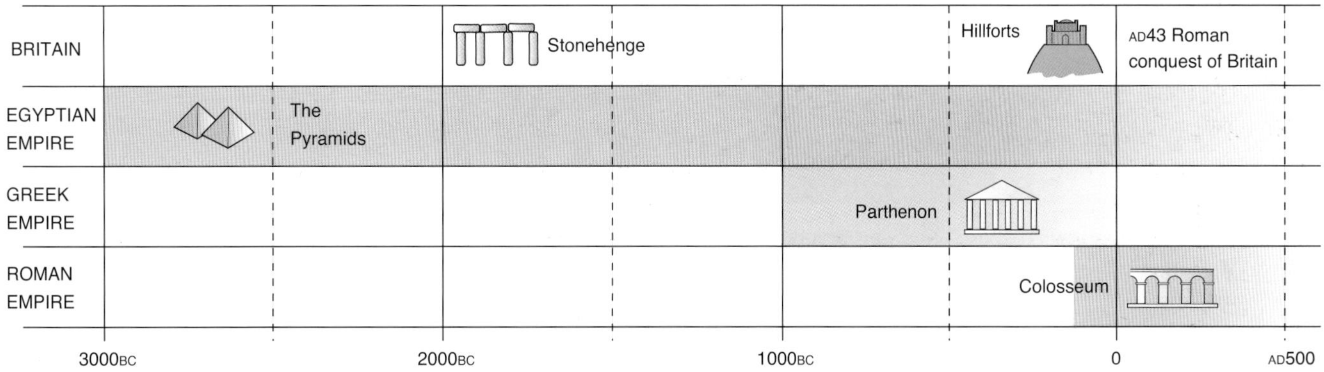

What difference did Galen make?

Now for somebody really important! Claudius Galen is one of the top five most important people in the history of medicine, possibly more important even than Hippocrates. Your task is to find out why – and use a photograph to sum up what you have found. You could even create your own photograph as an example of Even Smarter Revision.

Activity

Sources 1 and 2 introduce some important aspects of Galen's career. What can you learn from them about Galen and why his work was so important in the history of medicine?

Source 1

From Galen's book *On Anatomy*, written C.AD190:

'Human bones are the subjects that you should first get to know. You cannot just read about bones in books but you must also acquaint yourself with the appearance of each of the bones, by the use of your own eye, handling each bone by itself. At Alexandria this is very easy because the doctors there let their students inspect human bodies. If you cannot get to Alexandria it is not impossible to see human bones. I have often done this where tombs have been broken. On one occasion a river carried a corpse downstream before depositing it on the riverbank. Here it lay, as though prepared by a doctor for his pupils' lesson. Once I examined the skeleton of a robber lying on a mountain-side. If you do not have the luck to do this you can still dissect an ape. Choose apes which most resemble men, which walk and run on two legs, where you will find other parts as in man.'

Source 2

▲ A wall painting in an Italian church showing Galen (left) and Hippocrates. The painting dates from the 1200s, 900 years after Galen died.

Smarter Revision: Digital camera

exam BUSTERS

Revision can be fun. You probably don't believe this but here's how to enjoy revision by thinking hard and being creative. This class wanted to sum up why Galen was so important so they created this picture.

This is how they did it:

1 They investigated Galen's work and completed a 'role of the individual' chart for him.

2 Then they started thinking creatively – how could they turn this information into a picture they could revise from? In this picture each feature they have included in the photo tells you something important about Galen's work.

3 The class took the picture and annotated it – writing in a short explanation of what each object tells us about Galen.

4 They added two think bubbles to sum up Galen's thoughts – but we've taken off those notes and thought bubbles!

Activities

Either
Annotate your own copy of this picture. All the information is on pages 36–39. The activity on page 38 will help you.
Or
You could even produce your own summary picture of Galen's work. Have fun!

Why was Galen so important?

Activities

1. On your own copy of this page:
   a. mark SIMILARITIES between the work of Galen and Hippocrates in BLUE.
   b. mark DIFFERENCES between the work of Galen and Hippocrates in RED.
2. What was Galen's contribution to:
   a. the understanding and treatment of disease and illness
   b. knowledge of anatomy and surgery?
3. Why is Galen so important in the history of medicine? Write down three reasons AND say which of them you think is the most important.
4. Use this information to place your cards on your 'washing line' on page 34.
5. **'Role of the individual' chart:** Build up a chart (see page 27) for Galen.

Claudius Galen was born in Pergamum in Greece in AD129, the son of an architect. Galen's father had a dream in which Asclepius said that his son would become a physician. Galen began studying medicine when he was 16, even travelling to study at the great medical school in Alexandria. He also became a surgeon at a gladiators' school, gaining experience treating wounds and increasing his knowledge of anatomy.

Age 20, Galen moved to Rome. He was a great showman and put on public performances, dissecting animals and giving talks. He also had a terrible temper, inherited from his mother, who he said 'bit her maids and was always shouting at my father'. When plague broke out, the Emperor Marcus Aurelius summoned Galen to take care of the royal family and he remained doctor to the emperors for the rest of his life.

The work of Claudius Galen

What really made Galen famous were the 60 books he wrote. They combined Greek ideas with what he had learned from his own work in Alexandria and Rome and presented it all so convincingly that they became the basis for medical teaching and learning for the next 1500 years. For most of that time nobody dared to say that Galen was wrong!

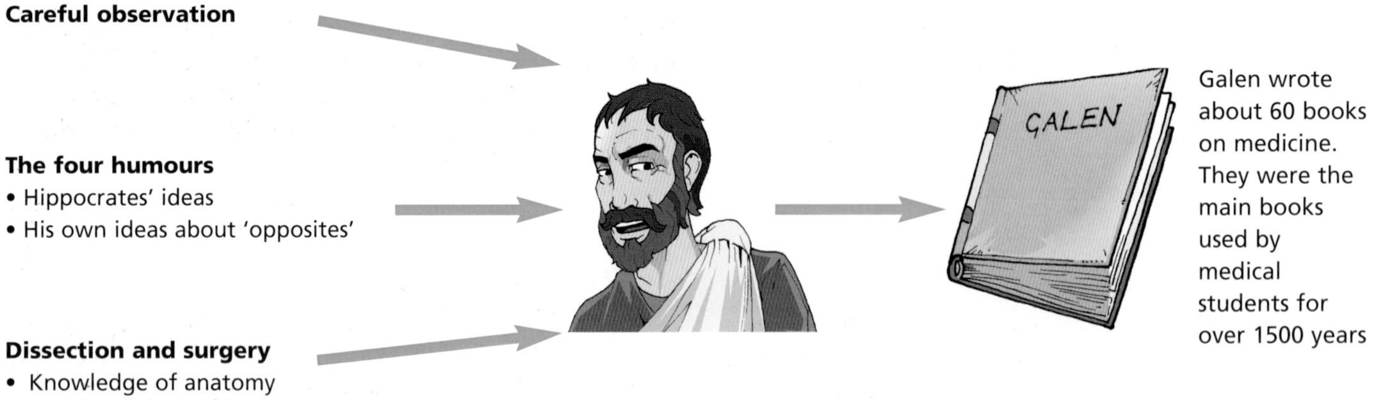

Diagnosis and the four humours

Galen's work was built on the key ideas in the Hippocratic Collection:

Four humours – Like Hippocrates, Galen believed that illness was caused by imbalances in the four humours.

Observation – Like Hippocrates, Galen told doctors to observe and examine patients carefully, taking the pulse and detailed notes of symptoms. In AD167 Galen made detailed notes on the plague sweeping across the empire, recording how his patients had fever, thirst, diarrhoea, skin rash and spat blood. His notes were so thorough this plague became known as 'Galen's plague'.

Treatments

Galen followed Hippocrates in giving advice on diet and exercise to prevent illness. His most common treatment was bleeding patients to restore the balance of the humours. He used bleeding far more than Hippocrates, who had preferred to interfere with the body as little as possible. Galen also developed the idea of using 'opposites' to balance the humours. For example, if a patient's symptom was too much phlegm then the illness was caused by cold. Galen's treatment was the opposite of cold – heat! He treated the patient by using hot ingredients such as peppers in his cures. If a disease was caused by heat, then the patient would need a cooling cure, perhaps treating this with cucumber in the medicine or diet.

Anatomy and dissection

Hippocrates had not done much work on anatomy and had not said that dissection was important. Galen disagreed. He believed that physicians should find out as much as possible about the structure and workings of the body, if possible dissecting human bodies themselves. If this was not possible, he advised doctors to dissect apes because they were most like humans.

Galen demonstrated his discoveries about the workings of the nervous system by dissecting a pig. As the pig squealed on the table, Galen cut into its neck, finding the nerves. He could have cut through the right nerve immediately to stop the pig squealing but that did not appeal to Galen's showmanship. Instead he announced, 'I will cut this nerve but the pig will keep squealing.' He cut, and the pig kept squealing. He cut again, building up the tension, and again the pig kept squealing. Then he announced, 'When I cut this nerve, the pig will stop squealing.' He cut and the pig was silent!

Although he often had to dissect animals, not humans, some of Galen's discoveries were important. He proved that the brain, not the heart, controlled speech, and that the arteries, and not just the veins, carried blood around the body. Inevitably he made mistakes because the bodies of apes and pigs are not the same as those of humans, but it was to be well over a thousand years before anyone dared to challenge Galen's findings.

Galen's influence

Galen wrote hundreds of books, covering every aspect of medicine in an extremely detailed and well-organised way. He included the work of earlier doctors such as Hippocrates but also added his own work on treatments and on the structure and workings of the body. It seemed as if Galen had covered everything, so people believed that his books had all the answers. That was one reason why Galen's books became the basis for medical training for over a thousand years.

A second reason why so many people believed Galen was always right was that his ideas fitted in with the ideas of the Christian Church, which controlled education in Europe in the Middle Ages. Although Galen was not a Christian, he believed that the body had been created by one god, who had made all the parts of the body fit together perfectly. This matched the Christian belief that God had created human beings, so for centuries Christians did not dare to question Galen's ideas.

Public health – the Romans' big idea

Information

What is public health?
Governments organise public health systems to protect their people from disease. This includes providing, for example, fresh water, sewers and hospitals and making laws to force people to try to prevent diseases spreading.

Activities

1 Why was the army so important to the Roman public health system?
2 Make two lists: a) the strengths and b) the weaknesses of the system.
3 Do you think the Roman public health system was an important step forward in the history of medicine?
4 Complete your 'washing line' activity on page 34.

Why did the Romans want to protect the public's health?

Roman rulers needed healthy soldiers to control the Empire. Healthy workers and merchants were needed to keep the Empire fed and prosperous. Therefore they built their towns, villas and army forts in healthy places, away from marshland and polluted water. They tried to keep army forts and cities clean and made sure people had fresh water.

Their public health schemes (see opposite page) used their great skills as builders and engineers. Engineers, often from the army, kept everything running and dealt with repairs.

How successful was Roman public health?

Roman public health schemes were the best there had been – and better than anything in Europe for the next 1500 years. But they were not perfect. What were the problems?

Problem 1

They could not stop plagues spreading. In the AD160s a plague (known as Galen's plague) killed 5 million people. A Roman writer said 'plague polluted everything with death. Everywhere fields and towns have no farmers or inhabitants.' Part of the problem was the army because soldiers carried disease wherever they were sent to fight or defend the Empire.

Problem 2

Sewers sometimes spread disease. In York the sewers were too large so water did not flow through quickly enough to clear sewage in the bottom of the sewers. The rough surface of stone sewers also trapped the bacteria that cause disease.

Problem 3

Towns could still be dirty places. People had to carry water upstairs. If they did not want to carry it down again they just heaved it out of a window. The poet Juvenal warned 'Each open window may be a death trap. So hope and pray, poor man, that the local housewives drop nothing worse on your head than a bedpan full of slops!'

The key features of Roman public health schemes in towns

Fresh water from springs

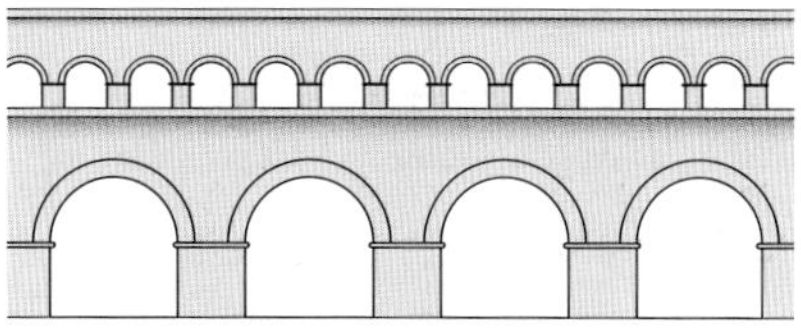

Aqueducts carried fresh water many miles to towns

> In the countryside little changed. The homes of the rich had bath-houses but across Europe most people's homes did not change.

Water pipes carrying the water around towns were made from lead or timber. Some people would have developed lead poisoning but the Romans could not know this was happening

Reservoirs held the water supply and distributed it to the piping system

Public fountains provided water for drinking and washing. Most people got their water from fountains, street pumps and rain-barrels because they were not rich enough to have water piped to their houses

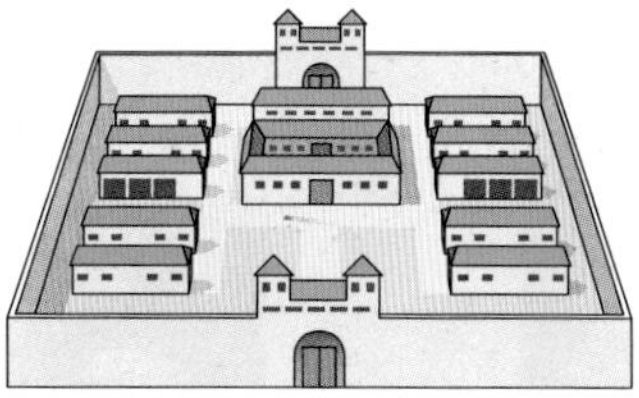

Forts had their own bath-house, water supply and latrines. Many also had hospitals for the soldiers

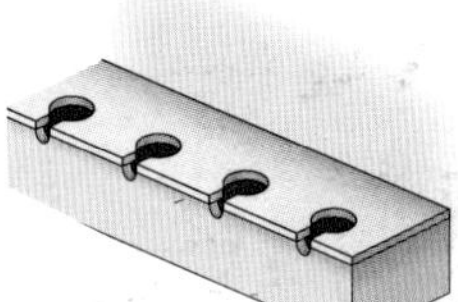

Public latrines were often flushed by water from the public baths and then drained into the sewers. They often seated twenty people in one room

Private homes of the rich were supplied with water but even here the water had to be carried upstairs in buckets by slaves. If there was a drought, the supply to houses was cut off to save water

Bath-houses were places for washing, exercise, talk and business. Even small towns had a bath-house charging users only a quadrans, the smallest Roman coin. In a large town such as Lincoln, 5,000 people used the baths every week though the water was only changed once a week

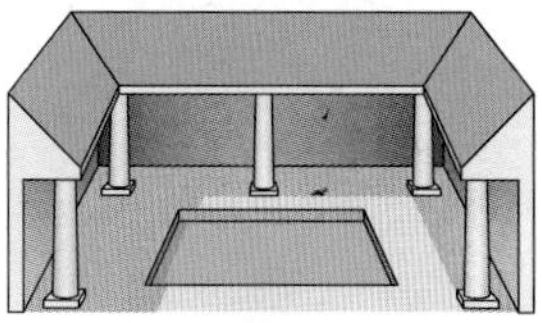

Sewers carried away waste from houses, latrines and baths. They were built of stone and depended on there being enough water in the system to flush them out. If there wasn't enough rain the waste built up in the sewers, spreading disease instead of stopping it

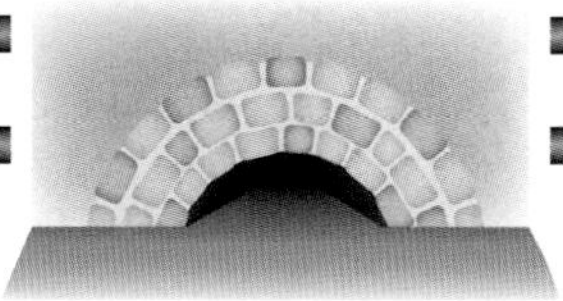

The sewers emptied into rivers, which were used to wash clothes and also for washing and drinking water

Did the Romans really improve public health in Britain?

Activities

1 Read Source 1. What does the author say:
   a is our usual image of public health in Roman towns
   b was the reality of public health in Roman towns?
2 Complete the chart below, collecting evidence of the impact of the Romans on public health in Britain.
3 Did the Romans really improve public health in Britain? Give your verdict and list the key pieces of evidence that support your view.

Public health improvements	Weaknesses of public health in Britain

Source 1

From Lindsay Allason-Jones, *Women in Roman Britain*, 1989. Dr Allason-Jones is a historian and archaeologist, an expert on life in Roman Britain.

'The impression given by most descriptions of town life in the Roman empire is of spacious, well-organised streets, water on tap, an efficient sewerage system; but this may not be the whole picture or even an accurate one. The great civic bath-houses, unless kept scrupulously clean, would have been hotbeds of disease. Housewives had to carry water from public water tanks or draw it from a well. Sewers were often open or built very close to the surface, leading to unpleasant smells and disease.'

Source 2

Away from the towns

▲ Before the Roman invasion in AD43, there were no towns in Britain. Britons lived in roundhouses like this in small farming communities. After AD43 this way of life continued for the majority of Britons. Only a minority lived in towns or villas with baths and heating. Keeping clean, collecting water and being hygienic was up to families and individuals, not organised by local rulers.

Source 3

The impact of disease

▲ Roman towns suffered from regular outbreaks of plague and other diseases despite their public health schemes. This mass grave in Gloucester contains victims of 'Galen's plague' in the AD160s. There were many more outbreaks of epidemic disease which killed hundreds of people or more in towns.

Source 4

Public health in towns

Water supply

Clay-lined channels were dug to bring fresh water to towns. The channel at Dorchester was 8 miles long, 5 feet (1.6m) wide and 3 feet (1m) deep). Two million gallons of fresh water flowed into Wroxeter each day and was distributed around the town through lead and timber pipes. Water supplies mostly went to baths and water tanks for public use. Few houses received their own water supplies.

Baths

Public baths have been discovered by archaeologists in most Roman towns. In a large town like Lincoln, 5000 people used the baths every week. However, this wasn't as wonderful as it sounds. The water was only changed once a week. Archaeologists have also discovered that the baths in Exeter and Wroxeter were demolished long before the end of Roman Britain. Using the baths may not have been as popular as we assume – but we can't be certain.

Sewers and toilets

Every town needed public toilets as few homes had toilets that emptied directly into sewers. At home, people used pots that they emptied into sewers or rivers. Most towns had timber or open sewers with only the largest towns, such as York, having stone sewers. However, even stone caused problems. In York the sewers were too large so water did not flow through quickly enough to clear sewage in the bottom of the sewers. This led to bad smells and helped to spread disease.

▲ The bath-house at Wroxeter in Shropshire was one of the best in Britain with a large outdoor exercise yard and pool, as well as indoor facilities.

Source 5

After the Roman army left

A reconstruction ▶ drawing of Canterbury in the fifth century. After the Roman army left Britain, life for the people changed. Towns were slowly abandoned. Public health systems gradually stopped working without the engineering skills of the Roman army.

2.5 Review: Why was ancient medicine so significant when people didn't even know what made them sick?

You have completed your investigation of each different society. Now it's time to put all those pieces together to see the overall pattern of ancient medicine. Why was it so important when so many of their ideas were wrong?

Disease and infection – see blue rows
Surgery and anatomy – see red rows
Public health – see green rows

	Prehistory	Ancient Egypt
DISEASE AND INFECTION HEALERS	Mothers and family members Medicine men	Priests at temples Army surgeons Specialist doctors
IDEAS ABOUT CAUSES	Gods and spirits	Blocked channels
TREATMENTS	Remedies made from herbs, animal parts, and Prayers, charms and chants 	minerals  Purging
SURGERY AND ANATOMY SURGERY	Simple surgery on visible wounds and tumours Splints for fractured bones Trephining (cutting hole in skull) 	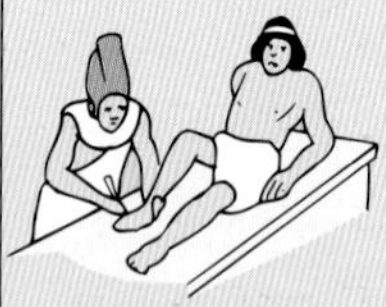 Herbal anaesthetics e.g. honey on wounds to stop infection
ANATOMY		The main bones and organs
PUBLIC HEALTH	Hunter-gatherers moved on, avoiding creating disease through waste	Individuals washed carefully because of religion People took care of themselves 

Activities

1 **Memory map:** On pages 14–15 you began to build up a memory map for ancient medicine. Use the information on this page to check and complete it.

2 **Living graph:** On page 6 we set you a task of keeping a record of changes and continuities in medicine using a living graph. Use the information on this page to check and complete your graph.

3 Which ancient medical ideas and methods do you think were important because:

a they made people healthier

b they lasted a long time and had great influence even if they were not correct?

Use pages 52–53, 84–85 and 112–115 to help you.

	Ancient Greece	Roman Empire
	Priests at Asclepia Specialist doctors – followers of Hippocrates and Galen	
	Theory of four humours	
	 Bleeding and purging Rest exercise and diet	Galen's treatment by 'opposites'
	Opium, alcohol, wine and vinegar to stop infection	
	Aristotle's work on the importance of the heart Discoveries at Alexandria about the brain and heart	Galen emphasised the importance of dissection
	Doctors emphasised the value of good cleanliness People took care of themselves	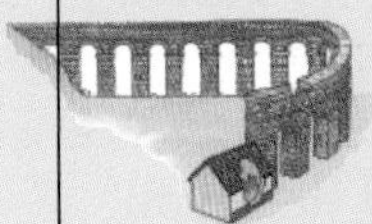 The army built public health systems. The Roman Government built aqueducts, sewers and baths although they could not prevent disease from spreading

Smarter Revision: Factors chart

1 How did their way of life affect medicine?

One important thing, true throughout history, that you need to remember is that **people's ways of life affected their ideas about medicine and their methods of treatment.**

Here are five important developments in the way people lived.

A Hunter-gatherer lifestyle

B Large cities

C Irrigation of fields

D Wealth and love of education and philosophy

E Use of papyrus and writing

2 The factor hunt

We have been concentrating on the continuities and changes in medicine, but you don't just need to describe **how** medicine and health developed. You need to explain **why** it changed at certain times and why it stayed the same at others. We began looking at explanations on pages 20–25 and now it's time to take part in a detailed factor hunt. Tracking the factors across the history of medicine will help you do this much more effectively – and get better marks in your exam.

Here's what you need to do, not just here but as you go through the whole history of medicine.

- Identify examples of how each factor affected medicine and health.
- For each example, record whether the factor helped or hindered the development of medicine and health.
- Assess the overall impact of each factor.

Factors chart

1 Factor	2 Evidence of factor helping development	3 Evidence of factor hindering development	4 Assessment – did this factor do more to help or hinder development?
War	*Battlefield surgery*		
Government		*It's not the Pharaoh's job to keep people healthy.*	
Religion			

Activities

Use the examples below to complete your own 'factors chart' like the one above. First fill in all the factors in the first column.

1. Take each ball in turn and decide which factor it's an example of. Put it in your chart in either column 2 or column 3 of the correct row. Some rows will have several examples in them.
2. Are there any links between two factors? (Think about any balls that might go in more than one row.)
3. Once you have filled up columns 2 and 3 complete column 4, assessing each factor, balancing out the ways it helped and the ways it hindered progress.
4. In one minute, explain to the rest of your class which factor you think had the greatest impact on ancient medicine.

Meet the Examiner: Introducing your examination

Your Medicine Through Time examination

The Medicine Through Time examination is 1 hour and 45 minutes long and is divided into three parts.

Section A covers one of the three themes – Disease and Infection, Surgery and Anatomy or Public Health. You WILL know which theme is being examined in Section A.

Section A contains one question with four parts. You must do all four parts. Spend around 55 minutes on Section A.

Answering Section A questions

Section A questions are based on a set of sources in a sources booklet. The sources may be any combination of text, pictures, diagrams or statistical information.

Source A

Source B

Source C

THEME

Focus on the theme for Section A – in this case, Public Health. You will show what you know about the other two themes in Sections B and C.

MARK ALLOCATIONS

Divide your 55 minutes to spend more time on the parts with higher marks. As a rough guide, spend 2 minutes per mark – so 8 minutes on a 4 mark question.

SECTION A

You **must** answer this question.

Total marks for this question: 26 marks

Public Health

1 Study **Sources A, B and C** in the Sources Booklet and then answer all parts of Question 1 which follow. In your answers you should refer to the sources by their letters.

(a) What does **Source A** suggest about attitudes to public health in Roman times? Explain your answer using **Source A** and **your knowledge**. *(4 marks)*

(b) What different attitudes to public health are suggested by **Source B**? Explain your answer using **Sources A** and **B** and **your knowledge**. *(6 marks)*

(c) Why were there different attitudes to public health at these times? Explain your answer using **Sources A** and **B** and **your knowledge**. *(8 marks)*

(d) Study **Source C**.
Public health has improved at different times for different reasons. Why was this?
Explain your answer using **Sources A, B** and **C** and **your knowledge**. *(8 marks)*

TIMING

Stick closely to 55 minutes for Section A. If you spend too much time on Section A, you are short of time for Sections B and C. Time yourself carefully.

TAKE TIME TO THINK

People who do well in exams don't just rush into writing. They take a few moments to think about their answers – what is most important to say? What order should I make my points in? You DO have time to think and plan.

USING SOURCES AND YOUR OWN KNOWLEDGE

Each part asks you to use both the sources and your knowledge – make sure you use both. This section isn't just about what's in the sources.

Answering Section A, part (a) questions

SECTION A
Surgery and Anatomy

1 (a) What does Source A suggest about the surgery carried out in the Roman period?
Explain your answer using Source A and your knowledge. *(4 marks)*

Source A

'A surgeon should be youthful or at any rate nearer youth than age; with a strong and steady hand which never trembles, and ready to use the left hand as well as the right; with vision sharp and clear, and spirit undaunted; filled with pity; so that he wishes to cure the patient, yet is not moved by his cries, to go too fast, or cut less than is necessary; but he does everything just as if the cries of pain cause him no emotion.'

An extract from On Medicine, *a book by Celsus, a wealthy Roman who wrote books on many aspects of medicine*

Decoding exam questions

Step 1: Read the question a couple of times.

Step 2: On your own copy, highlight the following. Use a different colour for each.

- **a** **Date boundaries** – What time period should you cover? Stick to this carefully, otherwise you waste time writing about events that are not relevant to the question.
- **b** **Content focus** – The theme the examiner wants you to focus on. The theme here is surgery and anatomy so you will not gain any extra marks for your knowledge of Roman public health.
- **c** **Question type** – For part (a) questions focus on what you can learn from the source and using your own knowledge. There is no need to evaluate how trustworthy the source is.
- **d** **Marks available** – This gives you a guide as to how much you are expected to write. Do not spend too long on questions that are only worth a few marks.

Step 3: To get high marks in part (a) questions you must ask yourself:

- **a** What can I **infer** from this source? This means what you can **work out** from the source rather than just repeating what it says. Identify the clues in the source that help you make inferences about Roman surgery. What can you infer from the words 'a strong and steady hand which never trembles'?
- **b** What do I already **know** that can help me make sense of this evidence? Use **your knowledge** to go beyond the clues in the source and to explain what the source is saying about surgery. What do you know about the kinds of operations the Romans carried out and how they dealt with pain during operations?

Activity

Read this student answer. Note how the student identifies key details and then explains what they say about surgery. Now complete the answer. Write in your best English – check punctuation, spelling and correct use of capital letters.

In Source A Celsus says that surgeons should be youthful and strong. This gives the impression that difficult surgery is carried out and we know from other sources that amputations were done. Celsus also says that surgeons should have 'spirit undaunted' and must 'not be moved by cries'. This suggests ...

Answering Section B and C questions

Sections B and C ask questions on the two themes not covered in Section A. So, if Section A is on Public Health, Sections B and C will be on Surgery and Anatomy and Disease and Infection, as in the example below.

Both Sections B and C contain two questions and you choose one question to answer from each section. You are advised to spend around 25 minutes on Section B and another 25 minutes on Section C.

DO THE RIGHT QUESTION
You must answer one of the two questions in each section. Answer BOTH parts (a) and (b) of each question you choose.

SECTION B
Surgery and Anatomy
Answer **either** Question 2 **or** Question 3.

EITHER

2 **Total marks for this question: 12 marks**

(a) Choose **one** of the medical pioneers below.
- Andreas Vesalius
- William Harvey

What did he do? *(4 marks)*

(b) Which of these medical pioneers contributed more to improved medical knowledge during the Renaissance?
Explain your answer. *(8 marks)*

OR

3 **Total marks for this question: 12 marks**

(a) Choose **one** of the historical periods below.
- Ancient Egypt
- Ancient Rome

What anatomical knowledge and surgery was there at that time? *(4 marks)*

(b) In which period was there more improvement in surgical and anatomical knowledge?
Explain your answer. *(8 marks)*

CHOOSING QUESTIONS
In both Sections B and C you have to choose one of the two questions. Read both questions carefully, including both parts (a) and (b). Do NOT make your decision about which question to answer just on part (a).

TIMING
Spend about 25 minutes on Section B and 25 minutes on Section C. Look at the marks awarded to parts (a) and (b). Spend roughly 2 minutes per mark on a question.

GOOD ENGLISH
Always check punctuation, spelling and correct use of capital letters. Do not use bullet points.

PART (a) QUESTIONS are worth 4 marks. They need a short answer about ONE of the items listed.

PART (b) QUESTIONS are worth 8 marks. They ask you to compare the two items in the bullet points. See the ExamBuster on pages 76–77.

SECTION C
Disease and Infection
Answer **either** Question 4 **or** Question 5.

EITHER

4 **Total marks for this question: 12 marks**

(a) Choose **one** of the factors below that have affected the development of medicine in the twentieth century.
- War
- Science and technology

Describe the effects of that factor on the fight against disease and infection. *(4 marks)*

(b) Which factor has contributed more in the fight against disease and infection in the twentieth century?
Explain your answer. *(8 marks)*

OR

5 **Total marks for this question: 12 marks**

(a) Choose **one** of the important theories in the history of medicine below.
- The theory of the four humours
- Germ theory

What was the theory? *(4 marks)*

(b) Which of these theories contributed more to the development of medicine?
Explain your answer. *(8 marks)*

Answering Section B and C, part (a) questions

SECTION C
Disease and Infection

(a) Choose **one** of the medical pioneers below.
- Hippocrates
- Galen

What did he do? *(4 marks)*

Decoding exam questions

You must stick to the **date boundaries** of the question. In this case, the question says 'What did he do?' So, for Hippocrates, you write about the Greek period. Details of how these ideas were used later will not gain you any extra marks.

The **theme** for this section is Disease and Infection. This must be the focus of your answer. There is no need to explore other themes. For example, do not write about Galen's work on anatomy which comes within the Surgery and Anatomy theme.

There are **4 marks available.** This indicates that only a short answer is required.

Spend 7 or 8 minutes on this question – 2 minutes per mark. One paragraph would be enough.

Exam tips and tasks

1 Stay relevant

The third sentence of the answer below does not gain any marks even though it is true.

- Why not? Look at the 'Decoding' notes above.

Hippocrates developed an important new theory about what caused disease. This theory was the basis for the treatments he used to make patients better. Hippocrates' work was really important because Galen built on it and it continued to be used for centuries afterwards.

2 Be specific

The answer above would gain more marks if it included more specific information. It makes general statements about Hippocrates' theory and about his treatments, but includes no detail to support these statements.

- Rewrite this answer adding specific detail to support the general statements the student has made.

3 Now write your answer, choosing Galen as your topic.

Practice questions

SECTION C
Disease and Infection

1
(a) Choose **one** of the theories about the cause of disease below.
- Blocked channels
- The theory of the four humours

What was the theory? *(4 marks)*

SECTION C
Public Health

2
(a) Choose **one** of the historical periods below.
- Ancient Greece
- Ancient Rome

What kinds of public health facilities were there at that time? *(4 marks)*

Section 3: Why didn't medicine improve during the Middle Ages?

About AD500 the Roman Empire in Europe was destroyed by attacks from Goths, Vandals and other tribes from Germany and the east. Over the next one thousand years medicine did not improve and in some ways got worse. Your task in this section is to find out why medicine did not improve in the Middle Ages.

Activities

Work in pairs.

1. You have **five minutes**. What evidence can you find in this picture of:
   a. surgery
   b. disease – ideas about causes and types of treatment
   c. public health?
2. You have **three minutes**. How many similarities can you find between medicine in the Middle Ages and medicine in the ancient world?
3. You have **two minutes**. What differences can you find between medicine in the Middle Ages and medicine in the ancient world?
4. What chance do Londoners have of surviving the terrible disease they have heard of? List three pieces of evidence to support your answer.

Medical Moments in Time: London, 1347

I treated arrow wounds with the King's army. A blacksmith made me a tool to take the arrow out. Then honey on the wound to help it heal. That'll teach you to walk behind the target at archery practice.
Get this filth cleaned up or I'll fine you two shillings.
Your humours are out of balance. Go to a surgeon who'll bleed you and go again in six months.
ALES
A terrible pestilence is killing everyone in France. I've heard it's caused by the planets. What can we do?
You ought to employ more rakers to clean the streets.
Pray to God for forgiveness. God sends plague as punishment for our sins.
Her eye's sore.
My sister has a good remedy – onion, garlic, bull's gall, wine. I'll run and get some.
Physicians trained by reading books by Hippocrates, Galen and Arab doctors such as Ibn Sina and al-Rhazes.
A certain cure for the pestilence! A holy remedy made from finest herbs and dust from the true Holy Cross on which Christ was crucified. Only one silver penny!

3.1 Why couldn't people stop the Black Death?

The pestilence that arrived in 1348 is better known as the Black Death. We can learn a lot about medicine in the Middle Ages from the Black Death. It acts as a linking thread throughout this section, so you need some basic information to begin with. That's what pages 54–57 are for.

The horror of the Black Death!

The Black Death was one of the most frightening outbreaks of disease in history. The epidemic began in China, spread to India and across Europe. In Britain people heard stories of the disease spreading through France. At the time they simply called it 'the pestilence'. What happened next was described by a monk writing at a monastery in Wiltshire:

> In 1348 the cruel pestilence arrived at a port called Melcombe in Dorset. It killed numberless people in Dorset, Devon and Somerset and then it came to Bristol where very few were left alive.
>
> It then travelled northwards, leaving not a town, a village or even, except rarely, a house, without killing most or all of the people there. There was such a shortage of people that there were hardly enough living to bury the dead.

Historians now estimate that at least 40 per cent of the population died, with towns and ports being even harder hit. The plague killed everyone, rich and poor, and they died quickly and painfully. Only remote villages and farms high up on the hills were likely to be safe.

What was the Black Death?

Even now historians are not completely certain what the pestilence was but it was probably bubonic plague. Bubonic plague is carried by rats and spread by fleas. A flea becomes infected when it bites an infected rat, then it passes the disease on to other rats and to humans when it bites them. People bitten by infected fleas suddenly felt cold and tired and then discovered painful swellings called buboes in their armpits and groins. Blisters appeared all over their bodies, followed by high fever, severe headaches, unconsciousness for several days and then death.

The impact of the plague was probably made worse by a second disease called pneumonic plague. This was spread by people coughing over others. The victims coughed up blood because the disease attacked their lungs, causing breathing problems. They died more quickly, in a day or two at most.

Activities

1 Information speed test! How quickly can you find the answers to these questions?
   - a When did the Black Death arrive in England?
   - b Which two diseases do historians think were involved?
   - c Which two animals probably spread the disease?
   - d What percentage of people in Britain died?
   - e What were buboes?

2 Use Sources 2–6.
   - a Choose three words to describe people's reactions to the Black Death.
   - b Why do you think they reacted in these ways?

3 Think back to your work on ancient medicine. Do you think the Black Death would have hit the Romans so hard?

Source 1

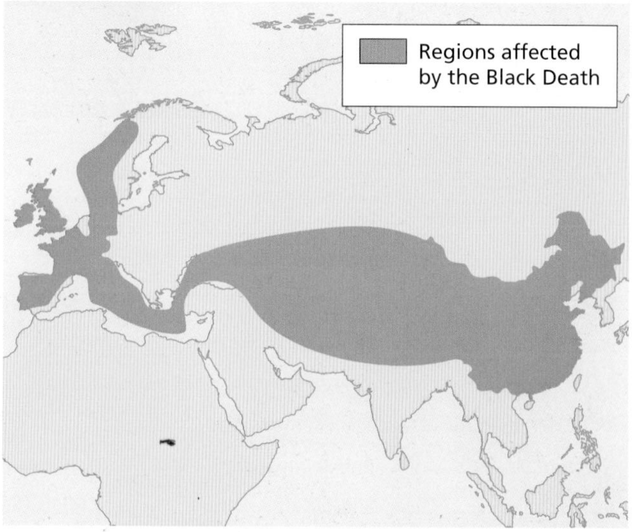

▲ The Black Death spread throughout Asia and Europe, probably carried by rats and fleas on trading ships and in packs of goods carried by merchants.

Source 2

An Irish monk, Brother John Clynn, wrote an account of the plague and concluded:

'I, waiting among the dead for death to come, leave parchment for continuing the work, in case anyone should still be alive in the future and any son of Adam can escape this pestilence and continue my work.'

Source 3

The Italian writer, Petrarch, wrote this letter to a friend in 1350:

'Where are our dear friends now? Where are the beloved faces? Where are the affectionate words, the relaxed and enjoyable conversations? What lightning bolt devoured them? What earthquake topped them? There was crowd of us, now we are almost alone. We should make new friends, but how, when the human race is almost wiped out; and why, when it looks to me as if the end of the world is at hand?'

Source 4

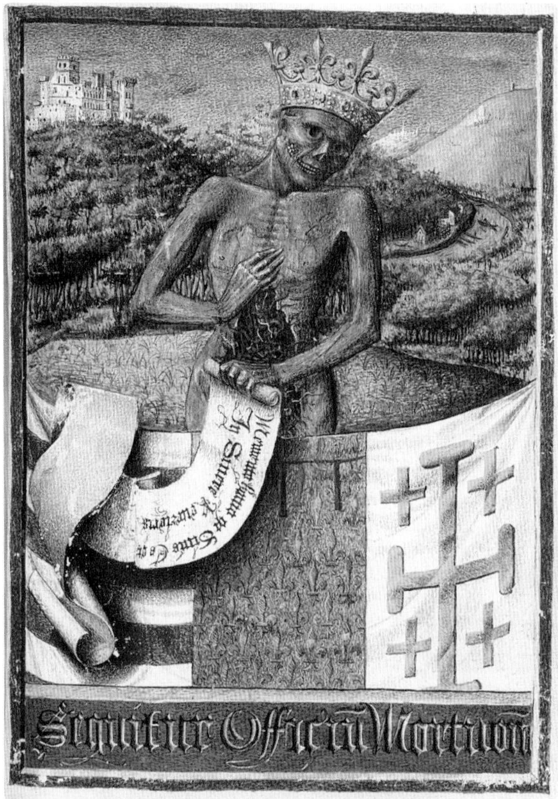

▲ King Death, an illustration in a French book of prayers from the early fifteenth century. The scroll he is holding reads: 'Remember man that you are ash [and] into ash you shall return'.

Source 5

▲ Black Death graves at Hereford cathedral. A chronicler wrote that in London 'they dug broad, deep pits and buried the bodies together, treating everyone alike, except the most eminent'.

Source 6

▲ Words scratched on the church wall in Ashwell, Hertfordshire: '1349 the pestilence 1350 pitiless, wild, violent, the dregs of the people live to tell the tale'.

What did people think caused the Black Death?

What did people think caused the pestilence and how did they try to deal with it? These two quick activities will help you answer these questions. Later in this section you can increase your understanding of these topics.

Activities

1 Which of Sources 1–5 would you use to support each of these statements?
 a The ideas of Galen were still accepted and followed.
 b Some people, at least, connected the Black Death to dirt and bad air.
 c In some places people took the chance to blame and attack outsiders.
 d Science in the Middle Ages was very different from science today.
2 Which of the explanations in Sources 1–5 do you think was the most widely believed? Use Sources 6–10 to help you.

Source 1

A Swedish bishop who had read work by John Jacobus, a French physician, suggested:

'Sometimes the pestilence comes from a privy toilet next to a chamber or some other thing that corrupts the air. Sometimes it comes from dead flesh or from standing water in ditches.'

Source 2

In September 1348 the Prior of Christchurch Abbey, Canterbury wrote to the Bishop of London:

'Terrible is God towards the sons of men … He uses plagues, miserable famines, wars and other suffering to arise and to terrify and torment men and so drive out their sins. Thus England is struck by the pestilence because of the increasing pride and numberless sins of the people.'

Source 3

▲ This fifteenth-century illustration shows the planet Saturn eating his children.

By the 1400s the science of astrology was an important part of medicine. Physicians believed the stars and planets affected people's bodies because both were made of the same four elements – air, earth, fire and water. Guy de Chauliac, a French surgeon, blamed the Black Death on two things. One was 'the state of each victim's body – bad digestion, weakness and blockage'. The other was 'the close position of Saturn, Jupiter and Mars in 1345 … always a sign of wonderful, terrible or violent things to come'.

Source 4

▲ A German woodcut showing the burning of Jews in Germany. Minority groups were blamed for the Black Death in many countries. Jews were said to have poisoned water supplies and in some places were burned as people looked for someone to blame.

Source 5

In 1365 a physician called John of Burgundy wrote:

'Many people have been killed by the plague, especially those stuffed with evil humours. As Galen says, the body does not become sick unless it contains evil humours.'

How did people try to treat or stop the Black Death?

Activity

3 Which of Sources 6–10 provide evidence of:
- **a** the belief that God sent the pestilence to punish sins
- **b** the ideas of Galen being still followed by physicians
- **c** public health in British towns being much worse than in Roman towns
- **d** doctors being helpless to stop the Black Death
- **e** activity that might have done a little good?

Source 8

▲ Flagellants walked through towns as the plague spread, whipping themselves to show God that they had repented their sins and asking God to be merciful.

Source 6

▲ One physician takes the victim's pulse while the other examines his urine, but even they cannot stop 'Death' taking the victim. This warning was in a fifteenth-century French manuscript.

Source 9

This advice comes from John of Burgundy, author of one of the first books about the plague, written in 1365:

'Avoid too much eating and drinking and avoid baths which open the pores, for the pores are doorways through which poisonous air can enter the body. In cold or rainy weather, light fires in your room. In foggy or windy weather, inhale perfumes every morning before leaving home. If the plague arrives during hot weather, eat cold things rather than hot and drink more than you eat. Be sparing with hot substances such as pepper, garlic, onions and everything else that generates excessive heat and instead use cucumbers, fennel and spinach.'

Source 7

◀ King Edward III and bishops ordered that services and processions be held in every church at least once a day, in which people prayed for forgiveness and asked God to put an end to the disease. Some people went further and made candles their own height and lit them in church as offerings to God. In Barcelona, the citizens made a candle 7 kilometres long that they hoped would encircle and protect the city.

Source 10

In April 1349, at the height of the Black Death, King Edward III wrote to the Mayor of London:

'Have the filth lying in the streets removed with all speed to places far distant, the city cleansed from all odours so that no great mortality may arise from such smells ... the filth from the houses is infecting the air, endangering people through the contagious sickness which is increasing daily.'

3.2 The Big Story of medicine in the Middle Ages

Pages 52–57 have introduced you to medicine in the Middle Ages. Now use your Smarter Revision techniques to get clear in your mind the key features of medieval medicine. This will set you up for this section's main question about why medicine didn't improve.

Disease and infection – see blue rows

Surgery and anatomy – see red rows

Public health – see green rows

	Medicine at the end of the ancient period
Healers	**a** Mothers and family members treated most illnesses. Women with skills and experience were often called to help, e.g. with childbirth. **b** Priests at temples to Asclepius.  **c** Surgeons, e.g. army surgeons, trained by observing others and improved their skills through practice. **d** Specialist doctors trained by reading the books of Hippocrates and Galen.
Ideas about causes of illness	**a** Many believed that illnesses were caused by gods and spirits. **b** Doctors said that many illnesses had natural causes. They followed Hippocrates' theory that illness was caused when the body's humours were out of balance.
Treatments	**a** Remedies were made up from herbs, minerals and animal parts.  **b** Prayers, charms and chants were used. **c** Bleeding, purging and other methods were used to restore the proper balance of the humours. Galen introduced treatment by 'opposites'.  **d** Rest, exercise and diet.
Surgery	**a** Simple surgery on visible wounds and tumours. 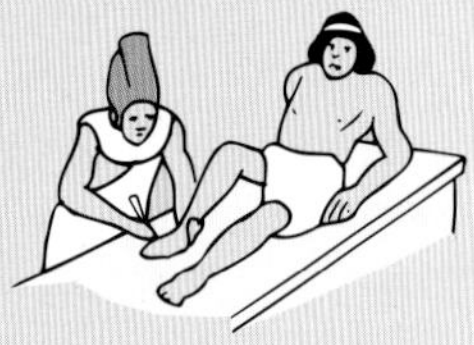 **b** Splints for fractured bones. **c** Trephining (cutting a hole in the skull). **d** Plants such as opium dulled pain a little but there were no effective anaesthetics. **e** Surgeons used wine, vinegar or honey to clean wounds but could not prevent infections spreading or stop heavy bleeding.
Knowledge of the human body	**a** Doctors knew about many of the main organs and bones from observation of wounds. **b** At Alexandria discoveries had been made through dissection but dissection was rarely allowed for religious reasons.
Public health	**a** The Egyptians and Greeks left people to look after their own hygiene.  **b** The Romans built aqueducts, sewers and baths in towns and forts. **c** Most people in the countryside in the Roman Empire did not have baths or sewers. **d** Even the Romans' public health system could not stop epidemic diseases spreading and killing millions. 

Activities

1 Memory map: On pages 14–15 you built up a memory map for ancient medicine. Use that model to create a memory map for medieval medicine. Do this in pencil at this stage and then finalise your graphs at the end of this section.

2 Living graph: On pages 6–7 you began to create living graphs which record developments across time. Use the information on this page to fill out your graphs for the Middle Ages. Do this in pencil at this stage and then finalise your graphs at the end of this section.

Medicine c.1400, at the end of the Middle Ages

Little had changed although from the 1200s physicians (specialist doctors) were trained at universities.

a Mothers and family members treated most illnesses. Women with skills and experience were often called to help, e.g. with childbirth.

b Priests said prayers to help the sick and protect from illness.

c Surgeons, e.g. army surgeons, trained by observing others and improved their skills through practice.

d Physicians trained at universities by reading the books by Hippocrates and Galen and some Arab medical writers. In the 1300s there were fewer than 100 physicians in England.

Nothing had changed.

a Many believed that illnesses were sent by God.

b Doctors said that many illnesses had natural causes. They followed Hippocrates' theory that illness was caused when the body's humours were out of balance.

Treatments were very similar.

a Remedies were made up from herbs, minerals and animal parts.

b Prayers, charms and rhymes were used.

c Bleeding, purging and other methods were used to restore the proper balance of the humours, following the methods of Galen.

d Rest, exercise and diet.

Surgeons improved their techniques and instruments a little through practice.

a Simple surgery on visible tumours and wounds.

b Splints for fractured bones.

c Trephining (cutting a hole in the skull).

d Plants such as opium dulled pain but there were no effective anaesthetics.

e Surgeons used wine, vinegar or honey to clean wounds but could not prevent infections spreading or stop heavy bleeding.

Nothing had changed.

a Doctors knew about Greek and Roman discoveries but did not learn any more.

b Dissection was carried out to illustrate what Galen had said, not make new discoveries.

The Roman public health systems had disappeared so in towns and wealthy homes public health was worse.

a Town governments employed people and made laws to try to keep streets clean but often had little success.

b It was very difficult to keep towns clean as they were full of animals. Houses were packed together and there were few paved streets.

c Kings were not expected to improve hygiene or protect public health. Their job was to defend the country and keep law and order.

d Epidemic diseases still could not be stopped.

3.3 Why didn't medicine improve in the Middle Ages? Part 1

Now you know that medicine did not change much in the Middle Ages and in some ways got worse. That's strange because people were just as intelligent then as we are today and they wanted to be healthy. So what stopped them improving their medicine and health? We'll tackle this in two stages – you'll find out at half-time that the word 'tackle' has been chosen deliberately!

The end of the Roman Empire

After the Roman Empire collapsed, Europe was split into many small kingdoms, frequently invading and fighting each other. Britain, for example, was taken over by tribes of Angles and Saxons who couldn't read and were not interested in Galen, baths or sewer systems. You can see the impact of all this war and destruction below.

1 Without the Roman army there were **no engineers** with the technological knowledge to keep public baths, sewers and aqueducts working effectively.

2 Invading tribes **destroyed or neglected** public health systems.

3 Invasions and wars **destroyed libraries** and books in monasteries.

4 The attitudes of rulers were different. **Kings spent their money on wars,** not on sewers and baths. They were illiterate so had no interest in education.

5 Wars made **travel more dangerous** so doctors travelled much less to gain experience and education.

6 All these wars meant there was plenty of **practice for surgeons.**

Collapse of Roman Empire | Europe full of small warring kingdoms

AD400 | AD500 | AD600 | AD700 | AD800

Saxon kingdoms in England

Smarter Revision: Using your factors chart to explain why medicine did not improve

exam BUSTERS

Activities

A 'factors chart' will help you build up your explanation throughout this section.

1. Prepare your own version of this chart, on paper or as a spreadsheet.
2. Fill in your 'factors chart' with examples from page 60. You will find plenty of examples of war but there are examples of other factors too.
3. Which aspect of medicine do you think the collapse of the Roman Empire and all the wars:
   - **a** hit hardest
   - **b** may have helped?

Factors chart

1 **Factor**	2 **Evidence of factor helping medicine improve**	3 **Evidence of factor keeping medicine at the same level**	4 **Evidence of factor hindering development of medicine**	5 **Assessment – did it do more to help or hinder or just keep medicine static?**
War				
Government				
Religion				

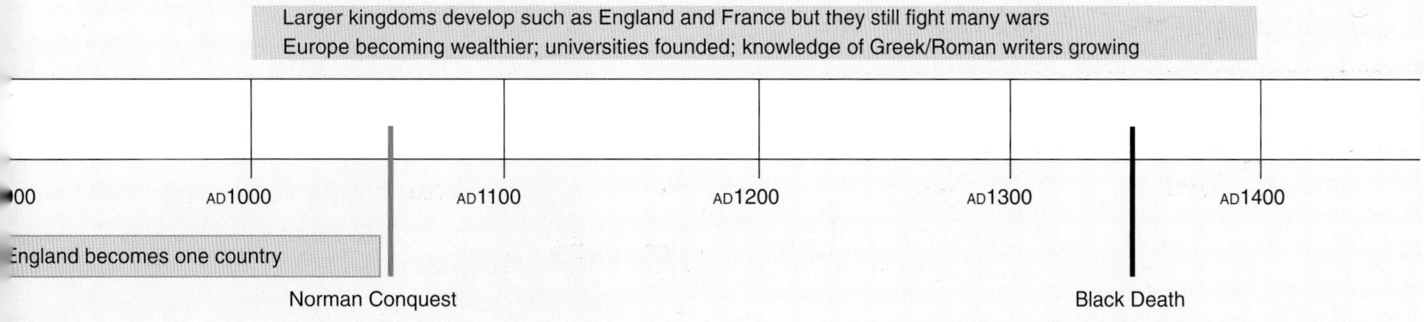

How did Christianity and Islam affect medical developments?

The warfare after the collapse of the Roman Empire nearly destroyed all the medical knowledge built up by the Greeks and the Romans. However, the two great religions, Christianity and Islam, made sure this knowledge was not lost. Firstly, they saved many Greek and Roman medical books from destruction. Secondly, they made sure that physicians continued to read and trust the work of Galen.

Activities

1 Summarise each effect in a sentence.

2 a How similar were Christianity and Islam in their attitudes to medicine?

b What differences can you find in their attitudes to medicine?

3 **Factors chart:** Now add evidence to your 'factors chart'. Think carefully about exactly which factors are affecting medicine.

The effects of Christianity

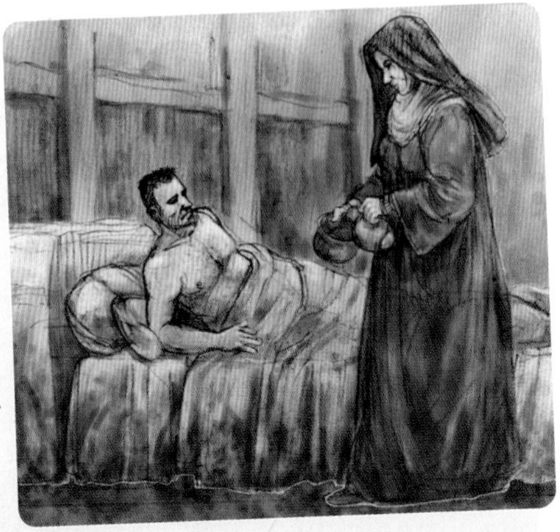

A

Caring for the sick

Christians believed that sickness was sent by God to punish people for their sins. Therefore the sick could be healed if they prayed for forgiveness to Jesus Christ and the saints linked to particular illnesses. St Apollonia was the patron saint of toothache because all her teeth had been knocked out when she was murdered because of her religion. In a hospital, nuns fed the sick and gave them herbal remedies but prayer was the most important treatment. At the end of the hall (or ward) was an altar where priests said mass seven times each day. The patients joined in, hoping that prayer would help them recover.

B

Preserving knowledge

The Christian Church preserved a great deal of knowledge handed down from the Greeks and Romans. Monks in monasteries copied out the Bible, histories and other Ancient books, including books by Galen and other medical writers from Greece and Rome.

C

Supporting Galen

Galen's books were the main books read by physicians in Europe for two reasons. Firstly, the Christian Church controlled the universities where physicians were trained and the Church believed that ancient writings should not be questioned. If people started questioning Galen they might question the Bible so questioning was not a good idea! Secondly, the Church supported Galen because he said that each part of the body had a definite purpose. This fitted the Christian belief that God had created human beings. Therefore when Roger Bacon said that doctors should do their own research instead of just reading Galen he was thrown into prison by church leaders.

The effects of Islam

Caring for the sick

The Islamic religion taught people to look after the sick and Arab hospitals were famous for the care they gave patients. The first was founded in Baghdad around 805 and by the 1100s every large town had a hospital. They provided medical care and prayers for the sick.

D

Preserving knowledge

E

The eighth century was a period of great wealth in the Islamic Empire, when Arab rulers believed it was important to develop education. Many Greek medical books were translated into Arabic by Islamic scholars.

The city of Baghdad was the main centre for collecting and translating medical texts. Without these translations the books by Galen and others could well have been lost amidst European wars.

Ibn Sina and Rhazes

Islamic doctors wrote multi-volume medical encyclopaedias which organised medical knowledge with great thoroughness. They included the work of Galen and other Greek medical writers. These books were later translated from Arabic into Latin and were used in Europe so that European physicians learned more about the work of Galen and Arab doctors. Two of the greatest Arab doctors were:

1 al-Razi (c.860–925) known in Europe as Rhazes. He wrote over 200 books, including his own ideas but also believed 'he who studies the works of the Ancients, gains the experience of their labour as if he had himself lived thousands of years'.

2 Ibn Sina (980–1037) known in Europe as Avicenna. His medical encyclopaedia, *The Canon*, was used to teach European physicians until the 1600s. He included the work of the Greeks and his own methods and was known as the 'Galen of Islam'.

F

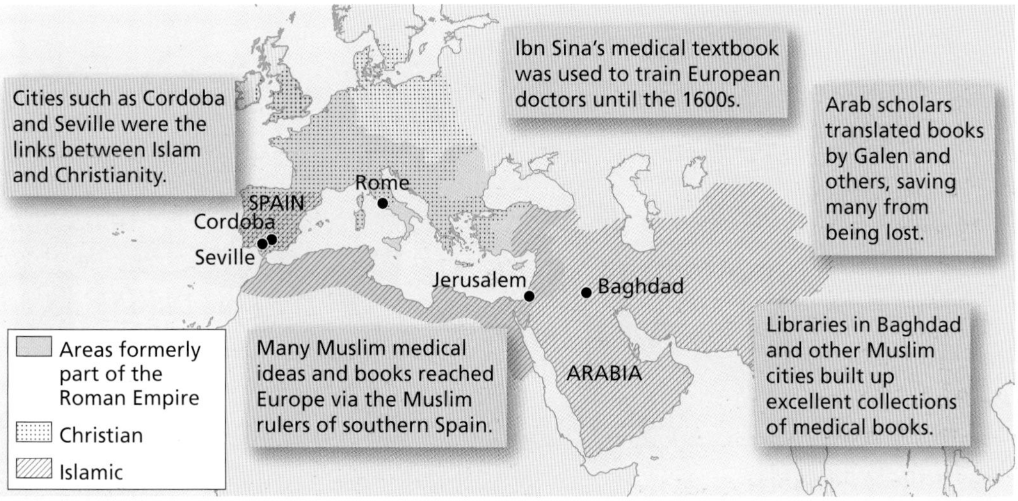

◀ After the Roman Empire collapsed, its lands became dominated by two great religions, Christianity and Islam. Europe was full of small countries that spent a lot of time fighting each other, but it was united by Christianity. By AD1000, most people in Europe had become Christians. Islam spread through Arabia, North Africa and into Spain.

3.4 Why didn't medicine improve? A half-time team talk

Now you can see why we said you'd be tackling this enquiry in two stages. This half-time team talk is here to make sure you are on the right lines in building up your factors chart before you start Stage 2 and then decide which factors were most important in preventing medical improvement.

Activities

In this match the Factors are trying to stop Medicine making progress.

1. The coach thinks that War has been the star factor so far, doing the most to stop Medicine developing. Do you agree? What evidence would you use to support your judgement?
2. Work in pairs. Take one of the topics below. Read that page and work out which factors are:
   - **a** putting in the strongest tackles and pushing medicine backwards
   - **b** stopping medicine's development but not pushing them back
   - **c** doing more to help medicine than hinder it.

   Topics:

   Hospitals and Healers (pages 66–67)

   Causes of disease and knowledge of the body (pages 68–69)

   Treatments (pages 70–71)

   Surgery (pages 72–73)

   Public health (pages 74–75)
3. Then complete your 'factors chart' as a class using the information you have collected.

3.5 Why didn't medicine improve in the Middle Ages? Part 2

Topic Who did hospitals look after?

> Care for the sick is of great importance. You must help them as you would help Christ, whom you help in helping the sick.

This extract from the rules of the Benedictine monks might make you optimistic about going to a hospital if you were ill. Looking after the sick was an important part of the work of the Christian Church and this led to many hospitals being founded in the Middle Ages. By 1400 there were over 500 hospitals in England, although many had only five or six beds. St Leonard's in York was unusually large with over 200 beds. However, hospitals were very careful about who they took in, as Source 1 shows. So you could not get into hospital if you had a disease that other people might catch!

Occasionally, hospitals were set up to care for particular cases. In London, Richard Whittington, the Lord Mayor, paid for an eight-bed hospital for unmarried pregnant women. In Chester there was a hospital for the care of 'poor and silly persons'. Leper houses were built outside towns to separate the victims of the disease leprosy from healthy people. Leprosy was particularly feared because it rotted people's flesh, a punishment from God for sin.

Source 1

From the rules of the hospital of St John, Bridgwater in the south of England, 1219:

'No lepers, lunatics or persons having the falling sickness or other contagious disease, and no pregnant women, or sucking infants and no intolerable persons, even though they be poor and infirm, are to be admitted. If any such be admitted by mistake they are to be expelled as soon as possible. And when the other poor and infirm persons have recovered they are to be let out without delay.'

▲ The Hôtel Dieu in Paris. The King's doctors worked there so this was not typical but it is one of the few illustrations of the inside of a medieval hospital. What evidence can you see of **a)** religion and **b)** medical help?

Information

Islamic hospitals

Islam also taught people to look after the sick, and Arab hospitals were famous for the care they gave patients. Like Christian hospitals they looked after the elderly and infirm but they also provided medical care. The hospital at Cairo, built in 1283, had specialist wards for mental and physical problems, a surgery, pharmacy, library, lecture rooms for teaching and a Christian chapel as well as a mosque.

What kinds of care could the sick get?

Most hospitals were like care-homes today, looking after the poor and elderly. They provided food, rest and, most importantly, prayer. At the end of the hall (or ward) was an altar where priests said mass seven times each day. People believed that God sent sickness to punish them for their sins so they joined in the prayers, hoping that God would realise they were sorry for their sins. Nursing care was provided by nuns who had a good knowledge of herbal and other remedies, often drawn from the books in their library.

Outside hospitals, women treated the vast majority of illnesses. Mothers and wives had a wide range of remedies at their fingertips although sometimes the local wise-woman was called in to use her skills and knowledge. Women also acted as midwives. In some towns, midwives had to be apprenticed and gain licences and were then paid for their expertise.

If you had a little money or were very worried about your illness you could see a local surgeon. Some surgeons were very skilful, learning through practice as apprentices to experienced surgeons. Guilds of Master-Surgeons required new members to gain licences by passing tests. Some surgeons read books by great European surgeons such as Guy de Chauliac. Women could qualify as surgeons by working as apprentices. Family links played an important part in giving women this opportunity. Records list Katherine, a surgeon in London around 1250, whose father and brothers were surgeons.

Only the rich could afford to go to a physician. Physicians were the highest-ranking doctors because they trained at universities. They treated kings, nobles and wealthy merchants and were well-paid, but there were few of them. In the 1300s there were fewer than 100 physicians in England.

Source 2

In *The Canterbury Tales*, Geoffrey Chaucer described a physician as:

'Well read was he in Asculapius, Hippocrates, and Hali, and Galen, Serapion, Rhazes, and Avicen …'

Activities

1. **Factor hunt:** What evidence can you find of the effects of religion?
2. **a** According to the information and sources, who did hospitals look after?
   b What kinds of help did hospitals provide?
3. How important a role did women play in medicine?
4. **a** How does Chaucer (Source 2) show that the physician was well-qualified?
   b How can you tell the man in Source 3 is a physician? (Look at page 70 to see if you are right.)

Source 3

▲ A picture of a physician from about 1400.

Topic Knowledge of the body and causes of disease – what did medieval physicians know?

Activities

1. **Factor hunt:** What evidence can you find on these two pages of the effects of:
   a. religion
   b. attitudes – conservatism (respect for tradition)
   c. attitudes – enquiry?
2. Look back to page 56. Which sources are examples of the ideas about the causes of disease below?
3. Why was new knowledge of the body or of the causes of disease not developed?
4. Why were regular dissections a small step forward?
5. Which new idea about the body was suggested by an Arab doctor?

1 God or the Devil

The most common belief was that God sent illnesses such as the Black Death to punish people for their sins. The Anglo-Saxons also believed that elves and spirits, the Devil's helpers, shot invisible arrows, known as elf-shot, to cause everyday illnesses such as headaches.

2 The four humours

Physicians followed the theories of Hippocrates and Galen and said that illness was caused when the body's humours were out of balance. Greek books were at the centre of university medical training. Many people accepted this theory because physicians were respected for their university training. Islamic doctors also believed in the importance of the four humours because of their studies of Galen.

Ideas about the causes of disease

3 Common sense – bad air and dirt

A common explanation was that bad air caused illness. At the time of the Black Death many people said that earthquakes had infected the air. Some people did link the bad air to dirt and filth in the streets but could not explain exactly what the link was. Another common-sense belief was that worms caused illness. This sounds strange but archaeological discoveries show that many people suffered from worms in their stomachs and they would have seen these worms in their faeces.

4 Desperate explanations

As the Black Death killed millions, a wide range of other desperate and bizarre explanations were put forward:

- An English monk blamed the outrageous fashions that people had been wearing in recent years.
- When another outbreak of plague in 1361 killed many children, another churchman said God was punishing children who did not respect or look after their parents.
- Minority groups were blamed. Jews were said to have poisoned water supplies and in some places they were burned as people looked for someone to blame.

Source 1

Understanding the human body

Bodies were dissected as Galen had recommended. In the 1300s human dissections were an important, if small, part of medical education in Italy and Spain. Universities in England copied this in the 1500s.

The physician (in the red robe on the right) was in charge but did not do the dissection. He told the surgeon which parts of the body to dissect.

He also told his assistant (middle right) which passages from Galen to read out to illustrate the dissection.

The students had to listen to Galen's words and watch the dissection. They weren't allowed to do anything!

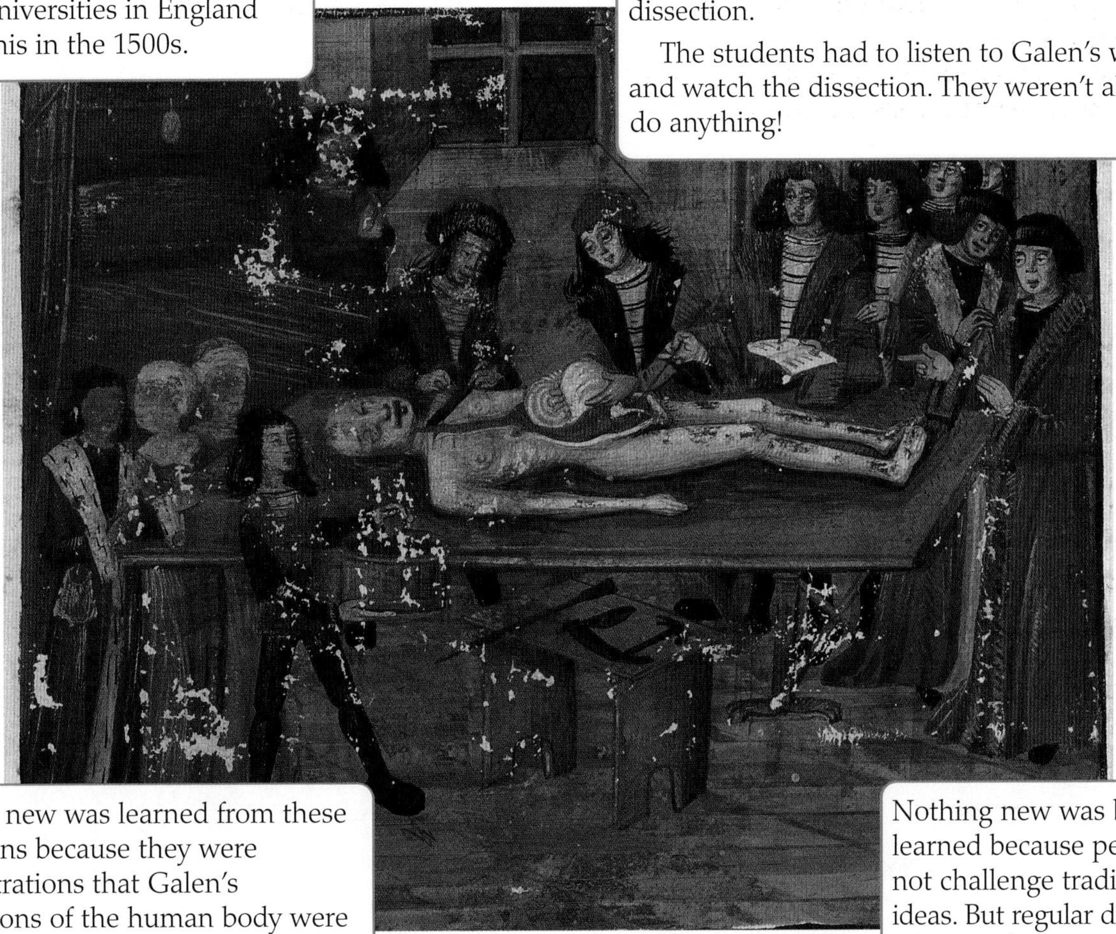

Nothing new was learned from these dissections because they were demonstrations that Galen's descriptions of the human body were correct, not investigations to make new discoveries. Physicians believed that Galen's books contained everything that needed to be learned about the human body.

Nothing new was being learned because people did not challenge traditional ideas. But regular dissections were a step forward because one day someone would use dissection to challenge Galen's descriptions of the body.

BUT

There were new ideas among Arab doctors. Ibn al-Nafis (1200–1288) investigated the anatomy of the heart and was brave enough to challenge Galen. Galen had said that the blood moves from one side of the heart to the other through invisible channels. Al-Nafis used his own observations to say that these channels did not exist. He suggested that blood moves from the heart to the lungs and then back to the heart, thus circulating round the body. This idea was correct, but nobody built on his work and it wasn't until the 1600s that this discovery was made in Europe.

Topic Treatments – how were the sick treated?

Activities

1 **Factor hunt:** What evidence can you find of the effects of:
  a attitudes – conservatism (respect for tradition)
  b attitudes – enquiry
  c religion and superstition?

2 What were the most important parts of a physician's equipment and what did he use them for?

3 Which new discovery was made by an Arab doctor?

4 How effective were herbal remedies?

The work of the physician

Diagnosing the illness

Source 1

The physician's most important piece of equipment was his urine chart. The physician matched the patient's urine against the colours, smell and density shown on the chart. He might also taste the urine to check that it was normal.

Wealthy patients sent their urine to their physician to make sure that they were not falling ill. This method of diagnosis (called uroscopy) fitted the theory of the four humours. For example, very white urine was a sign of too much phlegm in the body.

▲ A urine chart

Physicians also followed Hippocrates and Galen by making careful observations of symptoms. This led the Arab doctor Rhazes to describe for the first time the difference between smallpox and measles.

Until then, all infections with rashes had been put together as one illness. Rhazes carefully noted the differences, writing 'the physical signs of measles are nearly the same as those of smallpox but nausea and inflammation are more severe, though the pains in the back are less. The rash of measles usually appears at once, but the rash of smallpox spot after spot.'

Timing the treatment

Source 2

Once the physician had decided on the treatment he then chose the best time to carry it out. This required knowledge of astrology because they believed that parts of the body were linked to signs of the zodiac and the planets. The Zodiac man showed the doctor when to avoid treating each part of the body. When the moon was in Pisces, for example, the feet should not be treated.

▲ A Zodiac man

The work of the surgeon

Source 3

This kind of chart showed the surgeon where to take blood from. Bleeding, urine and zodiac charts were the three most common illustrations in medical books.

Treatments such as bleeding were carried out by a surgeon. Bleeding was done by warming a bleeding cup, placing it over a small cut and letting the warmth draw blood out of the cut. Alternatively, leeches were used to sink their jaws into the patient and draw off blood, a method still used in the nineteenth century.

People were bled regularly as a way of avoiding illness. One medical book said that bleeding 'clears the mind, strengthens the memory, cleanses the guts, sharpens the hearing, curbs tears, promotes digestion, produces a musical voice, dispels sleepiness, drives away anxiety, feeds the blood and rids it of poisonous matter and gives long life, cures pains, fevers and various sicknesses and makes urine clear and clean'.

Not surprisingly, after that list, bleeding was frequent. In some monasteries monks were bled between seven and twelve times a year to prevent illness. On occasion this was carried out until the monk was on the point of unconsciousness, which means he lost three or four pints of blood!

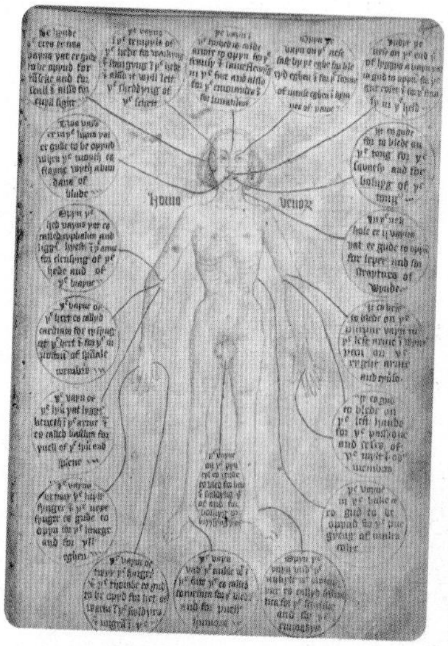

▲ A bleeding chart

Home remedies

Source 4

This cure for a stye comes from Bald's *Leechbook*, a tenth-century collection of treatments. Many ingredients in such remedies were helpful. Honey and plantain, both very common ingredients for problems such as cuts, wounds and dog-bites, acted like modern antibiotics in fighting infection.

Common remedies were based on plants or herbs, minerals and animal parts. Most women knew these by heart but increasingly they were written down in commonplace books or 'herbals', books illustrating each plant and other ingredient, the exact quantities required and how to mix up the potion. They also included prayers to say while collecting the herbs to increase the effectiveness of the remedy.

Some cures combined all kinds of ideas, a mixture of prayer, magic and folklore, such as this Anglo-Saxon cure written down c.AD900: '[scratch] the neck after the setting of the sun and silently pour the blood into running water. After that, spit three times, then say: Have thou this unheal and depart with it.'

An example of a cure that was less likely to work was for treating quinsy (an abscess in the throat):

'Take a fat cat, flay it well and draw out the guts. Take the grease of a hedgehog, the fat of a bear, resins, fenugreek, sage, honeysuckle gum and virgin wax and crumble this and stuff the cat with it. Then roast the cat and gather the dripping and anoint the sufferer with it.'

Topic Surgery – what kinds of surgery were there?

Activities

1 **Factor hunt:** What evidence can you find on these two pages of the effects of:
  a war
  b attitudes – enquiry?

2 The French surgeon Guy de Chauliac (c.1300–1368) wrote: 'The surgeon must be ingenious and able to adapt himself'. How do Cases A and B support de Chauliac's statement?

3 Read Case C. Explain which idea was being challenged and how it came to be challenged.

4 Why were surgeons more likely than physicians to have ideas of their own and disagree with Galen?

Case A: The battle of Shrewsbury, 1403

The royal army had beaten the rebels but the 16-year-old Henry, Prince of Wales, lay wounded. An arrow, glancing off a helmet, had thudded through his left cheek and penetrated to the back of the base of his skull. The royal surgeon, John Bradmore, could not see exactly where the arrowhead was but knew it had to be removed. If he left pieces in the wound they would poison and kill the Prince.

First Bradmore designed a metal forcep to pass through the cheek wound, take hold of the arrowhead and pull it out. While a blacksmith made this new instrument, Blackmore kept the wound open by pushing wooden probes through it, each time using a wider probe to enlarge the hole. Each probe was wrapped in clean linen smeared with honey, good for keeping wounds free of infection. When the forcep was made, Bradmore pushed it through the wound and removed the arrowhead. For three weeks he dressed the wound with barley and honey. It healed free from any infection.

Case B

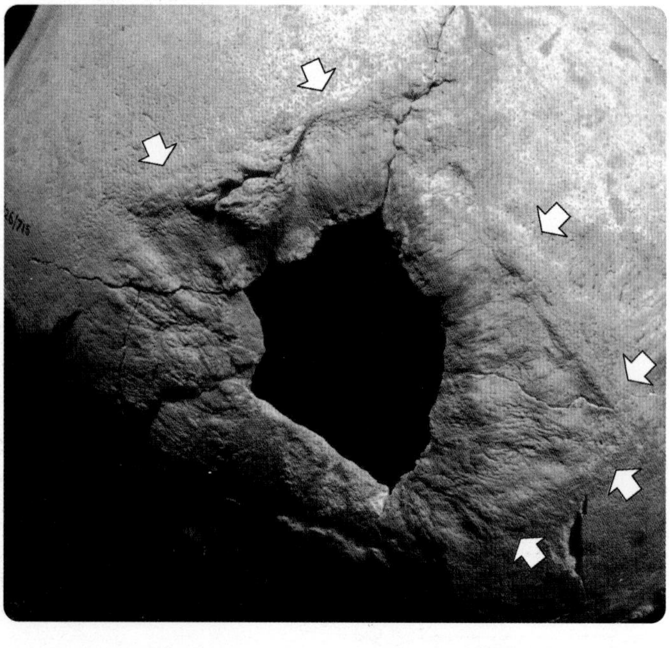

This skull was found in Yorkshire. It belonged to a man who died aged about 40. He had been hit on the head, leaving bone splinters in the brain but a surgeon cut a hole, removed the splinters and the man lived for some time after the operation. Some surgeons could also remove stones that had grown and lodged, extremely painfully, in the bladder.

Case C: What to do with pus

Everyday practice even led a handful of surgeons to dare to disagree with Galen on the lovely topic of pus! Since the Greeks, doctors had said that wounds were more likely to heal if pus (known as praiseworthy pus) developed. They believed the pus carried away poisoned blood that caused infection. Doctors therefore covered wounds in ointments and bandages designed to make pus develop.

Then Hugh and Theodoric, a father and son from Lucca in Italy, dared to say this idea was wrong! Hugh was a surgeon who went on Crusade in 1214 and later taught medicine. Theodoric (1205–1296) was also a surgeon. He wrote 'It is not necessary for pus to form in wounds. There can be no greater mistake! Such a procedure is quite against nature, prolongs illness, prevents healing and hinders the closing up of wounds. My father used to heal almost every kind of wound with wine alone, and he produced the most beautiful healing without any ointments.' Hugh's methods would have been effective. Wine, like honey, attacks infections.

Galen didn't know everything!

Henri de Mondeville (c.1260–c.1320) was another military surgeon and teacher. He taught his students to bathe and cleanse wounds, then close them up quickly without trying to form pus. Henri also wrote a surgical textbook in which he made the two important statements shown on the right, suggesting that surgeons could make new discoveries and challenge Galen's conclusions.

Surgeons could read too!

Most surgery was similar to the operations carried out by Greeks and Romans. Surgeons removed small tumours on the skin's surface, sewed up or cauterised large cuts, dealt with dislocations or broken limbs. The most skilful surgeons used extremely fine needles to remove cataracts from eyes, thus restoring or improving sight.

Surgeons did not just rely on practice. They read books too. Roger of Salerno wrote the first European textbook on surgery c.1180. Guy de Chauliac (c.1300–1368) dedicated himself to proving that a surgeon required just as much education and intelligence as a physician. He wrote a seven-volume book, *Chirurgia Magna* (Great Surgery), and filled it with references to the works of great doctors. There are 890 quotations from Galen, 661 from the Arab Ibn Sina and 120 from Hippocrates.

Source 1

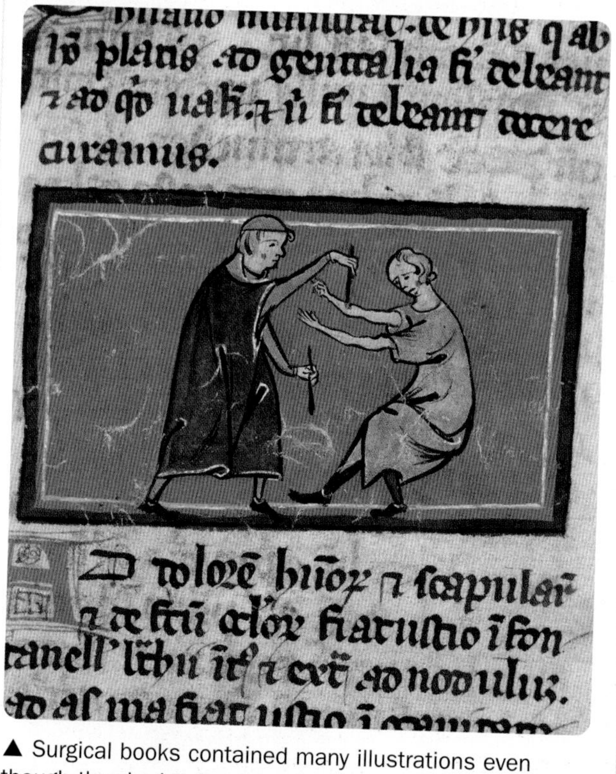

▲ Surgical books contained many illustrations even though they had to be drawn by hand. This shows cauterising, a common method of closing wounds by sealing them with a burning iron.

Source 2

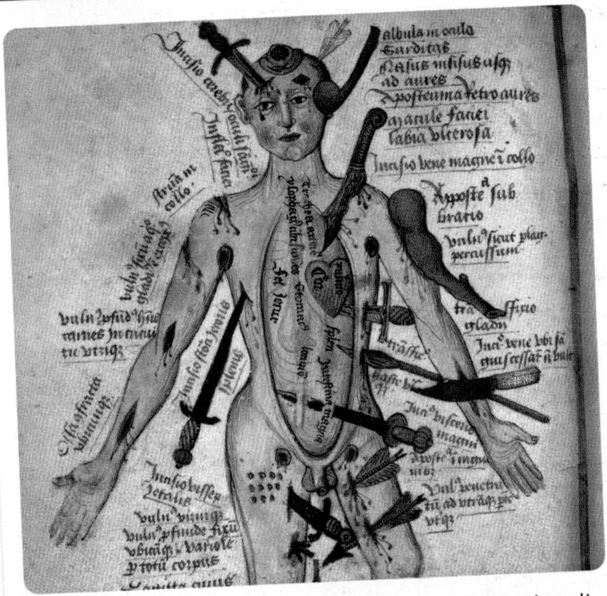

▲ A 'wound man' was a common medical illustration. It showed surgeons how to deal with different kinds of wounds. However, surgeons could not undertake complex surgery inside the body. They did not have enough detailed knowledge of anatomy nor effective anaesthetics. They did use herbs such as mandrake, opium or hemlock, which made patients drowsy, but there was always the danger of using too much of a drug and putting the patient to sleep permanently.

Topic Public health – why did public health deteriorate?

Medieval towns were much dirtier than Roman towns. Viking Jorvik (York) was a filthy place around AD1000. Water for drinking and cooking was collected from the river or storage pits, which were often next to the cesspits people used as toilets. Pigs and chickens roamed the streets. Rats, mice and hawks scavenged in streets full of rotting fish bones, animal dung, food waste and even human faeces.

Animals were always a problem. People used horses for transport. Cattle, sheep and geese constantly arrived to be butchered for food. But, conditions did improve a little. By 1200 many houses in cities like London and York had stone foundations. A few were built entirely of stone. Cesspits were lined with brick or stone and so were less likely to leak into drinking water supplies.

However, the problems were always greater than the solutions. Medieval towns were dirtier than Roman towns but the Romans had army engineers with good technological knowledge, slaves to do at least some of the building, and the wealth to afford aqueducts and public baths. Even so, the Romans had been no better at stopping plague than people were in the Middle Ages.

Why didn't people's efforts work?

▲ King Edward III

▲ Lord Mayor of London

▲ Londoner in the 1300s

Activities

1 **Factor hunt:** What evidence can you find on these two pages of the effects of:
   a government
   b religion and superstition?
2 Was public health always really bad in medieval towns?
3 Study Source 1.
   a What was good about the monastery's public health system?
   b Why was the monastery's public health system better than London's?
   c Compare Canterbury Abbey with a Roman fort (see page 41). Which had the better public health system? Explain the reason for your choice.
4 The Romans were not any better at stopping plague than people in the Middle Ages. Why?

The best public health facilities were in monasteries because they could afford them. Monks were better fed than most people, did less physical work and had the advantages you can see in this plan.

Source 1

▼ A plan of the water system at Canterbury Abbey, drawn by the engineer who designed it in the 1100s.

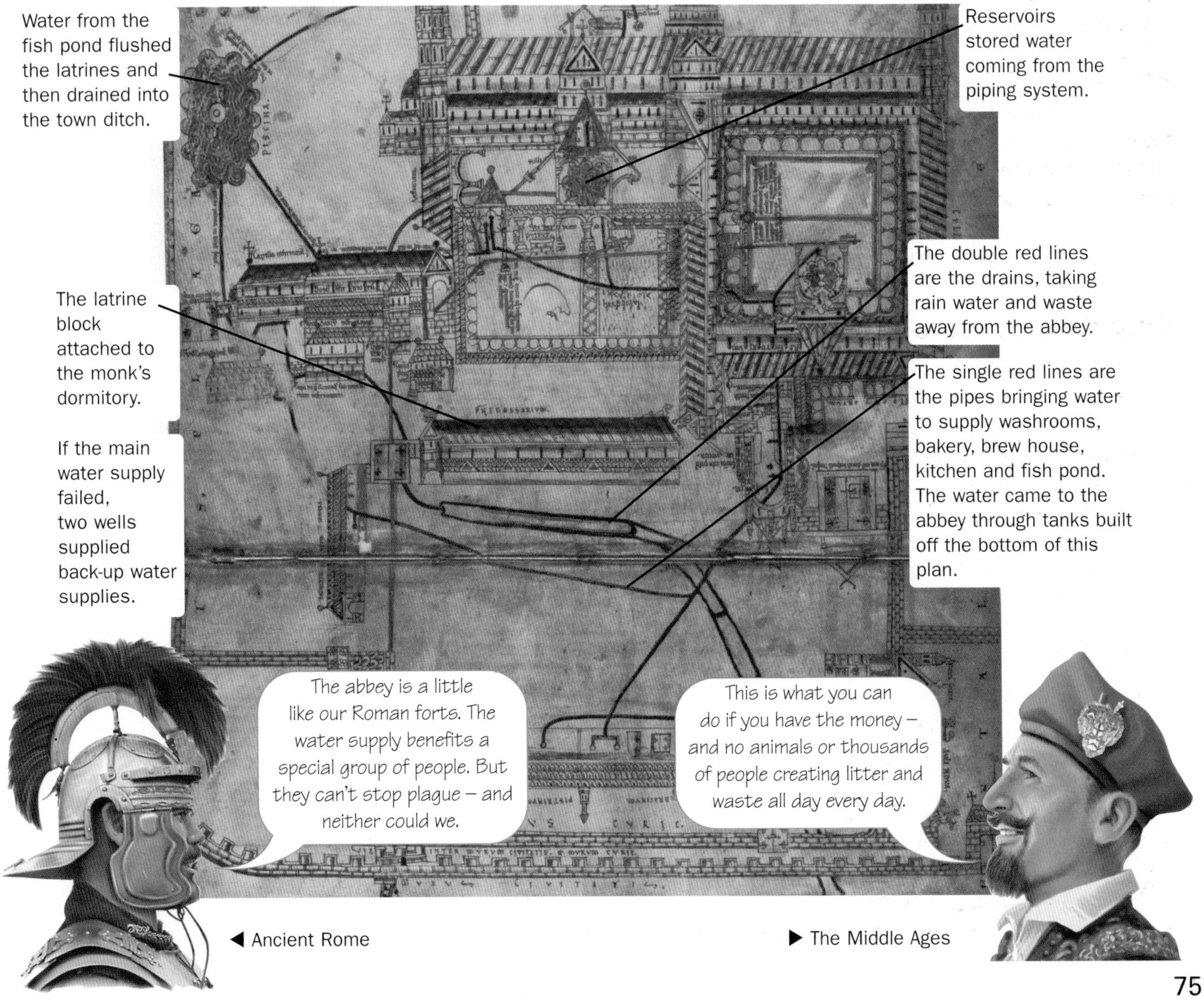

Meet the Examiner: How to answer comparison questions – part 1

exam BUSTERS

Now for some more advice on tackling Section B and C questions which we began on pages 50–51. This page gives you more help with the shorter part (a) answers. The page opposite helps you with longer part (b) answers.

> **SECTION C**
> **Disease and Infection**
>
> (a) Choose **one** of the factors below that affected the development of medicine in the Middle Ages.
> - War
> - Religion and superstition
>
> Describe the effect of that factor on the fight against disease and infection. *(4 marks)*

Answering part (a) – using connectives to describe effects

Step 1: Focus on the question.
(See pages 49–51 for help on decoding questions.)

a What are the **date boundaries** of the question?

b What is the focus **theme**?

c What is the **task** in part (a) – and what do you NOT have to do?

d How many **marks** is part (a) worth and roughly how long should you spend on it?

Step 2: Choose which factor you will write about, then jot down its effects.

Did it help or hinder understanding and treatment of diseases during the Middle Ages? Use the factors chart you produced on the Middle Ages to help you.

Step 3: Select at least two effects of the factor to write about.

Do not try and cover everything! Choose at least two where you are confident that you can explain the specific impact of the factor.

Step 4: Use connectives to tie in what you know to the question.

Do not 'say' that religion had an impact, **prove it**! You can do this by using connectives such as 'this meant that …', 'this led to …' and 'this resulted in …' to explain the impact of religion.

Activity

Look at the answer below. The student has used connectives to link religion to specific developments.

During the Middle Ages, religion had a major impact on the development of medicine. The most common belief was that God sent illnesses such as the Black Death to punish people for their sins. People believed that the sick could be healed if they prayed for forgiveness. This meant that people did not look for scientific ways to explain the causes of disease and that medical treatments did not improve. Also, the Christian Church supported Galen's ideas, they controlled universities and said that his work should not be questioned. This resulted in doctors being discouraged from researching and developing new ideas.

Now write your own paragraph explaining the impact of war on disease and infection. Use the sentence starters and connectives provided or develop your own.

War disrupted people's chances of developing … After the fall of the Roman Empire … This resulted in … Kings believed their main duty was … This meant that …

Answering part (b) – writing effective comparisons

SECTION C
Disease and Infection

(b) Which factor had the greater impact on the fight against disease and infection in the Middle Ages? Explain your answer. *(8 marks)*

The second part of every question in Sections B and C of your exam asks you to compare two things – two people, two theories or medical methods, two factors or developments in two periods. This page focuses on writing effective 'comparison' answers, using the example above on factors. There is help on comparing individuals on pages 100–102.

Remember to reach a decision!

Writing about the impact of both factors is not enough. A common mistake is to sit on the fence and avoid reaching a decision about which factor had the greater impact.

Sitting on the fence is a dangerous position. Your answer collapses and you lose marks!

Instead, you must be confident and reach an **overall judgement**. Imagine that you could put the evidence on scales. Which side would the scales tip – towards war, or religion and superstition? Which side has the strongest evidence to support it? Check your factors chart.

How can you write an effective concluding comparison?

Things to avoid:

- a detailed summary of every impact of each factor – with no final judgement
- a one-sentence comparison which reaches an overall judgement but does not explain it or show that there are two sides to the argument
- a weak comparison that sits on the fence and does not reach an overall judgement.

Things to do:

- Focus on the question. You could use words or phrases from the question in your final paragraph.
- Come to a strong overall judgement.
- Explain your main reason for reaching this judgement.
- Show that you recognise that there is evidence that agrees and disagrees with the statement.

How to structure a conclusion

Start by conceding that the weaker argument has some strengths. Give an example.

- *War did have an impact on understanding of disease in the Middle Ages. For example, after the fall of the Roman Empire ...*

Then make it clear that the other argument is stronger.

- *However, the impact of war was not constant throughout the Middle Ages ...*

Provide your main piece(s) of evidence that support this.

- *In contrast, religion and superstition ...*

Try to end with a memorable final sentence.

- *The greatest impact of religion was to ...*

Activities

1. Do you agree with the way this comparison is developing?
2. How would you finish this comparison?

Section 4: Why was the medical Renaissance important when it didn't make anyone healthier?

The Renaissance is the period of European history between around 1400 and 1600. It is famous for discoveries in science, geography and art. There were also breakthroughs in medicine but, by 1700, people were no healthier than in the Middle Ages. So, if they weren't any healthier, why were these medical discoveries important?

Activities

1. Sources 1–4 were all important developments in the period of the Renaissance. How do you think each development influenced medicine?
2. Which breakthroughs do you think each of the three medical pioneers shown on page 79 made use of in his work?
3. Think about the three medical discoveries made by these pioneers. Why do you think they did not immediately lead to people being healthier and living longer?

Renaissance breakthroughs

Source 1

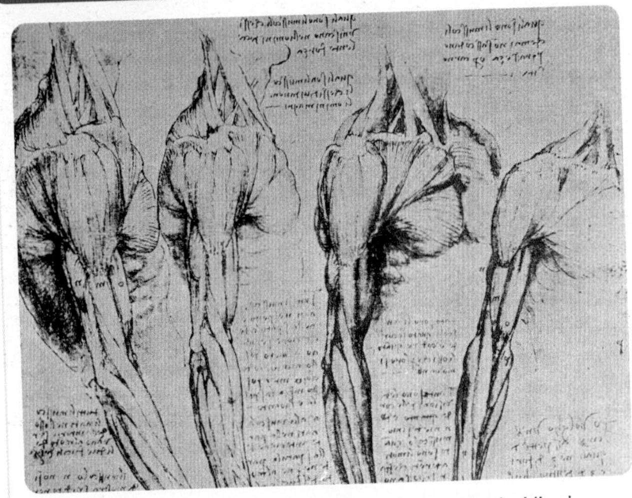

▲ Drawings of parts of the body by Leonardo da Vinci (1452–1519). Da Vinci gave this advice to young artists:

'The painter who has knowledge of sinews, muscles and tendons will know exactly which sinew causes the movement of a limb. He will be able to show the various muscles in the different attitudes of his figures. You will need three dissections to have a complete knowledge of the arteries, three more for the membranes, three for the nerves, muscles and ligaments, three for the bones and cartilages. Three must also be devoted to the female body.'

Source 2

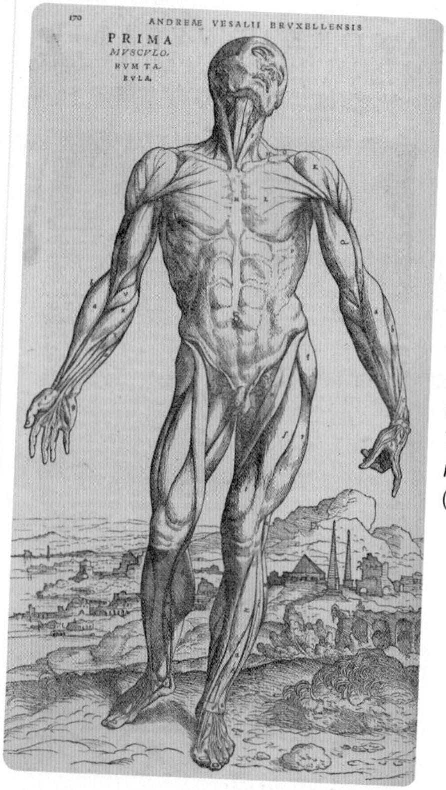

◀ The printing press was invented by Johannes Gutenberg in the 1450s. By 1500 printing presses were being used throughout western Europe. Some books were highly illustrated such as this page from Andreas Vesalius' book on anatomy, *The Fabric of the Human Body* (1543).

Source 3

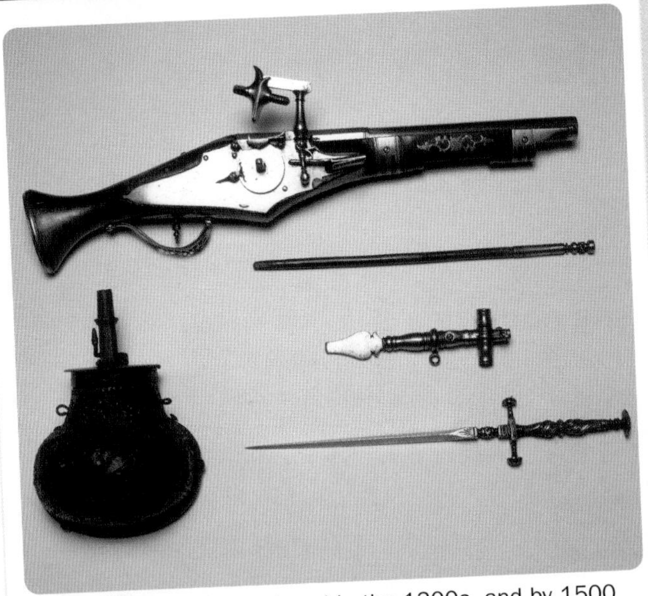

▲ Gunpowder was developed in the 1300s, and by 1500 cannons and guns were widely used on battlefields.

Source 4

◀ The first effective microscopes were developed in the 1600s by instrument makers including Robert Hooke in England and Antoni van Leeuwenhoek in Holland. They allowed people to see things they could not see with the naked eye.

Renaissance medical pioneers

▲ Andreas Vesalius made new discoveries about the anatomy of the human body.

▲ William Harvey discovered that the blood circulates around the body.

▲ Ambroise Paré pioneered new surgical methods for treating gunshot wounds and stopping bleeding.

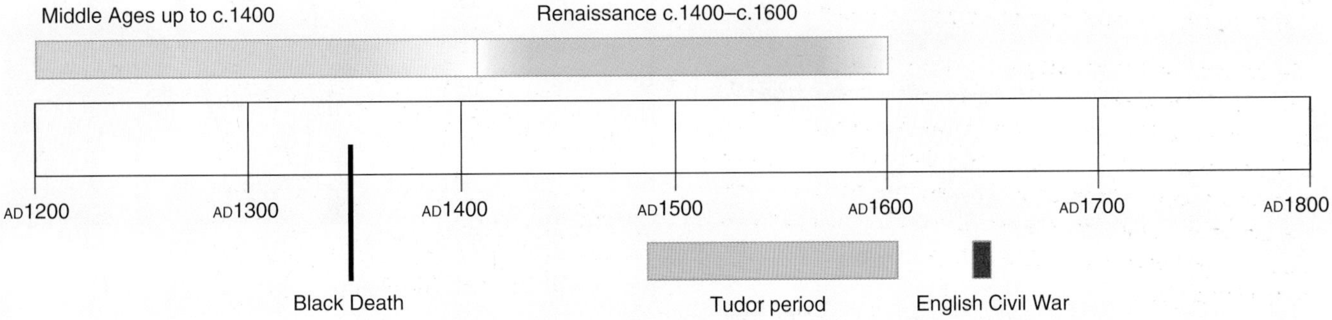

4.1 What was re-born in the medical Renaissance?

Renaissance means 're-birth'. In general the Renaissance period was a time of 're-born' interest in all things Greek and Roman, their books and ideas, buildings and sculptures. But, in medicine, interest in the Greeks and Romans had never gone away because physicians had kept reading and relying on Galen. So what exactly was being re-born in the medical Renaissance?

The Renaissance struggle: conservatism versus enquiry

In the Big Fight of the Middle Ages, conservatism beat enquiry. This wasn't surprising as conservatism had the experienced and powerful Christian Church in his corner. Enquiry only had a couple of surgeons in his corner suggesting new moves but they did not hurt conservatism at all. What happened next?

Then came the Black Death. Afterwards many of the survivors were better-off because employers had to pay higher wages to attract workers. Many people had spare time and spare money and they spent some of this time and money on education.

Wealth and education helped trigger the Renaissance, the re-birth of interest in the Greeks and the Romans. Educated people during the Renaissance thought that the Greeks and Romans were just like them – intelligent and thoughtful. They looked down on the people of the Middle Ages as ignorant.

They made new translations of Galen. Greeks and Romans, like Galen, had never gone away in medicine. Medieval doctors had studied them in detail. In universities in the 1500s scholars were still reading translations of Galen but now they were worried. The translations had been made in the Middle Ages. What if they were wrong? What if vital knowledge had been missed out or misunderstood by ignorant people in the Middle Ages? They decided to make new translations to make sure they were right. They published new editions of Greek and Roman books, including nearly 600 editions of Galen's books.

This work changed attitudes. In the Middle Ages, people respected traditional ideas and simply copied Greek knowledge and ideas. They did not challenge them. But in the Renaissance, people realised that the Greeks loved enquiry – asking questions, challenging old ideas (like the gods causing disease) and suggesting new ones (the theory of the four humours). If the Greeks could ask questions and challenge old ideas, then so could they, the people of the Renaissance.

So what was re-born? It was not just interest in Greek and Roman ideas that was re-born but, far more importantly, their love of enquiry and willingness to challenge existing ideas. Once they began to ask questions and look carefully some people began to realise that Galen had not known everything – and had even made mistakes!

But not everyone agreed. Many people still conservatively stuck to tradition, not daring to think for themselves, still saying it was wrong to challenge Galen. So what developed was a battle between attitudes – between people defending the old ideas and people fighting for new ones.

Activities

1 What exactly was being re-born in the Renaissance?
2 Conservatism beat enquiry in the Middle Ages.
   a What kinds of changes in medicine do you think would be needed to change the result and give enquiry a knock-out victory over conservatism?
   b Look at the possible results below. Which do you think was the likely result by 1700?

The Big Fight 1400–1700 – how will it end?

So who did win the Big Fight between the attitude twins – conservatism and enquiry? Your task is to create your own commentary on the great 'conservatism versus enquiry' contest. Your commentary will link all the topics in this section together by assessing how much medicine really changed between 1400 and 1700. And there's a bonus – you will have begun your revision months before you complete your course and take your exam!

Disease and infection – see blue rows

Surgery and anatomy – see red rows

Public health – see green rows

Activities

Over the next twelve pages you will be gathering information to fill in the Big Story chart on the opposite page. You could do this on computer. You will then use the chart to write your own audio commentary on the big fight of 1400–1700. Each topic in the table will be one 'round' in the big fight.

Stage 1: get an overview

Use pages 84–85.

a Pencil information about each topic into column 3 of your Big Story chart.

b On a separate sheet of paper draft first ideas for your commentary for each 'round'. Just a sentence to summarise what happened will be enough at this stage. This is your set of starter ideas to build on.

Remember:

Round 1 is Knowledge of the human body (pages 86–89)
Round 2 is Surgery (pages 90–91)
Round 3 is Healers (pages 92–93)
Round 4 is Ideas about causes of disease (pages 92–97)
Round 5 is Treatments (pages 94–95)
Round 6 is Public health (pages 96–97).

Stage 2: fill in the detail

Now work through the tasks on pages 86–97. Some of them will get you working in groups or listening to other groups present, but all the time it is your responsibility to fill in your Big Story chart.

Stage 3: decide on the winners of each round

Complete the final column of your chart giving points to each boxer: conservatism or enquiry. Use the table to help you.

If there are ...	Then Conservatism gets ...	And Enquiry gets ...
No discoveries at all	3	0
Traditional ideas that still dominate medicine even if one or two new ideas begin to be accepted	2	1
Important discoveries that begin to change this aspect of medicine	1	2
Really important discoveries that completely change this aspect of medicine	0	3

Stage 4: write your commentary

a Now you are ready to write your commentary. It should say in sports-commentator style: who is winning this round (is it a close run thing or an easy win?); which punches (evidence) have the biggest impact?

b Record your commentary as a podcast. You can also listen to it for revision.

The Big Story of medicine during the Renaissance

	Medicine c.1400, at the end of the Middle Ages	The impact of the Renaissance – medicine c.1700	Who won this round: conservatism or enquiry? Which were the strongest punches?
Round 1 Knowledge of the human body (pages 86–89)	Doctors knew about Greek and Roman discoveries but did not learn any more. Dissection was carried out to illustrate what Galen had said, not to make new discoveries.		
Round 2 Surgery (pages 90–91)	**a** Simple surgery on visible tumours and wounds. **b** Splints for fractured bones. **c** Trephining (cutting a hole in the skull). **d** Plants such as opium dulled pain a little but there were no effective anaesthetics. **e** Surgeons use wine, vinegar or honey to clean wounds but could not prevent infections spreading or stop heavy bleeding.		
Round 3 Healers (pages 92–93)	**a** Mothers and family members treated most illnesses. Women with skills and experience often called to help, e.g. with childbirth. **b** Priests said prayers to help the sick and protect from illness. **c** Surgeons, e.g. army surgeons, trained by observing others and improved their skills through practice. **d** Physicians trained at universities by reading the books by Hippocrates and Galen and some Arab medical writers.		
Round 4 Ideas about causes of disease (pages 92–97)	**a** Many believed that illnesses were sent by God. **b** Doctors said that many illnesses had natural causes. They followed Hippocrates' theory that illness was caused when the body's humours were out of balance.		
Round 5 Treatments (pages 94–95)	**a** Remedies made up from herbs, minerals and animal parts. **b** Prayers, charms and rhymes were used. **c** Bleeding, purging and other methods were used to restore the proper balance of the humours, following the methods of Galen. **d** Rest, exercise and diet.		
Round 6 Public health (pages 96–97)	**a** Town governments employed people and made laws to try to keep streets clean but had little success. **b** It was very difficult to keep towns clean as they were full of animals, houses were packed together and there were few paved streets. **c** Kings were not expected to improve hygiene or protect public health. Their job was to defend the country and keep law and order. **d** Epidemic diseases still could not be stopped.		

Medical Moments in Time: London, 1665

Activities

This drawing helps you to develop a quick overview of how medicine was changing and whether conservatism was still beating enquiry in 1665. You can add this to your Big Story chart on page 83.

1. Divide the six topics among the class. What evidence can you find to start your chart? Who is winning each round?
2. What evidence helps to explain why people were no healthier nor living longer than in the Middle Ages?

No meetings of the Royal Society while there's plague.
I'll miss the lectures and experiments. They're talking of transfusing blood from a dog to a man.
The new microscopes are wonderful – detail you can't see with the naked eye.
Hush. She's got tummy ache. Pass my copy of *New Herbal*.
Mother dosed us with rhubarb. It's excellent.
I like this copy of Vesalius. Good illustrations of anatomy.
They never had books like this before printing was invented.
Cure for the plague! Straight from America where it saved my friend Pocahontas. One spoonful a day and you'll live to be 80.
BOOKS
TAVERN
I like Harvey's theory that blood circulates round the body.
Nonsense! It goes against Galen.
Another cross. More plague – why?
God sends plague to punish our sins.
No, it's bad air or the planets. I'm leaving London today.
Physicians trained at universities, reading books by Greek, Roman and Arab writers. They studied discoveries by Vesalius and Harvey but new ideas were rarely accepted immediately.
Even if he's right it won't help anyone who's sick.

4.2 What did people discover during the medical Renaissance?

Pages 86–91 tell you about the three most important developments of the medical Renaissance. They make it look as if medicine is changing completely, as if enquiry has won. But is it that simple? Were these punches really knocking out conservatism or just the start of a much longer contest?

Activities

Pages 86–91 will help you complete the first two rows of your Big Story chart on page 83: 'Knowledge of the human body' and 'Surgery'.

1 Work in groups. Each group will tackle one of the developments:
   - Vesalius and anatomy (pages 86–87)
   - Harvey and blood (pages 88–89)
   - Paré and surgery (pages 90–91).

   Report your findings to the rest of the class.

2 **'Role of the individual' chart:** Convert your findings into charts for revision.

Pioneer 1 Andreas Vesalius – breakthroughs in anatomy

Biography

- Born 1514, died 1564.
- Father a doctor. Studied medicine in Paris and Padua, Italy.
- Professor of Surgery in Padua.
- Wrote *The Fabric of the Human Body* (1543), a detailed and fully illustrated description of human anatomy.

Anatomy – the story so far

1 Doctors believed Galen had given a fully correct description of anatomy.

2 Dissection was carried out to show Galen was right, not to check or challenge him, even though Galen had said it was important to learn by dissecting human bodies. He sometimes had to use animals because human bodies were not available.

Vesalius' achievements – Galen could be wrong!

The Fabric of the Human Body was the first highly illustrated book on human anatomy.

Vesalius respected Galen's work but proved that Galen was sometimes wrong by showing that:

- the human jaw bone is made from one bone, not two as Galen said
- the breastbone has three parts, not seven as Galen said
- blood does not flow into the heart through invisible holes in the septum – such holes do not exist.

He showed that doctors could learn more about anatomy and had to carry out human (not animal) dissection to learn more.

Source 1

▲ The title page of Vesalius' *The Fabric of the Human Body* tells us about his attitudes to dissection. Vesalius is shown in the centre, dissecting the body himself. In the Middle Ages, professors sat and read Galen aloud while demonstrators did the dissection. Galen and other Greek doctors are shown at the same level as Vesalius, not higher up as if superior. Students crowd round the body so they can see what Vesalius is doing rather than simply listening to Galen being read out.

How did he do it?

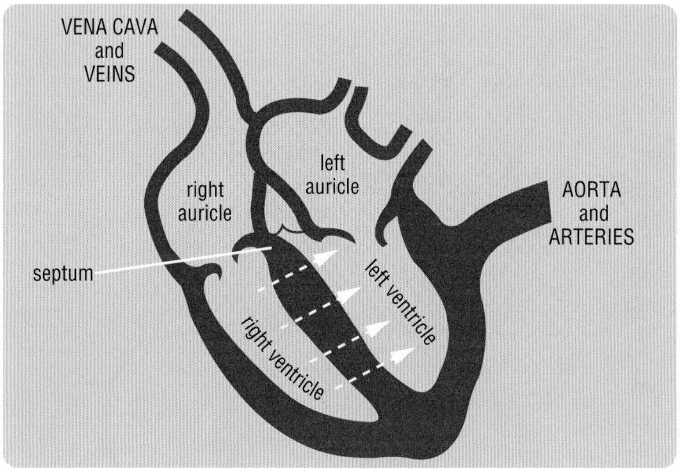

▲ Diagram showing Galen's idea about how blood reached the heart. Vesalius's dissection proved this was not true.

But …

- **Many doctors refused to accept that Galen could be wrong.** Some said that Vesalius's work only showed that the body had changed since Galen's time. The heavy criticism led Vesalius to leave Padua and work for the Emperor Charles V.
- **Nobody was healthier as a result of Vesalius's work.** His work was only the start. Many more discoveries were needed before people would live longer, healthier lives.

Stepping stones to the future

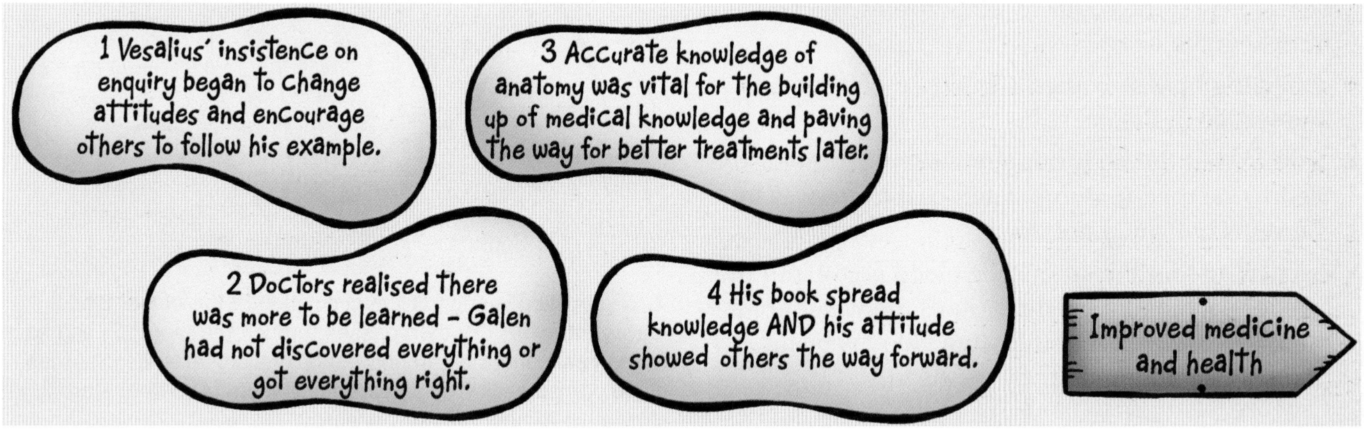

Pioneer 2 William Harvey – discovering the circulation of the blood

Biography

- Born 1578, died 1657.
- Studied medicine in Cambridge and Padua, worked as a doctor in London.
- Published his book *An Anatomical Account of the Motion of the Heart and Blood,* in 1628, which described how the blood circulates round the body.
- Became doctor to King Charles I.

Blood – the story so far

Galen had said:

1 new blood was constantly manufactured in the liver to replace blood burned up in the body just like wood is burnt by a fire

2 blood passed from one side of the heart to the other through invisible holes in the septum. This had been challenged by Ibn al-Nafis (1210–1288) and Vesalius but neither could provide an alternative explanation.

Two other doctors had made discoveries that paved the way for Harvey:

- Realdo Columbo (1516–1559) said that blood moved along the veins and arteries.
- Fabricius (1533–1619), Harvey's tutor at Padua, proved there are valves in the veins.

Despite these pieces of knowledge, nobody could explain how blood moved around the body!

Source 1

▲ A water pump being used to fight a fire in the 1600s. Pumps like this had valves to direct the flow of water.

Harvey's achievements

Harvey proved that the heart acts as a pump, pumping blood around the body. He did this by:

- dissecting live cold-blooded animals whose hearts beat slowly so he could see the movement of each muscle in the heart
- dissecting human bodies to build up detailed knowledge of the heart
- proving that the body has a one-way system for the blood – he tried to pump liquid past the valves in the veins but could not do so
- calculating that the amount of blood going into the arteries each hour was three times the weight of a man. This showed that the same blood is being pumped round the body by the heart.

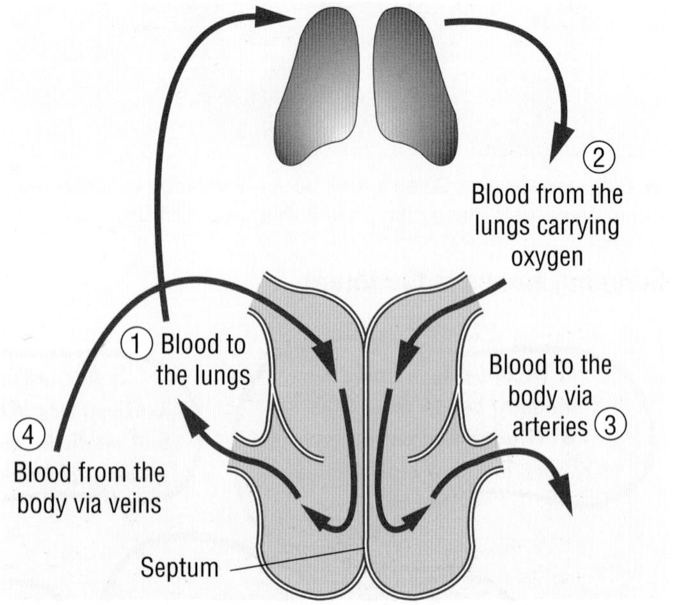

▲ A simplified version of the circulation of the blood. Blood leaves the heart (1), then passes through the lungs (2) and back to the heart and then around the body along arteries (3). Then blood comes back to the heart along veins (4) before starting its circulation around the body again.

How did he do it?

Source 2

◀ Harvey could not explain everything about the circulation of the blood. He did not know how blood moves from the arteries to the veins but later in the 1600s Professor Marcello Malphigi used one of the first effective microscopes to discover the capillaries, which carry blood from arteries to veins. The development of microscopes was a vital technological development helping to transform medical knowledge.

But …

- **There was still much more to discover about the blood.** Doctors could not make blood transfusions until they discovered blood groups in 1901.
- **Harvey's discovery was only gradually accepted.** Some doctors ignored his theory. Others said that he was wrong because he was contradicting Galen. It was nearly fifty years before the teachers at the University of Paris taught Harvey's ideas rather than Galen's.
- **Harvey's discovery did not make anyone better.** The writer John Aubrey noted 'All his profession agree Dr Harvey to be an excellent anatomist, but I never heard any that admired his treatment of the sick.' Harvey himself said that after he published his discovery fewer patients came to see him. Many thought his idea mad.

Stepping stones to the future

1 Harvey's discovery laid the groundwork for future investigation of the blood and physiology (the workings of the body) – see Source 2.

2 Many aspects of medicine depend on understanding the blood system. Surgery, for example, could not develop until after Harvey's discovery.

3 Harvey proved that Vesalius was right about the importance of dissection. He wrote 'I prefer to learn and teach anatomy not from books but from dissections.'

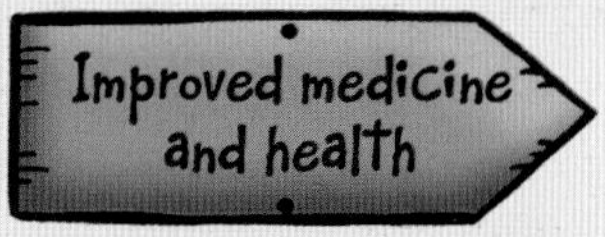

Pioneer 3 Ambroise Paré – breakthroughs in surgery

Biography

- Born 1510, died 1590.
- Learned surgery as apprentice to his brother, then worked at Royal Hospital, the Hôtel Dieu, Paris.
- From 1536 spent 20 years as an army surgeon, then was surgeon to kings of France.
- Most famous surgeon in Europe because of his books *Ten Books on Surgery* and *Apology and Treatise.*

Surgery – the story so far

1 Practice in wartime had helped surgeons make minor improvements to techniques but there had been no major breakthroughs.

2 Gunpowder in gunshot wounds was thought to be poisonous so wounds were treated by pouring boiling oil onto them to kill the poison or by ramming an oil-soaked cloth into the wound and binding it up. Both were extremely painful.

3 Open wounds and amputations were closed by putting a red-hot iron called a cautery onto the wound to seal the blood vessels. Cauterising a wound was also incredibly painful.

Paré's achievements

- Paré changed the treatment of gunshot wounds. He replaced the use of boiling oil on wounds with his own mixture of egg yolks, oil of roses and turpentine.
- He used ligatures to stop bleeding – silk threads tied around individual blood vessels. He did this instead of using a cauterising iron, which he called the 'old and too cruel way of healing'.
- He designed and arranged the making of false limbs for wounded soldiers, and included drawings of them in his books to spread the idea.

Source 1

▲ A wound being cauterised. In reality the patient would have been struggling and screaming with pain. This wood engraving dates from around the 15th–16th century.

Source 2

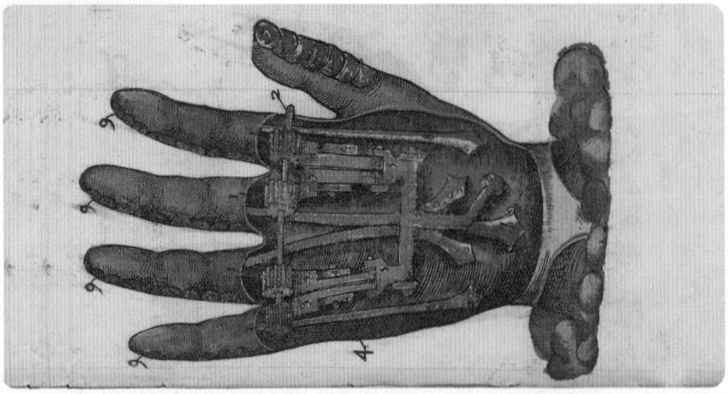

◀ Skilled armourers sometimes made the false limbs designed by Paré. The best even allowed the user to hold a sword and fight. This wood engraving appeared in 1564.

How did he do it?

Source 3

Paré's description of his breakthrough in treating gunshot wounds in the middle of a battle:

'Other surgeons applied the oil, as hot as possible, into the wounds. I took courage to do as they did. Eventually I ran out of oil. I was forced instead to use an ointment made from egg yolks, oil of roses and turpentine. That night I could not sleep, fearing what would happen because the wounds had not been cauterised and that I should find those on whom I had not used the burning oil dead or poisoned. This made me rise up very early to visit them. To my surprise I found those to whom I gave my ointment feeling little pain, and their wounds without inflammation or swelling, having rested reasonably well during the night. The others, on whom I used the boiling oil, were feverish, with great pain and swelling around the edges of their wounds.'

But …

- **Stopping bleeding with ligatures was slow.** Fifty-three ligatures had to be tied when a thigh was amputated. In the chaos of war, using a cautery was faster and could be effective.
- **Ligatures were dangerous** because the thread could carry infection deep into a wound, causing death. A better antiseptic than turpentine or wine was needed but this wasn't discovered for another 300 years, in the late 1800s.
- **Paré's discoveries were still small scale** compared with the major problems facing surgeons – they had no effective anaesthetics, they had no effective antiseptics to stop infection and they did not understand about blood groups or have fast ways of stopping major bleeding.

Stepping stones to the future

1 Paré's work became widely known through his books, which were written in French and translated into other everyday languages so that they could be read by more surgeons then if they had only been in Latin.

2 Paré encouraged surgeons to think for themselves and try new methods. He showed that improvements were possible.

3 Ligatures did stop bleeding, although other improvements were needed (see warning) before they were widely used.

Improved medicine and health

4.3 Did new discoveries help the sick?

It looks as if enquiry was winning thanks to the work of individuals, but conservatism was fighting hard.
Use pages 92–97 to complete your chart and decide who really won the Big Fight.

Healers and their training

A Physicians

University-trained physicians still accepted Hippocrates' theory that illness was caused by an imbalance in the body's humours. Their training concentrated on the writings of Greek doctors, especially Galen, and Arab doctors such as Ibn Sina. They also read the work of Vesalius, Paré and Harvey, but were still reluctant to accept that Galen could have been wrong. Therefore, Harvey's discovery was not accepted immediately. Like their ancient and medieval predecessors, physicians also advised their clients on how to stay healthy through a good diet and exercise.

Source 1

▲ Uroscopy, examining the appearance of urine, was still one of the most common means of diagnosing illness in the seventeenth century.

Activities

1. Work in teams. Each team will tackle one topic:
   Healers (pages 92–93)
   Treatments (pages 94–95)
   Public health (pages 96–97)
   Record what you find in the correct row of your Big Story chart then report back to the class.
2. All teams will have discovered something about 'Ideas and disease' because there is evidence about that on every page. Pool your findings and add the details to your Big Story chart.
3. Discuss: Why do you think Thomas Hobbes, one of the greatest philosophers in history, said 'he had rather have the advice or take medicine from an experienced old woman, who had been at many sick people's bedsides, than from the learnedest but unexperienced physician'?

B Women healers and wisewomen

Most people could not afford physicians and took their illnesses to women in the family or local wisewomen, skilled in the use of herbal remedies. Wealthy ladies often provided care for local families. Lady Grace Mildmay (1552–1620) began learning as a child, being set to read William Turner's book *A New Herbal* by her governess and later read books by Galen and Ibn Sina. She kept records of her patients and the treatments she used. Women also worked as midwives, although the first handbooks for midwives were written by men who had little practical experience. The first English handbook by a woman was *The Midwives Book* by Mrs Jane Sharp in 1671.

However, wealthy patients were becoming less willing to go to women healers and preferred fashionable physicians instead.

This was nothing to do with experience or effectiveness but wanting to be seen to be going to the most expensive doctors! Women were still not allowed to go to university, so could not match the theoretical knowledge of men, no matter how good their practical skills.

Another development that downgraded women's role was a secret discovery. About 1620, Peter Chamberlen invented the obstetrical forceps, used to free a baby from the womb during a difficult birth without hurting or killing baby or mother. The Chamberlens, refugees from France, passed the design from father to son until the death of the last of the family in 1728 revealed their secret. After this, male physicians said that only men should use forceps because only they had been to university to gain anatomical knowledge.

C Paracelsus versus Galen – new versus old

> 'Galen is a liar and a fake. Avicenna [Ibn Sina] is a kitchen master. They are good for nothing. You will not need them. Reading never made a doctor. Patients are the only books.'
>
> 'I tell you, one hair on my neck knows more than all you authors, and my shoe-buckles contain more wisdom than both Galen and Avicenna.'

▲ Paracelsus, 1493–1541. His real name was Philippus Aureolus Theophrastus Bombastus von Hohenheim. Fortunately, he changed it to Paracelsus, which means 'better than Celsus'. Celsus was a renowned Roman doctor. By choosing this name, Paracelsus was showing what he thought about the ideas of ancient medicine.

The person who said these amazing things was Paracelsus, a town doctor and professor of medicine in Basel, Switzerland in the 1520s. And he didn't just criticise Galen in words. One day he burned the books of Galen and Ibn Sina in a great public bonfire! Nobody else dared be so outspoken. Other doctors, such as Vesalius and Harvey, corrected details of Galen's work. Paracelsus dared to say that Hippocrates and Galen were wrong – about almost everything!

Paracelsus even said that the theory of the four humours, the basis of the work of all physicians, was wrong. He said illnesses were caused by chemicals in the body and that treatments, therefore, should be based on chemicals. He experimented with treatments whose ingredients were salt, mercury and sulphur.

This sounds more scientific, but Paracelsus's work illustrates the mix of old and new in the Renaissance. He was very religious and believed that God had sent secret messages about how the world works. These messages included clues (called 'signatures') about how to cure illnesses. These signatures included plants that resembled an illness. For example, the plant 'eyebright' looks like a blue eye and so he used it to treat eye problems. He used orchids, shaped like a testicle, to treat sexually transmitted diseases.

But was Paracelsus successful in winning support away from Galen? No! Some individual doctors followed his ideas, but most said he was a crank. Physicians in universities did not teach about his work. Their students did not read his books. Paracelsus's career shows how hard it was to challenge doctors' faith in the work of Galen, even during the Renaissance when old ideas were beginning to be overturned.

Were everyday treatments changing – and doing more good?

1 Bleeding and purging

Physicians continued to believe that many illnesses were caused when the humours in the patient's body were out of balance. Therefore, they used bleeding and purging to correct the balance, even though this must have weakened the patient considerably.

Source 1

▲ Bleeding was still one of the most common medical treatments and was recommended as a method of preventing illness, too.

2 Herbal remedies

Many home remedies were handed down through generations from mother to daughter. Girls learned how to mix up remedies, using ingredients such as honey, which we now know kills some bacteria. More people were writing down home remedies because more people could now read and write. Mary Doggett noted a remedy for scurvy which used a mixture of horseradish roots, white wine, water and a quart of orange juice or twelve thinly cut oranges. We know that scurvy, which leads to internal bleeding and death, is the result of not eating enough fruit and vegetables so long practice had produced an excellent remedy, even if Mary did not know why it worked.

Source 2

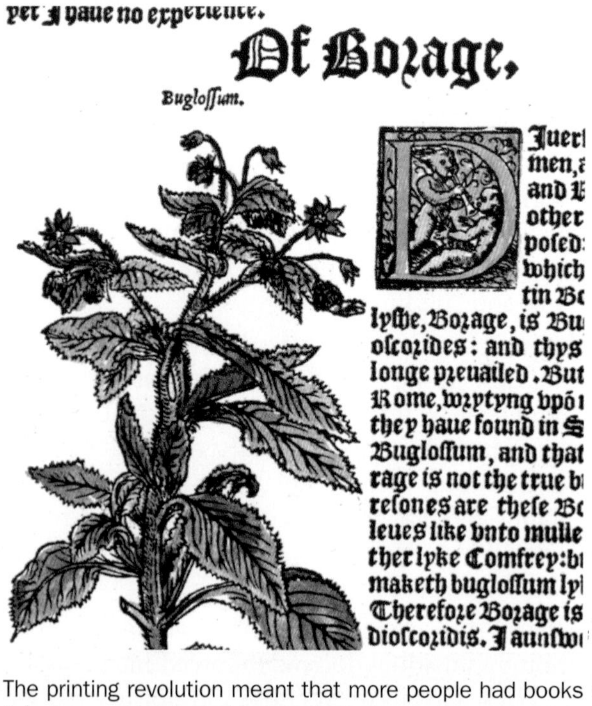

yet I haue no experience.

Of Borage.

Buglossum.

Diuer men, and other posed: which tin Bo lyshe, Borage, is Bu oscorides: and thys longe preuailed. But Rome, wrytyng vpo they haue found in Buglossum, and that rage is not the true b resones are these Bo leues lyke vnto mulle ther lyke Comfrey: b maketh buglossum ly Therefore Borage is dioscoridis. I aunswe

▲ The printing revolution meant that more people had books in their homes containing advice on herbal remedies. One of the most popular was Nicholas Culpeper's *The Complete Herbal* which recommended simple homegrown herbal remedies.

3 New ingredients from abroad

European travels to America and Asia led to the arrival of new ingredients for medicines. Rhubarb from Asia was widely used to purge the bowels. Ipecacuanha from Brazil was prescribed for dysentery and used to make people vomit. The bark of the cinchona tree was imported from South America because of its effectiveness in treating fevers. In Europe it became known as quinine and helped many who suffered from malaria.

Less helpfully, opium was imported from Turkey and used as an anaesthetic. Tobacco was greeted as a cure-all when it arrived from America, being recommended for toothache, poisoned wounds, joint pains and as protection from plague. A schoolboy at Eton College commented that he had never been flogged so much as during the Plague of 1665, when he was beaten for not smoking often enough!

4 The bezoar stone – testing a magical cure

In 1566 a visitor to King Charles of France gave the king a bezoar stone, which came from the stomach of goat-like animals. The visitor insisted that it would cure all poisons but when King Charles asked Ambroise Paré, his surgeon, Paré said that it could not possibly cure all poisons because a hot poison needed a cold antidote and vice-versa. Paré then suggested a test on a live patient! A cook who had been sentenced to death for theft was offered the chance to live if he took poison and then the bezoar stone. If the bezoar stone worked he would be free! The cook accepted the chance, took poison and then the stone. He died in agony several hours later. It was another triumph for experiment and enquiry, though not so good for the cook.

Source 3

From James Woodforde's diary (Woodforde was a parson in Norfolk and Somerset):

27 May 1779 'My maid Nanny taken very ill with dizziness and a desire to vomit but could not. Her straining to vomit brought on the hiccups which continued very violent. I gave her a dose of rhubarb before going to bed.'
1 March 1778 'Ben brought me a letter saying that Juliana is in a decline on account of lately having had measles and catching cold after, which has affected her lungs. She has been bled seven times.'
17 May 1778 'Ben brought letters which gave the disagreeable news of Juliana's death.'
11 March 1791 'The stye on my eye was still swelled and inflamed very much. As it is commonly said that rubbing the eyelid with the tail of a black cat would do it much good, and having a black cat, I made a trial of it. Very soon after dinner I found my eyelid much abated of swelling and almost free of pain. Any other cat's tail may have the above effect in all probability but I did my eyelid with my own black tom cat's tail.'
16 March 1791 'My eyelid rather better. Just before dinner I washed it well with cold water and the evening appeared much better for it.'

Source 5

Two suggestions from the 1660s on how to help plague sufferers:

'To draw the poison from the plague sore, take the feathers from the tail of a chicken and apply the chicken to the sore. The chick will gasp and labour for life. When the poison is drawn by the chicken, the patient will recover.'
'Wrap in woollen clothes, make the sick person sweat, which if he do, keep warm until the sores begin to rise. Then apply to the sores live pigeons cut in half or else a plaster made of yolk of an egg, honey, herb of grace and wheat flour.'

Source 6

From *The New London Dispensary*, published in 1682:

'To cure malaria, take the hair and nails of the patient, cut them small and either give them to birds in a roasted egg or put them in a hole in an oak tree or a plane tree. Stop up the hole with a peg of the same tree.'

Source 4

◀ Between 1660 and 1682 over 92,000 people visited the King's court, believing that if Charles II touched them they would be cured from scrofula, a skin disease known as the King's Evil. People even travelled to be touched by the King from as far as Bamburgh in Northumberland.

Had public health improved?

Plague – the disease that would not go away

After the Black Death of 1348 plague never completely disappeared. Leicester, for example, suffered ten outbreaks of plague between the 1550s and 1640s. In 1604, 30 per cent of the people of York died from plague. Outbreaks like these happened all over the country.

One major reason was that towns were still overcrowded and full of dirt. The Government did issue some orders, such as saying that bundles of straw had to be hung as a warning outside the homes of plague victims and that people who came from infected houses should carry a white stick in public. However, little was done to enforce regulations because of the cost of employing people to do this at a time when there was no police force.

Then, in 1665, another outbreak of plague killed around 100,000 people in London, a quarter of the city's population, and many thousands more all over Britain.

What had not changed since the Black Death in the 1340s?

On 7 June 1665 Samuel Pepys noted in his diary 'I did in Drury Lane see two or three houses marked with a red cross upon the doors and "Lord have mercy upon us" writ there.'

Many people still believed that God had sent plague to punish them for their sins. The government ordered days of public prayer and fasting so that people could publicly confess their sins and beg God to be merciful. Others blamed the malevolent movements of planets or poisonous air, just as in the fourteenth century.

Doctors still had no cures for the plague. Many physicians followed their wealthy clients out of London into the countryside. Some stayed, including Dr George Thomson who carried out an autopsy on a plague victim, hoping to learn more about the disease. Thomson caught plague, but survived. Perhaps his own remedy – putting a dried toad on his chest when he felt the first symptoms – worked.

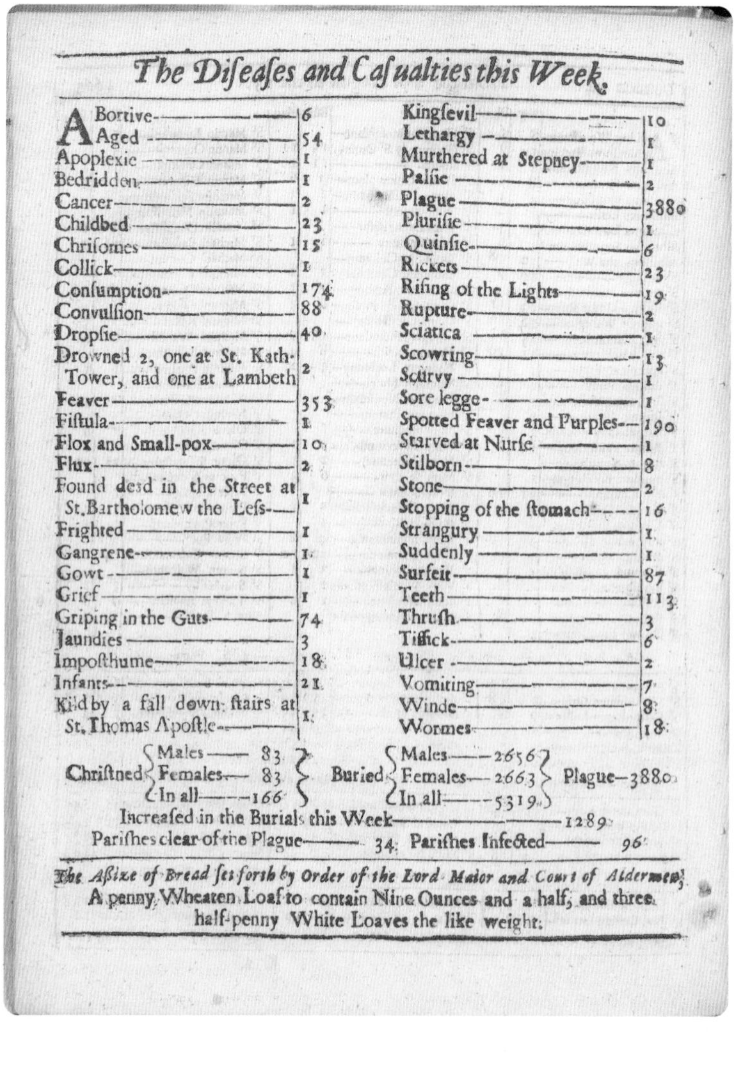

The Diſeaſes and Caſualties this Week.

Abortive	6	Kingſevil	10
Aged	54	Lethargy	1
Apoplexie	1	Murthered at Stepney	1
Bedridden	1	Palſie	2
Cancer	2	Plague	3880
Childbed	23	Pluriſie	1
Chriſomes	15	Quinſie	6
Collick	1	Rickets	23
Conſumption	174	Riſing of the Lights	19
Convulſion	88	Rupture	2
Dropſie	40	Sciatica	1
Drowned 2, one at St. Kath-Tower, and one at Lambeth	2	Scowring	13
Feaver	353	Scurvy	1
Fiſtula	1	Sore legge	1
Flox and Small-pox	10	Spotted Feaver and Purples	190
Flux	2	Starved at Nurſe	1
Found dead in the Street at St. Bartholomew the Leſs	1	Stilborn	8
Frighted	1	Stone	2
Gangrene	1	Stopping of the ſtomach	16
Gowt	1	Strangury	1
Grief	1	Suddenly	1
Griping in the Guts	74	Surfeit	87
Jaundies	3	Teeth	113
Impoſthume	18	Thruſh	3
Infants	21	Tiſſick	6
Kild by a fall down ſtairs at St. Thomas Apoſtle	1	Ulcer	2
		Vomiting	7
		Winde	8
		Wormes	18

Chriſtned: Males — 83, Females — 83, In all — 166
Buried: Males — 2656, Females — 2663, In all — 5319; Plague — 3880
Increaſed in the Burials this Week — 1289
Pariſhes clear of the Plague — 34. Pariſhes Infected — 96

The Aſſize of Bread ſet forth by Order of the Lord Maior and Court of Aldermen,
A penny Wheaten Loaf to contain Nine Ounces and a half, and three half-penny White Loaves the like weight.

▶ In 1665, another outbreak of plague killed around 100,000 people in London, a quarter of the city's population and many thousands more all over Britain. A general mortality bill for the year 1665, listing the number of deaths in each parish and the overall different causes of death. This kind of evidence demonstrated how the plague hit the crowded, poorest parishes hardest.

What was different in the 1660s?

There were signs of a more scientific approach to understanding the plague, based on observation of the evidence. From the weekly Bills of Mortality (see Source 1), some observers linked dirt and disease after realising that the highest numbers of deaths were in the poorest, dirtiest parishes where people lived crammed into the worst housing.

Methods of preventing the spread of plague were more carefully thought-out and organised. The Mayor of London did his best to stop the plague spreading. Victims were shut up in their homes and watchmen stood guard to stop anyone going in or out. When anyone died, the body was examined by 'women searchers' to check that plague was the cause. Their findings were confirmed by surgeons. Bedding had to be hung in the smoke of fires before it was used again. Fires were also lit in streets to cleanse the air of poisons.

Other regulations showed that people were making a connection between dirt and disease, even if they could not explain the link scientifically.

Householders were ordered to sweep the street outside their door. Pigs, dogs, cats and other animals were not to be kept inside the city. Plays, bear-baitings and games were banned to prevent the assembly of large crowds. These methods helped a little, but it took a combination of cold weather, the disease reaching the end of its natural course and then the Great Fire of London to put an end to the Great Plague.

▲ In 1666 London was destroyed by fire and was completely rebuilt to the design of the architect, Christopher Wren. In place of the narrow, dirty streets and wooden buildings were stone and brick buildings with wider, better-paved streets. For a time London was healthier but, as the city became more and more crowded again, the benefits of the rebuilding began to fade.

Smarter revision: Concept map

So far this section has mostly been investigating the changes and continuities in medicine. To finish we'll concentrate on WHY medicine was slow to change with the help of a concept map. On this page we're going to show you how to build up a concept map.

Using concept maps

The students on the opposite page are building a concept map. Concept maps help you develop good explanations. They will:

- help you identify the factors that explain why medicine changed or stayed the same
- show how the factors worked together
- show which factors were the most important (that's what the crowns are for!).

Activities

We have built up this concept map for you. It explains why medicine was slow to develop. It's almost finished. All you have to do is copy it and finish it off.

1 The factors linked to the question with red string were important in hindering medical developments.
The pink cards provide evidence of this. On your own version of the map write or place the cards in the correct places on the red string.

2 The green string links the factors that worked together to prevent progress.
The green cards explain these links. On your own version of the map write or place the cards in the correct places on the green string.

3 The crown shows which factor we think was most important in hindering medical progress. Do you agree? Why or why not?

A. Opposition to Vesalius' criticism of Galen.

B. Prayers said in 1665 to prevent plague.

C. Continued belief in the theory of the four humours.

D. Opposition to Harvey's ideas about blood.

E. Touching for the King's Evil.

F. Governments did not try to improve public health except in emergencies.

G. The Church still supported many traditional ideas.

H. Kings still believed their task was making decisions about war and religion, not improving living standards and health.

Why was medicine so slow to change during the Renaissance?

Meet the Examiner: How to answer comparison questions – part 2

Comparing the significance of individuals

Look at this question.

> **SECTION C**
> **Surgery and Anatomy**
>
> **2 (a)** Choose **one** of the medical pioneers below.
> - Ambroise Paré
> - William Harvey
>
> What did he do? *(4 marks)*
>
> **(b)** Which of these medical pioneers contributed most to improvements in surgery and knowledge of anatomy during the Renaissance.
> Explain your answer. *(8 marks)*

Part (b) of this exam question is challenging. It tests your knowledge of medicine during the Renaissance period *and* your ability to use this knowledge to **compare** the significance of two people. Follow the steps below to help you achieve a high grade on questions that ask you to compare individuals.

Step 1: Explaining an individual's significance

Part (a) of the question asks you to describe what one person did. Therefore, you need to do more than describe and list what people did to get good marks in part (b). You also need to do more than make a general statement about significance.

Look at the following answer.

Paré made important discoveries about surgical methods. Many surgeons read his books and changed their methods.

The student starts by making a general point but has to go on to say more to prove this point is true.

At the start of the period, surgeons used boiling oil to treat gunshot wounds. They thought it killed the poison gunpowder brought into wounds. The boiling oil caused great pain and many soldiers died. By the end of the Renaissance many surgeons had stopped using boiling oil because Paré had discovered how to treat gunshot wounds with other mixtures and many more soldiers survived with much less pain. So he was important because of his original discoveries and because they were widely used.

The student scored extra marks by proving their point by comparing surgical methods at the start and the end of the period.

The student whose answer is on the previous page had thought about why Paré was significant, using a table like the one below. These criteria help you to decide exactly why someone was significant and to compare the significance of two people.

How would you fill in this chart? Include details and a score.

Criteria for judging significance – award up to 3 marks for each criterion	**Paré**		**Harvey**	
	Details	Score	Details	Score
Impact – how many people were helped at the time?				
Correctness – was the discovery correct? Did they understand why it was correct?				
Longevity – how long did someone's impact last?				
Consequences – did it lead on to other important discoveries?				
Overall significance – total marks				

Step 2: Writing your conclusion

This is a crucial part of your answer that students sometimes forget or answer poorly. Just producing a balanced answer is not enough. You have been asked to **decide** which man made the greater contribution. It would be easy to sit on the fence and avoid reaching a conclusion. Sitting on the fence is a dangerous position. Your answer collapses and you lose marks!

Instead, you need to be confident and reach an **overall judgement**. Imagine that you could put the evidence on scales. To which side would the scales tip – towards Paré or Harvey? Which side has the strongest evidence to support it? Think about your significance table (above). Write down your opinion and explain the key reason you have come to your conclusion.

What makes an effective concluding comparison?

Things to avoid:

- a detailed summary of everything that has already been said
- a one-sentence conclusion which reaches an overall judgement but does not explain it or show that there are two sides to the argument
- a weak comparison that sits on the fence and does not reach an overall judgement.

Things to do:

- Focus on the question. You could use words or phrases from the question in your final paragraph.
- Come to a strong overall judgement.
- Explain your main reason for reaching this judgement.
- Show that you recognise that there is evidence that agrees and disagrees with the statement.

How to structure a conclusion

Start by conceding that the weaker argument has some strengths. Give an example.

• Harvey made one of the most important discoveries in medical history.

Then make it clear that the other argument is stronger.

• However, Harvey's discovery made no difference to people's health during the Renaissance and many physicians even refused to believe him.
• In contrast, Paré ...

Provide your main piece(s) of evidence that support this.

Try to end with a memorable final sentence.

Activities

1 Do you agree with the way this conclusion is developing?
2 How would you finish this conclusion?

Meet the Examiner: How to cross-reference and compare sources

This page returns to Section A questions in which your answers are based on a set of sources and your own knowledge. You have already looked at answering part (a) questions on page 49.

SECTION A
Public Health

1 (a) What does **Source A** suggest about attitudes to public health in the Middle Ages? Explain your answer using **Source A** and **your knowledge**. *(4 marks)*

(b) What different attitudes to public health are suggested by **Source B**? Explain your answer using **Sources A** and **B** and **your knowledge**. *(6 marks)*

Activity

Answer part 1(a), using the advice on page 49.

Source A

'London's streets have tubs of putrid water positioned here and there, supposedly in case of fire but more often than not full of decaying rubbish. In the streets the stench and obstruction of the animal dung, vegetable rubbish, fish remains and entrails of beasts present huge problems … with 40,000 permanent citizens and sometimes as many as 100,000 mouths to feed and bowels to evacuate it is impossible for a city with no sewage system to cope.'

A description of London in the 1300s from a modern history book The Time Traveller's Guide to Medieval England *by Ian Mortimer, published in 2008.*

Source B

'It is ordered that every Householder do cause the street to be daily prepared before his door and so to keep it clean swept all the week long. That the sweeping and filth of houses be daily carried away by the Rakers. That no hogs, dogs or cats or tame pigeons or conies to be kept within any part of the city or any swine stray in the streets or lanes and that the dogs be killed by the dog killers.'

An extract from Orders issued by the Lord Mayor of London after the outbreak of plague in 1665.

Some students answer part (b) questions poorly because they waste a lot of time describing what each source says before they begin to answer the question. Students sometimes also try to explain why the sources are different but there's no need – that comes in part (c)! Look at the two approaches below.

Approach A scores very few marks, but Approach B picks up marks from the start as the entire answer focuses on the question by:

- making direct comparisons between the sources from the start of the answer
- using the student's own knowledge to make inferences from the sources.

APPROACH A

Paragraph 1 –
Lengthy description of Source A.

Source A tells us there were tubs of putrid water in the streets and the city was full of animal dung and vegetable rubbish ...

Paragraph 2 –
Lengthy description of Source B.

Source B says that the householders had to sweep the streets outside their houses every day and the dirt had to be taken away by the rakers every day ...

Paragraph 3 –
Answer ends with a broad statement.

Source B is therefore different from Source A.

APPROACH B

Paragraph 1 –
Explains one difference in attitudes suggested by the two sources.

Source A suggests that people did not care about keeping the streets clean because the streets were full of animal dung and vegetable rubbish. Source B gives a different impression because people have to sweep the streets outside the houses and rakers take away the dirt.

Paragraph 2 –
Explains a second difference using knowledge as well as sources.

Source B suggests that people knew that animals were a problem in the city, creating a lot of dirt, so orders had been given to keep them out. Source A does not say that animals were a problem but there is plenty of evidence that ...

Paragraph 3 –
Reaches an overall judgement about differences in attitudes based on the sources and own knowledge.

Overall, the two sources show how attitudes had changed between 1300 and 1665. In the 1300s people took little care over public health, but by the 1660s ...

Activities

1. What is the importance of the words underlined in paragraph 1?
2. Complete paragraph 2 using your own knowledge to explain how animals caused public health problems in the Middle Ages.
3. How would you use your own knowledge to complete paragraph 3?

Writing effective explanations using sources and your own knowledge

(c) Why were there different attitudes to public health at these times?
Explain your answer using **Sources A** and **B** and **your knowledge**. *(8 marks)*

This question is about **why** the attitudes to public health were so different. There are three things to think about before you start to write: **Time, Author, Place (TAP)**.

Activities

4 Use what you know about the sources (including the information about the source as well as the source itself) and your own knowledge.
Which TAP reason(s) best explain the differences in attitudes between the sources?

5 On your own copy of the answer below, highlight in different colours:
- **a** parts of the answer taken from the sources
- **b** parts using own knowledge
- **c** parts which *directly* answer the question
- **d** understanding that attitudes had changed over time
- **e** good practice, e.g. starting with a key point to directly answer the question rather than leaving it to the end – showing thought and planning before writing.

Time: Are the sources about different periods of history? Had important changes taken place between these different times?

Author: Were the authors both well-placed to know what life was like at that time? Do they both provide reliable evidence about this topic?

Place: Are the sources about different places? For example, living conditions in monasteries during the Middle Ages were very different from living conditions in towns.

The attitudes to public health are so different because they come from different periods of history. Source A is about attitudes in towns during the Middle Ages. This was after the collapse of the Roman Empire and their public health system fell into ruin. During the Middle Ages most people didn't care about their living conditions because they didn't understand the importance of cleanliness and their rulers did little if anything to help them. Medieval kings spent their money on wars and becoming more powerful.
Some people during the Middle Ages, however, lived in better conditions than Source A shows; for example, monks in monasteries had clean water supplies, washing facilities, toilets and drains. Source B tells us about attitudes at the time of the Great Plague in London. It shows how the rulers of London were trying to stop the plague spreading. Although they still did not know the real cause of disease, they had much more experience of dealing with the plague since it first broke out in 1348 (the Black Death).

Section 5: Medicine in 1800 – on the brink of progress

We have reached 1750 and, although changes have begun to take place, people are not living longer and are no healthier. This section rapidly summarises everything you have done so far, investigates one of the greatest discoveries in medical history and then takes you on a quick tour of the medical breakthroughs that finally improved health and life expectancy.

Disease and infection – see blue rows

Surgery and anatomy – see red rows

Public health – see green rows

5.1 Why hadn't life expectancy improved by the 1750s?

	Ancient medicine			
	Prehistory	**Egypt**	**Greece**	**Rome**
Disease and infection Healers	Medicine men Women and family members	Priests → Specialist doctors	Asclepius 	
Ideas about causes of disease	Gods and spirits	Blocked channels	Four humours	Bad Air
Treatments	Herbal remedies  Prayers and charms 	Purging	 Bleeding and purging Rest, exercise and diet	
Surgery and anatomy Surgery	Simple surgery and trephining 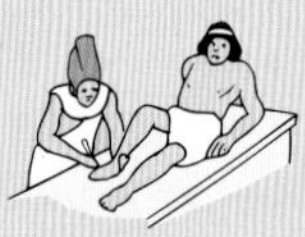 	→ Honey, vinegar, wine as antiseptics Simple anaesthetics made from plants		
Knowledge of the body		Knowledge of main bones and organs		Galen emphasises importance of dissection
Public health		Individuals took care of themselves		Romans built public health facilities in towns and forts 
Individuals			 Hippocrates Aristotle	Galen

Activities

1. Life expectancy had not increased since Ancient times.
   - **a** How do each of the three themes in the chart below help to explain this lack of progress?
   - **b** Which theme do you think is most significant in explaining why life expectancy had not increased?
2. What medical changes and discoveries do you think were needed to make significant progress in the future?
3. **Living graph:** Look at the living graphs you began on pages 6–7. Use the details on this page to make sure they are complete to 1750.

Middle Ages	Renaissance
Wise women →	→
Followers of Galen and Hippocrates → University training →	Still reading Galen and Hippocrates →
Gods and spirits →	→
→	Four humours →
→	Bad air →
→ Herbal remedies →	More herbs from overseas →
→ Leeches →	Bleeding and purging →
Battlefield surgeons make minor improvements →	Improved treatment of gunshot wounds
Use of cauteries to stop bleeding →	Use of ligatures to stop bleeding
	Vesalius pioneers human dissection and challenges Galen
	Harvey discovers blood circulation
	Use of microscopes
Monasteries developed their public health systems	
Kings did very little to improve public health or stop diseases spreading	
al Rhazes	Vesalius
Ibn Sina	Paré
	Paracelsus
	Harvey

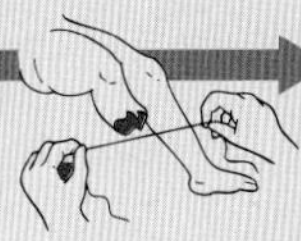

5.2 What does the story of Jenner and vaccination tell us about medicine in 1800?

Source 1 is titled 'The Curse of Humankind'. It probably doesn't make a lot of sense to you so you'll have to take our word for it when we say it's really interesting! Your task is to find out exactly what it's telling us – about the story of vaccination and about how far medicine had developed by 1800.

Activities

1. Look carefully at the picture. What can you work out in answer to the questions before reading pages 109–111?
2. Now read pages 109–111 and come back and answer the questions round the picture. (Remember to use your speed-reading skills.)
3. Who or what is the 'curse of humankind' and what is the artist's attitude to vaccination?
4. Think back to the struggle between enquiry and conservatism. What evidence is there in this picture about the strength of each of the two attitudes around 1800?

Source 1

What work did these three men do?

What are they talking about?

What is he holding?

Who is the man in the black coat?

What is the angel doing?

What are they holding and what is written on them? Why is it written on them?

Who are the people in the background and on the ground?

The roll of paper says 'Bill to . . .' – what is this?

Explain what he's saying in your own words.

▲ 'The Curse of Humankind', drawn by Isaac Cruikshank in 1808.

Smallpox – the story so far

Smallpox killed more children than any other disease in the 1700s. Survivors were often severely disfigured by scars from the scabs that formed on the skin.

To stop people catching smallpox the technique of inoculation was used in China and other parts of Asia and Africa. This involved spreading pus from a smallpox pustule into a cut in the skin of a healthy person. If the person was lucky they got a mild dose of smallpox and did not catch it again because their body had developed antibodies against smallpox – although they did not know this. If the person was unlucky they got a bad case of smallpox and died.

Lady Mary Wortley Montagu watched inoculation carried out in Turkey where her husband was British Ambassador. During a smallpox epidemic in England she had her daughter inoculated in front of important doctors and the method rapidly became popular.

Inoculation became big business. Robert and Daniel Sutton became very wealthy by carrying out many thousands of inoculations, charging up to £20 per patient.

However, there were dangers with inoculation:

- The person inoculated could get a strong dose of smallpox and die.
- The person inoculated could pass smallpox onto someone else.
- Most people could not afford inoculation so were not protected.

Some people thought that the milder disease of cowpox seemed to give protection against smallpox so deliberately infected themselves with cowpox. However, no doctors had written about or tested this idea scientifically.

Jenner's achievements

Jenner learned a lot from the surgeon John Hunter, who told his students to observe patients carefully and experiment to test their ideas. Jenner's discovery of vaccination followed Hunter's advice exactly. Jenner had long known the story that milkmaids who caught cowpox never seemed to get smallpox and he kept this idea in his mind, thinking about how to test it.

In the 1790s Jenner carried out experiments to test the theory, observing and recording all the details carefully (see Source 2). Then in 1798 he published his book describing vaccination and presenting his evidence, describing 23 different cases. He called this method vaccination because the Latin word for cow is *vacca*.

Activities

5 How did inoculation come to be used in Britain?

6 Why did Jenner believe that vaccination was an improvement on inoculation?

Edward Jenner

Biography

- Born 1749, died 1823.
- Aged 13 apprenticed to a surgeon for 6 years. Aged 21 studied with John Hunter in London, the greatest surgeon of the time.
- In 1772 began work aged 23 in Berkeley, Gloucestershire as a country doctor but kept in touch with Hunter about medical developments.
- In 1798 published his book *An Enquiry into the Causes and Effects of Variola Vaccinae, known by the Name of Cowpox*. This showed that vaccination could save people from catching smallpox.

Source 2

Extracts from Dr Jenner's casebook, published in 1798:

Case 16

'Sarah Nelmes, a dairy maid, was infected with cowpox from her master's cows in May 1796. A large sore and the usual symptoms were produced.'

Case 17: James Phipps

'I selected a healthy boy about 8 years old. The matter was taken from the cowpox sore on Sarah Nelmes' hand and inserted on 14 May 1796 into the boy by two cuts each half an inch long. On the seventh day he complained of uneasiness, on the ninth he became a little chilly, lost his appetite and had a slight headache and spent the night with some degree of restlessness but on the following day he was perfectly well.

In order to ascertain that the boy was secure from the contagion of smallpox he was inoculated with smallpox matter but no disease followed. Several months later he was again inoculated with smallpox matter but again no disease followed.'

How did Jenner develop and spread vaccination?

Source 1

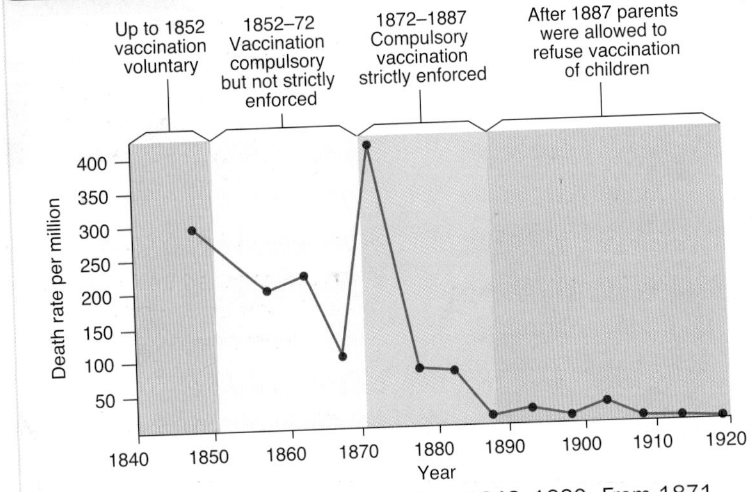

▲ Graph showing deaths from smallpox 1848–1920. From 1871 people were fined for not having their children vaccinated.

But ...

- **Many people opposed vaccination.** An anti-vaccine league was formed in 1866.
- **Governments could not decide how much to force people to be healthier.** The graph shows the changes in laws about vaccination being compulsory.
- **Jenner did not know that germs cause disease** so did not know exactly how vaccination worked. Therefore it was not possible to learn from this discovery how to prevent the spread of other diseases.
- **In the later 1800s other factors played a part in keeping people healthier,** such as clean water supplies, cleaner housing and a better diet.

Stepping stones to the future

1 An excellent example of experiment and enquiry and showed that a killer disease could be beaten, encouraging other doctors and scientists to solve medical problems.

2 Used worldwide.

3 Vaccination made compulsory in Britain in 1852, leading to a significant reduction in deaths. Other factors like public health reforms played a part in this.

4 In 1980 smallpox was declared eradicated from the world.

Improved medicine and health

Why was there opposition to vaccination?

Activities

1. This diagram summarises what the story of vaccination tells us about medicine in 1800. Your task is to draw your own version and add an example or examples to each heading, using what you have read on pages 108–111.
2. **'Role of the individual' chart:** Create a chart for Jenner to help your revision.
3. Remember to go back and finish Activity 2 on page 108.

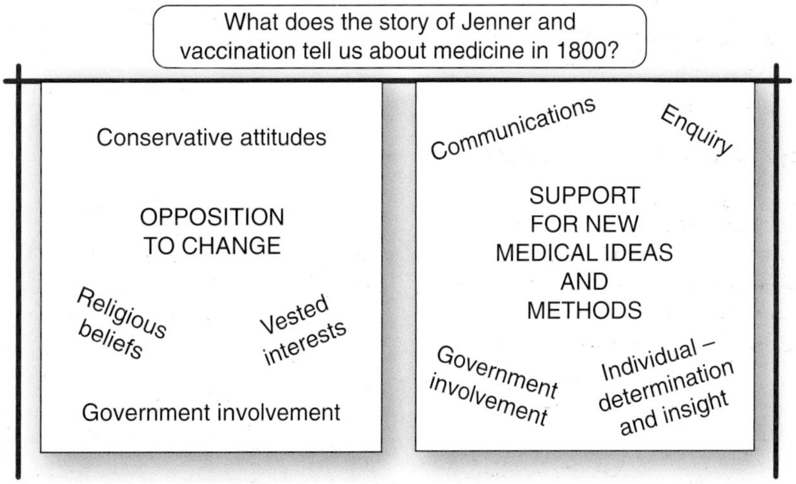

5.3 When and why did life expectancy improve after 1800?

Jenner's breakthrough begins the story of huge medical improvements. Pages 116–121 give you an overview of these changes so you can begin thinking about why they have happened. But first travel back in time to 1848 and then to 1935 – how quickly was medicine and health changing?

Activities

1 What evidence can you find in the 1848 picture of:
  a surgery
  b ideas about causes of disease and types of treatments
  c public health?
2 What adjectives would you use to describe the degree of change between 1665 (see page 84) and 1848?
3 In 1848, the average life expectancy was still only around 40 for men and a few years lower for women. Which factors do you think explain why:
  a life expectancy was still low
  b it might improve later in the 1800s?

Medical Moments in Time: London, 1848

In 1848 the government passed a Public Health Act setting up a national Board of Health. It said:
• local taxes could be charged to improve water supply and sewers
• the Board of Health could force towns to improve water supply and sewerage if the local death-rate was very high
• local Boards of Health with Medical Officers could be set up.
Hold your arm out. Bleeding does you good. And I've a good laxative that'll clear out your whole body.
50,000 people dead from cholera. It's worse than 1832.
It's this miasma of bad air that's causing it. People need clean air.
FINE ALES
TOBACCO
TAILOR
CARRIAGES
EEL PIES
Toilets and cesspits were cleaned out by night-soil men and the waste was carried through streets on carts.
It's consumption. He's been coughing all week.
Back home, people with coughs ride a donkey in a circle seven times. Worth trying?
There's talk of taxes to pay for cleaning streets and building sewers and water pipes.
I'll pay for where I live but not for keeping anyone else clean.

Activities

1. What evidence can you find in the 1935 picture of:
   a. changes in medical methods, ideas and attitudes since 1848
   b. continuities in medical methods, ideas and attitudes with the Middle Ages or earlier?
2. What adjectives would you use to describe the degree of change between 1848 and 1935?
3. In 1935 the average life expectancy was just over 50 for men and a few years higher for women. Which factors do you think explain why life expectancy had improved since 1848?
4. Create your own version of 'Medical Moments in Time' for today.
   a. Include details that show changes since 1935.
   b. Explain why life expectancy in many parts of Britain has risen to nearly 80.
   c. Describe any problems that continue to threaten people's health.

Medical Moments in Time: London, 1935

Governments had passed laws saying that:
• every town and county had to have a medical officer responsible for safeguarding the health of the people
• everyone received fresh water and had good sewers. All new houses had to have their own toilets.
After the First World War (1914–1918), many slum houses were demolished and new housing was built.
FINE PIES
I wish I didn't have to charge for visits and medicines. Many people can't afford to pay so never see a doctor.
Now then, mothers. This class helps you keep your children healthy. Remember the law says that you must get your children vaccinated. Let's start with keeping your babies clean.
SHOP
Jill's got measles. I'd better call in the doctor.
But we haven't finished paying him for last time.
We have to. The girl down the road got measles and now she's deaf in one ear.
From the early 1900s children could receive free school meals and had medical inspections to check their health.
Don't play out in the cold in bare feet. No wonder they hurt.
Mother used hot turnip mash to treat chilblains. No need for anything else.
SCHOOL

What were the key breakthroughs in medicine after 1800?

Source 1

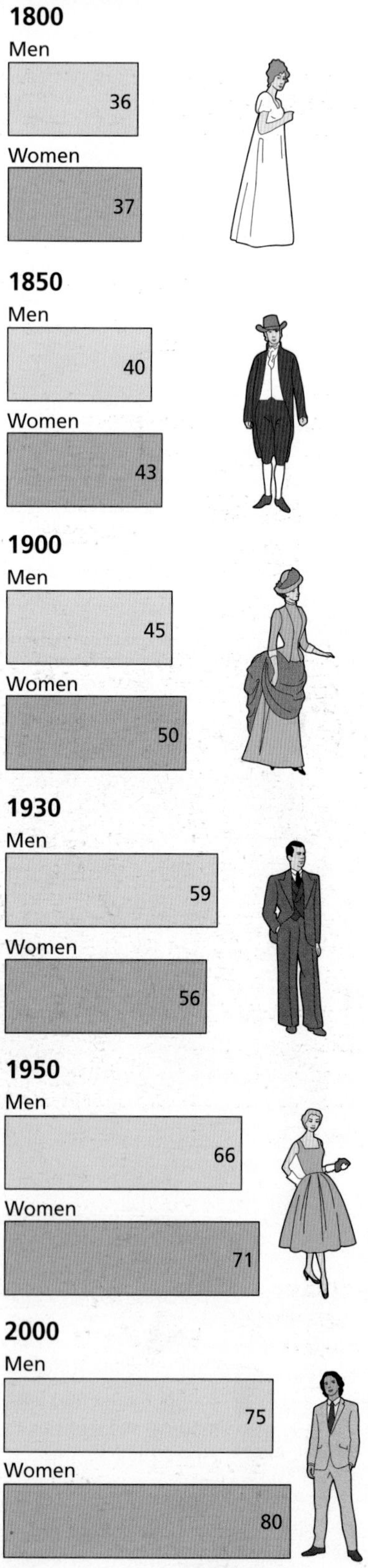

▲ Life expectancy, 1800–2000

Activities

The timeline in Source 1 continues the summary timeline you used on pages 106–107.

1 Life expectancy increased after 1800. Look at Source 1. How would you describe the pattern of that increase?

2 Create your own set of cards like those in the diagram below.
   - a Jot down on each card the developments in its theme which you think were particularly important in increasing life expectancy.
   - b Now organise the cards into a pattern showing which theme or themes were **most important** in explaining why life expectancy had increased. You could use one of the examples we've given or decide on your own pattern.

3 **Living graph:** Look at the graphs you began on pages 6–7. Pencil in how you think each graph develops after 1800. Finalise these graphs as part of your course conclusion.

Using your cards to explain why life expectancy increased

Theory 1

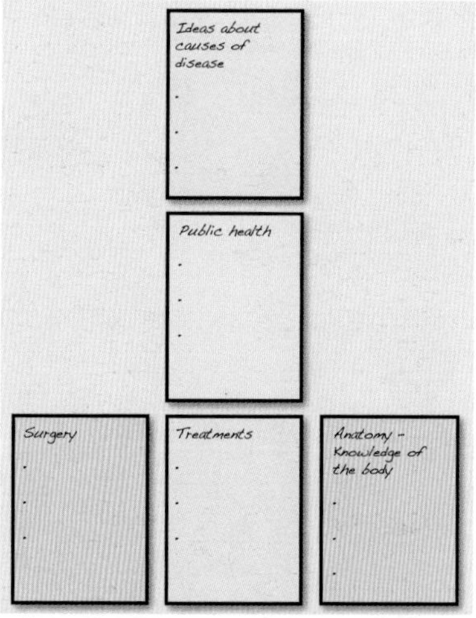

Theory 2

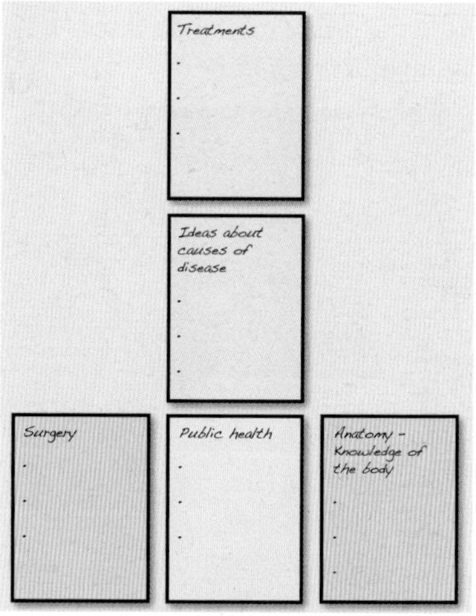

Theory 3

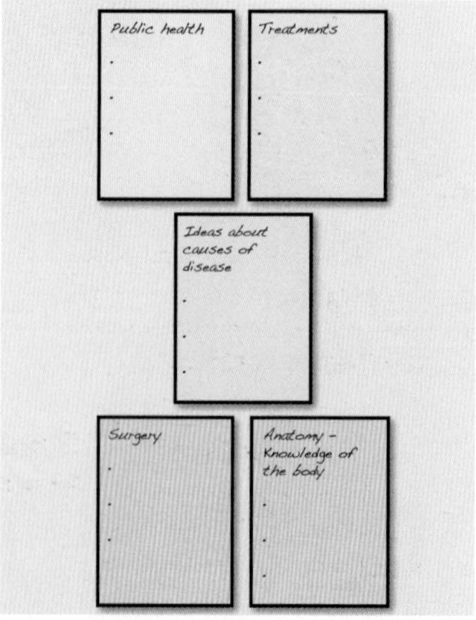

Theory 4

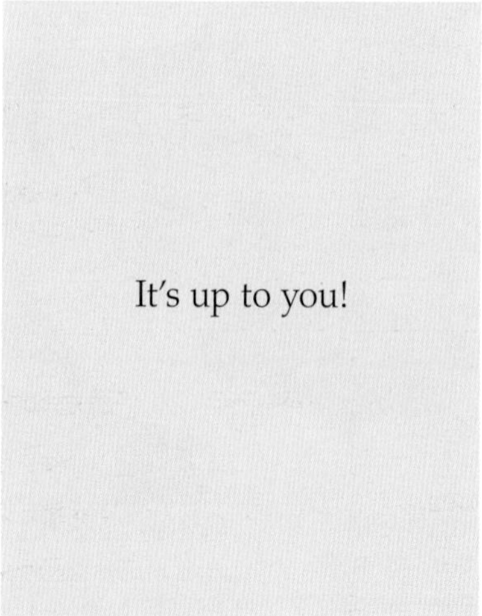

Disease and infection – see blue rows

Surgery and anatomy – see red rows

Public health – see green rows

		1800s	1900s and after
	Healers	Reform of nursing Women win right to become doctors	
Disease and infection	Ideas about causes of disease	Bad Air Spontaneous generation Germ theory 	Genetic causes – DNA 
Disease and infection	Treatments	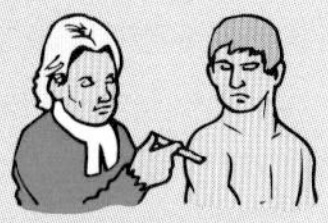 Vaccination against smallpox Vaccination against a range of diseases 	Chemical drugs – sulphonamides 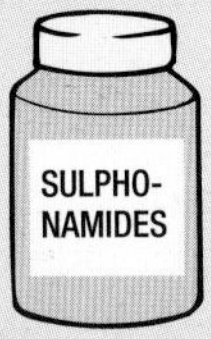 Antibiotic (Penicillin) Genetic medicine
Surgery and anatomy	Surgery	Chloroform – effective anaesthetic Carbolic – effective antiseptic	Discovery of blood groups Plastic surgery Transplants Blood Transfusions  Keyhole and microsurgery
Surgery and anatomy	Knowledge of the body	Use of microscopes to develop detailed knowledge	X-rays Discovery of DNA
Public health		Governments become increasingly involved in safe-guarding health 1848 – encourages reform  1875 – enforces reform	1900s help for poor, sick, unemployed 1942 Beveridge report  1948 NHS
Individuals		Jenner Simpson Snow Chadwick Pasteur Koch Blackwell Anderson Nightingale Seacole Lister Hill	Booth and Rowntree Lloyd George McIndoe Beveridge and Bevan Fleming, Florey and Chain Crick and Watson Barnard

Section 6: Fighting disease after 1800 – which medical hero deserves the statue of honour?

If you had been born into a poor family in London, Leeds or Manchester in 1800, your life expectancy would have been as low as 18. The chances were still very high that you would die from cholera or typhoid, smallpox or tuberculosis, diphtheria or measles. Today, deaths from these diseases are very rare. Some of these diseases have disappeared completely. Your task is to decide which individual should get the statue of honour for making the greatest contribution to defeating disease.

6.1 Who were the key people in the fight against the killer diseases?

Discovery 1	Discovery 2	Discovery 3
Bacteria (germs) are the true cause of diseases BUT scientists cannot identify which individual bacteria cause which individual diseases.	Identification of the bacteria which cause individual diseases.	Now that individual bacteria had been identified, vaccines based on those bacteria are developed to prevent individual diseases.
Understanding ▶	**Prevention** ▶	
Who did what?	**Who did what?**	**Who did what?**
Louis Pasteur published his 'germ theory' in 1861. He had carried out a series of experiments to prove that bacteria (germs) make milk and beer go bad and that bacteria cause diseases in animals. His theory was that germs also cause human diseases. In 1864 he convinced other scientists that this theory was correct.	In the 1870s **Robert Koch** and his research team developed the scientific methods that helped scientists to identify specific bacteria. Koch then made the first discovery of the bacterium that causes a human disease – tuberculosis. Other scientists then followed Koch's methods and discovered the bacteria that cause other diseases.	In the 1880s **Pasteur** discovered how vaccination works and developed vaccines, firstly against animal diseases – chicken cholera, anthrax – and then against a human disease, rabies. Other scientists then developed vaccines against other diseases.
 ▲ Louis Pasteur	 ▲ Robert Koch	 ▲ Louis Pasteur

Activities

1. Work in a pair and examine one of these six discoveries. You have one minute to explain to the rest of the class **why** it was so important. Include briefly:
   - **a** before the discovery – what was thought or what couldn't be done
   - **b** what the discovery was and who made it
   - **c** what it led to.
2. Can you spot links between any two discoveries?
3. Can you see evidence of the impact of any of the factors on page 9?

Discovery 4

The first cures for people who have already become sick with diseases. These cures attack the bacteria developing in the body. They are made from chemicals and called sulphonamide drugs.

Discovery 5

A second group of cures which attack bacteria. These cures are based on other bacteria which kill the bacteria causing a disease. They are called antibiotics.

Discovery 6

Treatments for diseases which have genetic causes rather than being caused by bacteria. These are based on the discovery of DNA and knowledge of the genetic make-up of the body.

Cures ▶ **Prevention and cures**

Who did what?

In 1909 **Paul Ehrlich** (who had been part of Koch's research team) developed the first chemical cure for a disease. This was Salvarsan 606, which he called a 'magic bullet' because it homed in on and destroyed the harmful bacteria that cause syphilis. It wasn't until the 1930s that **Gerhard Domagk** developed Prontosil, the second chemical 'magic bullet', to cure blood poisoning. Scientists then discovered that the important chemical in these cures was sulphonamide and drug companies then developed more sulphonamide cures for diseases such as pneumonia.

▲ Paul Ehrlich

Who did what?

Magic bullets could not kill staphylococcus germs, which caused major infections and often killed the victims. These germs were beaten when **Fleming**, **Florey** and **Chain** developed the first antibiotic medicine, penicillin. In 1928 Alexander Fleming made the initial discovery that penicillin killed bacteria and later Howard Florey and Ernst Chain developed Fleming's idea into a medical treatment.

▲ Alexander Fleming

▲ Howard Florey

▲ Ernst Chain

Who did what?

In 1953 **Francis Crick** and **James Watson** discovered the structure of human DNA and how it is passed on from parents to children. In the 1990s the Human Genome Project, a worldwide project, began working out exactly how each part of human DNA affects the human body.

▲ James Watson (left) and Francis Crick

What could your statue look like?

Activities

Here is an outline design for the statue that you can develop in your own way – or you could come up with your own design!

1. What initial ideas do you have for your statue now that you have read pages 118–119?
   a. Think about how many individuals you want to include – one, two or more?
   b. What else could you include on the statue base besides individual people's names?
   c. Should Edward Jenner (see below) be part of this statue? What are the reasons for and against including him?
   d. What about the base of your statue? We have shown it as interlocking links because no single element was responsible for conquering disease. How else could you present it?
2. Now use the three case studies on pages 122–125, 126–127 and 128–131 to fill out your knowledge of the battle against disease. Then return to this task and complete the design of your statue.

Edward Jenner

In 1798 Jenner had proved that vaccination prevents people catching smallpox. This discovery saved many thousands of lives but Jenner did not understand what caused smallpox or exactly how vaccination worked. Therefore this method could not be transferred to preventing other diseases.

Recap: What did they think caused disease in the early 1800s?

Activities

Before the case studies, here is a reminder of what people in the early 1800s thought caused disease.

3 Why was 'bad air' a logical explanation for disease?
4 Why did the microscope make a breakthrough possible?
5 Explain the theory of spontaneous generation in your own words.
6 Why hadn't Jenner's discovery of vaccination changed ideas about what caused diseases?

Fading beliefs

Two ideas had dominated explanations of the causes of disease for thousands of years but in 1800 both were fading fast.

The popular explanation – bad air/miasma

The idea that bad air causes diseases had been around for centuries. People could see rotting food and flesh and even faeces in the streets. They knew that this dirt gave off terrible smells and they assumed that these smells caused and spread disease. They called these poisonous fumes miasma. This made even more sense in the early 1800s when towns were even more crowded and filthy than ever before.

The microscope – a key development

In the 1600s a Dutchman, Anthony van Leeuwenhoek, made a microscope that magnified things by 300 times. He wrote descriptions of what he saw, including tiny living organisms that he found in food, water and human waste. He called them 'animacules' but nobody connected these organisms with diseases. In the 1800s Joseph Lister developed a much more powerful microscope, magnifying things 1000 times. Now scientists could study these 'animacules' in detail.

The latest theory – spontaneous generation

Scientists used the new microscopes to study the micro-organisms (which we call bacteria or germs) on rotting food and tried to work out where these organisms were coming from. They decided that the organisms were spontaneously (automatically) generated (created) by the process of decay in, for example, meat and then the organisms spread disease. This was the theory of spontaneous generation.

Case study 1: How did Pasteur and Koch make their breakthroughs?

For hundreds of years the names of Hippocrates and Galen had dominated medicine. In the 1800s they were finally replaced by Louis Pasteur and Robert Koch.

Pages 122–125 help you work out how they achieved so much. Do they deserve to be on the statue by themselves because they achieved everything through their own genius – or should they share the statue with other people or things?

Pasteur's work 1857–1865

1 What did Pasteur conclude from his work with liquids?
2 How did he prove he was correct?
3 What was important about his work with silkworms?
4 What examples can you find of the impact of: technology, government, attitudes – enquiry?

5 What problem did Pasteur fail to solve?

Koch's work 1873–1880

6 What did Koch achieve that Pasteur had failed to do?
7 What examples can you find of the impact of: war, technology?

8 Which of Koch's discoveries did Pasteur use when investigating chicken cholera?

Pasteur's work 1879–1881

9 Which discovery did Pasteur make that would really be important in the future?
10 What did he mean when he said 'Chance only favours prepared minds'?
11 Which factors helped Pasteur at this time?

12 How did Koch react to Pasteur's discovery of vaccines?

Koch's work 1881–1882

13 What was important about Koch's discovery?
14 What is Koch holding in the cartoon on page 125 and why has it been included?

Pasteur's work 1881–1885

15 How was Pasteur's key discovery in this period a step forward?

Activities

1 Draw your own version of this diagram and as you read through pages 123–125 write notes on it to explain the developments. Use questions 1–15 on the diagram to help you.
2 Choose each man's two major achievements and explain why you chose them.
3 The work of the two men was often linked together. Choose one link and explain how it led to a new discovery.
4 Which two factors played the greatest part in their discoveries? Explain your choices.
5 Who do you think made the greater contribution to the development of medicine – Pasteur or Koch? Jot down two or three reasons for your choice.

Louis Pasteur (1822–1895)

Born in France, Pasteur was a university scientist, not a doctor. He loved to demonstrate his experiments in public, especially if he could show that he was right and someone else was wrong. He was also a hugely determined man. He suffered a stroke in 1868 and was paralysed down the left side of his body but kept working and went on to make some of his greatest discoveries.

▲ Pasteur in his laboratory. Which vital piece of equipment is shown?

1 Louis Pasteur – his work from 1857 to 1865

- He helped the alcohol industry in Lille. The alcohol was going sour. Pasteur studied the liquid under his microscope and saw two differently-shaped **micro-organisms**: one in the fresh liquid, one in the sour liquid. He concluded that it was the organism that was making the alcohol go sour. Next he was asked by the government to help the wine and milk industries. He suggested that gently heating the liquids (**pasteurisation**) would kill these organisms or bacteria, making them safe to drink.
- As a result of this work Pasteur was convinced that **germs** in the air were causing the liquids to go sour and perhaps causing disease. His ideas were mocked by scientists who believed in the theory of **spontaneous generation** but he had the support of the Emperor of France and the government, who believed that Pasteur's success was making France respected abroad. They paid for his research assistants and a new laboratory to carry out his experiments with specially designed equipment. Improvements in technology made it possible to have much more precisely designed flasks.
- In 1864 he carried out a series of experiments (see Source 1) that convinced scientists that his **germ theory** was correct and that the theory of spontaneous generation was wrong. He showed that **bacteria were causing decay** – not being caused by decay.
- In 1865 he was called in to help the silk industry because a disease was killing the silkworms. He proved that the disease was being **spread by germs in the air**. This was the first time it was proved that germs were causing disease in **animals**.
- In 1865 Pasteur's young daughter's death and a cholera outbreak led him to investigate **human diseases**. He took samples of air from a cholera ward in a hospital but under his microscope he could only see a mass of bacteria. He could not discover which one was causing cholera.

Source 1

THEORY	EXPERIMENT
The air contains living micro–organisms	He took sterile flasks out into the streets of Paris, opened them briefly, then sealed them again. Bacteria grew in them. 
Microbes are not evenly distributed in the air	He repeated the experiment in various places around France including high mountains. The number of bacteria varied. 
Microbes in the air cause decay	He filled two flasks: one with stale air and the other with ordinary air. In the first there was no decay; in the second decay proceeded as normal. 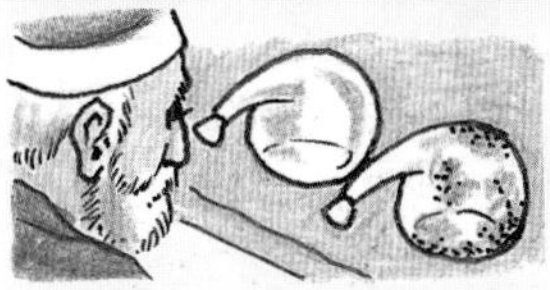
Microbes can be killed by heating	He heated a material in a flask to make it sterile. He drove the air out, then sealed the flask. It remained sterile even 100 years later. 

▲ Pasteur's theories and the experiments that proved them correct.

Robert Koch (1843–1910)

Born in Germany, Koch was a doctor who became interested in Pasteur's work and began to study bacteria himself. He was just as ambitious as Pasteur and just as brilliant at detailed, painstaking work in his laboratory and at working with a team of assistants. They saw each other as rivals, especially after the war between France and Germany in 1870–1871, which was won by Germany. Both men wanted to be successful to glorify their countries.

2 Robert Koch – his work from 1873 to 1880

- Koch investigated anthrax, a disease affecting animals and people, and discovered the specific bacterium that causes anthrax. This was the first time the specific germ that caused an individual disease had been identified and it was the final proof of Pasteur's germ theory.
- Koch then developed a method of proving which particular bacterium was causing a disease, which could then be used by other scientists.
- Koch improved methods of studying bacteria. He developed ways of staining bacteria so they could be photographed using a new high-quality photographic lens and studied in detail. He also discovered how to grow bacteria on potatoes, which made them easier to study than in a liquid.

3 Louis Pasteur – his work from 1879 to 1881

- Pasteur was determined to match Koch's discoveries and so built up a research team to make faster progress. The team started work trying to help the farming industry because an epidemic of chicken cholera was killing many thousands of chickens. Pasteur quickly found the bacterium causing chicken cholera, something that was impossible before Koch's work just a few years earlier. In summer 1880 Pasteur left one of his team, Charles Chamberland, to inoculate a batch of chickens with the germs but Chamberland forgot and then the laboratory closed for the summer. When Chamberland came back he finally inoculated the chickens, expecting them to die from cholera. What happened next? You can see in the drawing below.

  Pasteur solved the riddle of the chickens that didn't die! He realised that the germs left over the summer had weakened and were not strong enough to kill the chickens but that, just like cowpox and smallpox, they then protected the chickens from a strong dose of cholera. Pasteur had studied Jenner's work in detail and made the link. When people said it had been a lucky discovery he replied 'No! Chance only favours prepared minds.'
- Now that he knew exactly how Jenner's vaccine had worked, Pasteur could create other vaccines. At first he continued to work on animals, producing a vaccine against anthrax. He tested this successfully in a public experiment and the news spread rapidly round Europe.

▼ How an effective vaccine against chicken cholera was discovered by Pasteur and his team.

Source 2

4 Robert Koch – his work from 1881 to 1882

Koch was angry when he heard of Pasteur's development of the anthrax vaccine. He thought Pasteur had stolen some of his research on anthrax. He decided to get ahead by becoming the first man to discover the specific germ that causes a human disease. He investigated tuberculosis and found a way of staining the bacterium causing the disease that made it stand out from other bacteria and human tissue – it was so small that it had been missed by other scientists.

This was the major breakthrough he had been searching for. His research team was able to use his methods to discover the specific bacterium that causes cholera. Other scientists joined in the hunt, finding the bacteria for the diseases in this list.

1882	Typhoid	**1883**	Cholera
1884	Tetanus	**1886**	Pneumonia
1887	Meningitis	**1894**	Plague
1898	Dysentery		

Source 3

◀ A cartoon from the 1880s showing Koch slaying the bacterium that causes tuberculosis.

5 Louis Pasteur – his work from 1881 to 1885

After his success with vaccines against animal diseases, Pasteur turned to human diseases. He investigated rabies, testing his vaccine successfully on dogs, but did not know if it would work on people. The chance to find out came in 1885 when he tested his vaccine on Joseph Meister, a boy who had been bitten by a rabid dog. If the vaccine did not work the boy would die. Pasteur gave Joseph thirteen injections over a two-week period. Joseph survived. Now other scientists set to work to follow Pasteur and find vaccines that could prevent other human diseases. Their successes included:

1896	Typhoid
1906	Tuberculosis
1913	Diphtheria
1927	Tetanus

Case study 2: How was penicillin discovered and developed?

Activities

We guided you carefully through Case study 1 on Pasteur and Koch, but this time we'll give you more freedom. You have two tasks:

1. Create a diagram like the one on page 122 to tell the story of the development of penicillin. Use the headings on this page to structure the diagram.
2. Fleming is often described as the hero of the story of penicillin. Who do you think played the most important part?
3. Create a concept map like the one on page 99.
   - **a** Identify from this page all the factors that played a part in the development of penicillin.
   - **b** Choose the factor or factors that you think played the most important part in the development of penicillin and explain your choice. Make a concept map to show how they are related to each other.

Stage 1: A false start

There are many examples in medicine of false starts, and penicillin is one of them. In 1872 a doctor called Joseph Lister (you'll find out more about him later) noticed that mould of bacteria called penicillin killed other bacteria. Years later, in 1884, he used this mould to treat a nurse who had an infected wound. But Lister did not use it again. A miracle cure lay waiting for someone else to rediscover it.

Information

Antibiotic
A drug made from bacteria that kill other bacteria and so cure an infection or illness.

Stage 2: 1928 – Fleming's discovery of penicillin – another false start?

During World War One a scientist called Alexander Fleming was sent to France to study soldiers' wounds infected with streptococci and staphylococci bacteria. These wounds were not healed by chemical antiseptics, and many soldiers died from them. Back home Fleming worked on finding a way of dealing with these bacteria.

Ten years later, in 1928, Fleming found what he'd been seeking. He was working at St Mary's Hospital, London. Going on holiday he left a pile of petri dishes containing bacteria on his laboratory bench. On his return he sorted out the dishes and noticed mould on one of them. Around the mould, as you can see in the picture, the staphylococci bacteria had disappeared.

Fleming carried out experiments with the penicillin mould on living cells. He discovered that if it was diluted it killed bacteria without harming the cells. He made a list of the germs it killed and used it to treat another scientist's eye infection. However, it did not seem to work on deeper infections and in any case it was taking ages to create enough penicillin to use.

In 1929 Fleming wrote about penicillin in a medical journal but nobody thought his article was important. He had not used penicillin on animals to heal infections so had no evidence of it being useful.

▲ Alexander Fleming

Source 1

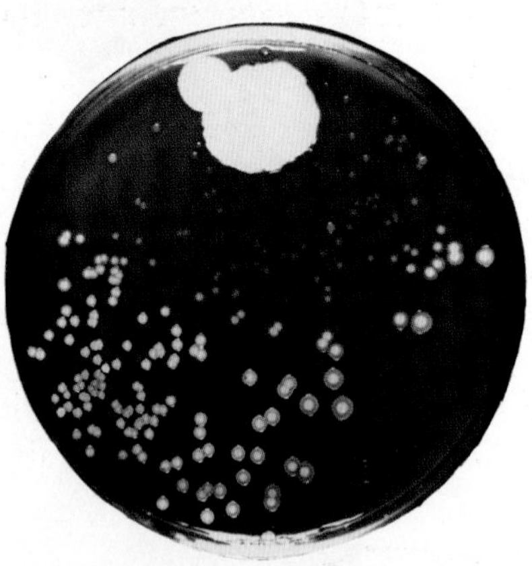

▲ Fleming's original dish. The mould is at the top. The bacteria originally around it have been killed but the bacteria further away have survived. The mould had probably been grown by another scientist in the room above Fleming's, and spores had floated out of the window, then downwards and in through Fleming's window before landing on the one place they could have an effect and then be noticed.

Stage 3: 1938 – Florey and Chain's research and trials

In 1938 Florey and Chain were researching how germs could be killed. They read Fleming's article on penicillin and realised that it could be very effective so they tried to get funding from the government. They got £25. With a war about to start and no proof that penicillin could help people, the government had other things to spend its money on. Instead Florey asked for money from America and got enough to pay for five years' research.

Florey and Chain discovered that penicillin helped mice recover from infections but to treat one person they needed 3000 times as much penicillin! Even large drug companies could not afford to fund this quantity of work. So Florey and Chain began growing penicillin in whatever they could, using hundreds of hospital bedpans, even though bedpans were now in demand to make Spitfires!

By 1941 there was enough penicillin to test it on one person. The volunteer was Albert Alexander, a policeman who had developed septicaemia – a bacterial infection that attacks the whole body – from a tiny cut. Alexander was dying. Chemical drugs had not killed the infection. Florey and Chain requested permission to try their new 'purified' penicillin, and injections began. The penicillin worked and Alexander began to recover. However, the penicillin ran out after five days, even though Florey and Chain were extracting unused penicillin from the man's urine and reusing it in a desperate attempt to keep treating him. The poor policeman became ill again and died. Penicillin had shown that it worked and that it wasn't harmful to the patient – but how could they make enough of it?

▲ Left: Howard Florey, Australian doctor and Head of Pathology at Oxford University. Right: Ernst Chain, a Jewish German who escaped persecution in Nazi Germany to become a scientist at Oxford.

Stage 4: 1941 – Wartime need for penicillin

Florey and Chain needed help to mass produce penicillin but English factories were busy helping the war effort and couldn't be used. So Florey went to America – at just the right time. In 1941 America was attacked by the Japanese at Pearl Harbour and entered the war. The American government realised the potential of penicillin for treating wounded soldiers and made interest-free loans to US companies to buy the expensive equipment needed for making penicillin. Soon British firms were also mass producing penicillin, enough to treat the allied wounded on D-Day in 1944 – over 2.3 million doses.

Source 2

▲ Tanks used to produce penicillin. The quantity needed is difficult to comprehend: 2000 litres were needed to treat one patient with infection. In June 1943, 425 million units of penicillin were being produced – enough for 170 patients.

Source 3

An account of the first use of penicillin in the British army in 1943, written by Lt Colonel Pulvertaft:

'We had an enormous number of wounded with infections, terrible burn cases among the crews of armoured cars. The usual medicines had absolutely no effect. The last thing I tried was penicillin. The first man was a young man called Newton. He had been in bed for six months with fractures of both legs. His sheets were soaked with pus. Normally he would have died in a short time. I gave three injections of penicillin a day and studied the effects under a microscope. The thing seemed like a miracle. In ten days' time the leg was cured and in a month's time the young fellow was back on his feet. I had enough penicillin for ten cases. Nine were complete cures.'

Why is this page so important?

The discovery of penicillin marks the start of modern antibiotics and has saved an estimated 200 million lives in less than 70 years.

Case study 3: Unravelling the secrets of DNA – the greatest development yet?

In the same week this page was written, two medical stories hit the headlines. One was about finding a way to help people paralysed in accidents to walk again. The other was about giving the newly-blind back their sight. Both possibilities still have a long way to go before they become fact, but they are both the result of one discovery – the discovery of the structure of DNA.

DNA stands for deoxyribonucleic acid, but you do not need to remember that – just talk and write about DNA. And you don't need to understand how DNA works or learn a list of scientific terms. We are interested in:

- causes: how the structure of DNA was discovered
- significance: why these discoveries are so important.

The discovery of DNA

Turning point 1 – Discovering the structure of DNA

DNA wasn't 'discovered' in one brilliant experiment. It took a series of discoveries over a long period. In the 1800s, scientists knew DNA existed and that it somehow controlled what we are like. However, they did not know how it did this.

The first step came in 1953, when two scientists in Cambridge, Francis Crick and James Watson, discovered the structure of DNA illustrated on the right. They proved that this DNA structure was present in every human cell and showed how it passed on information from parents to children. This was the launch pad for further discoveries.

Turning point 2 – Mapping the human genome

The complete set of genes in a living creature is called a genome. In 1986, the Human Genome Project began to identify the exact purpose of each of the genes in the human body, compiling a complete map of human DNA. The task was completed in 2001, fifteen years later.

This research was so complicated it needed teams of scientists in eighteen countries to take part, including the USA, Britain, Japan, France and Canada. Each team worked on a different part of human DNA. This work could not have been done before computers. The information carried in human DNA would fill 80,000 books the size of this one, but the electronic equivalent can be passed around the world instantly via the internet.

What is DNA?

- Inside every cell of your body are several identical strings of DNA.
- A tiny part of your DNA looks like this:

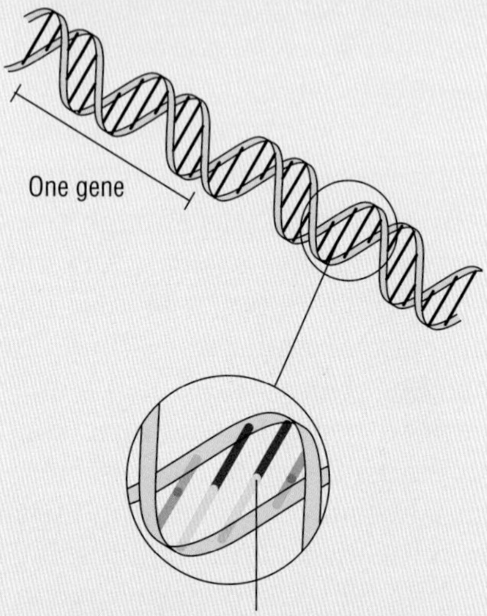

The structure of DNA is a double helix – a pair of interlocking spirals. They are joined by 'bases', set in pairs, which are like the rungs of a ladder.

- Think of DNA as a long list of instructions like a computer program that operate every cell of your body. There are more than 3000 million letters of code in your body's program.
- These instructions are grouped together into sets of instructions called **genes**.
- Each gene has a different function. Some decide your eye colour, some how much hair you have, some whether you will develop a disease or disability.
- Everybody's DNA carries slightly different instructions – which is why human beings are all different.

Why was the structure of DNA discovered in 1953?

Activities

1 Draw a diagram with four boxes like the one below.
2 Read the information in the diagram and decide on a suitable factor heading for each box. Use the factors on page 9 for three boxes – you will have to think of another heading for the fourth!
3 Write your own summary in each box of your diagram, explaining how each factor helped to make this discovery.

Francis Crick and James Watson were great scientists, and very adventurous in their ideas. They tried out ideas and methods other scientists did not try.

Crick and Watson did not work alone. They had help from a team of scientists with a wide range of skills and knowledge. Maurice Wilkins was an expert in X-ray photography. Rosalind Franklin developed a technique to photograph a single strand of DNA and was the first person to take X-ray photographs of DNA.

Why was the structure of DNA discovered in 1953?

Crick and Watson had the latest and best equipment, using new technologies such as X-ray photography and improved microscopes. They also built on new knowledge in other types of science, such as genetics and biochemistry.

Their research was very expensive because of the cost of complex equipment and the number of highly skilled people involved. Most of the money came from the government, but industries also made a contribution.

Why is DNA so important?

What has the discovery of DNA got to do with Superman?

In 1995, the actor Christopher Reeve, known worldwide as Superman, was paralysed after a riding accident. For the rest of his life (he died of a heart attack in 2004, aged 52) he was confined to a wheelchair. From his wheelchair, he campaigned for scientists to have the right to develop research to help people who are paralysed. In particular, he campaigned to support the use of stem-cell research which is one of the scientific developments that has followed on from the discovery of DNA.

To understand the importance of DNA in medicine it's helpful to compare this discovery with Pasteur's germ theory.

▲ The actor and activist Christopher Reeve campaigned for the use of stem-cell research.

Why was germ theory so important?

In the hundred years after Pasteur's germ theory, the average life expectancy increased from about 45 to 70 – the first significant, long-term increase in life expectancy in history. This was because germ theory affected medicine in all kinds of ways:

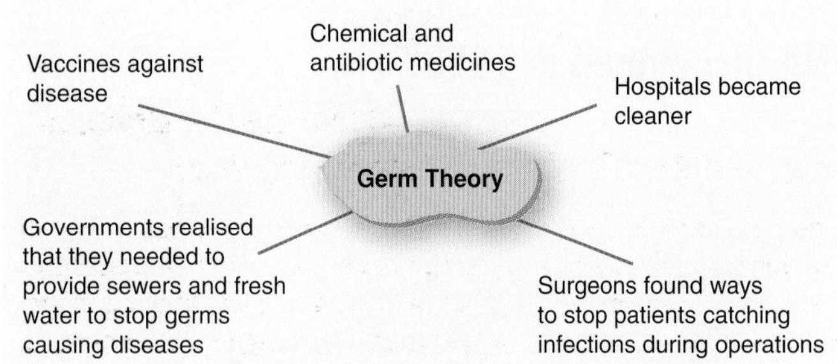

BUT ...

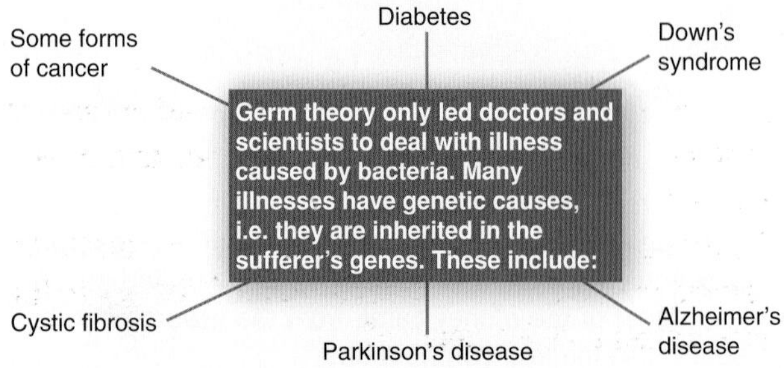

Other problems, such as paralysis or some cases of blindness, can be caused by accidents.

Work on DNA holds out the hope that scientists can find ways of helping sufferers from these and many more genetic illnesses, and help people paralysed in accidents.

That is why the discovery of DNA may turn out to be an even more important breakthrough than Pasteur's germ theory.

How could research on DNA affect health and medicine?

There are lots of 'mays' and 'mights' here. This is because we are still at the beginning of the DNA revolution, even if there have been headlines about 'breakthroughs' for the past several years. We do not know where these discoveries will lead. Remember – when Pasteur developed his germ theory, scientists did not know exactly what it would lead to. It took many years for the full impact to be clear. We cannot say for sure what these DNA discoveries will lead to – even in five years' time, let alone a hundred!

However, here are some of the possibilities:

Understanding DNA could lead to ...

Gene therapy – using genes from healthy people to cure the sick

Research has shown that some diseases and disabilities, such as cystic fibrosis, Huntington's chorea, sickle-cell anaemia and muscular dystrophy, are caused by a single abnormal gene passed down from parent to child. Gene therapy would take normal genes from a donor and put them into the DNA of someone suffering from one of these illnesses.

One approach to this is to use 'stem cells' from embryos. In 2009, the possibility of trialling the use of such cells became headline news. Trials of one type of cell would see if they could reverse a common form of blindness. Another cell could be used to re-grow damaged nerves and restore movement to people paralysed in accidents. However, there is a major ethical debate about this stem-cell research because the process of taking the cells from the embryos usually kills the embryos.

Customised drugs – creating drugs to cure one person's particular health problem

Drug treatments of the future could be designed to deal with a particular gene in a particular person.

These 'custom drugs' would be less haphazard than at present where the same drug is given to millions of different people regardless of their genetic make-up.

Genetic engineering – choosing the nature of a child

Genetic modification of plants is already happening. For example, a gene from a drought-resistant wheat can be added to the DNA of a high-yielding wheat to make a new variety of wheat that produces lots of grain, even in dry conditions. In theory, the same techniques could be used to produce more perfect human beings – with parents being able to 'design' their children: not only their gender, but also their appearance and intellectual ability.

Genetic screening or testing – identifying the illnesses people could suffer from and preventing them

If doctors know the exact gene responsible for medical conditions, they can test or screen patients as part of preventive medicine. For example, they can spot who is likely to get cancer and help them to avoid activities that might trigger the cancer to start. This is already done to check unborn babies for possible conditions such as Down's syndrome. This, however, raises one important ethical question – if an embryo is found to be carrying a gene that's linked to a major disability, is that justification for the embryo to be aborted?

Activity

During the week that you cover this topic, look at a news site such as http://news.bbc.co.uk.

- **a** Which medical developments linked to DNA are being reported on and what benefits might they lead to?
- **b** Are any moral or ethical issues mentioned in relation to the developments? If so, what are they and how important are they?
- **c** Do these debates about using new medical methods remind you of any past breakthroughs? What are the similarities and differences?

Review: Who and what deserves to be part of the 'Conquerors of Disease' statue?

Your statue can have more than one person on it – if you think more than one person deserves the credit for beating the killer diseases. And, as you have discovered, no one made their discoveries completely independently. There were many links between them. This page helps you sort out those links and reach your decision – who was the most important person in the fight against the killer diseases.

Activities

1. Study the concept map on page 133. Write the speech bubbles for each of the other people in the concept map, summarising their greatest achievement. (Do not do this for 'Other scientists' – this person represents all the other scientists who built on the discoveries by the five main people.)
2. How many links can you find between the people on the concept map? We have drawn in two but there are others. Use the clues to identify the links and write cards to go on the linking string to explain them.
3. Look at your completed map with all the links showing. Who has the most links connecting him to other people? Why?
4. Now make your choice about which person or people should be on the statue. To help you, think about this question:
   'Was there one discovery that had to happen before any others could take place?'
5. Finally, complete the base of your statue using your work on the impact of factors in the case studies.

Clue 1

Koch used Pasteur's germ theory to identify the first ...

Clue 2

Pasteur had studied Jenner's work in detail, which helped him develop ...

Clue 3

The rivalry between these men spurred both on to new discoveries.

Clue 4

Ehrlich had learned a lot from Koch when ...

Clue 5

Without the germ theory these men would not have been able to make their discoveries.

Clue 6

Pasteur used Koch's new methods of studying bacteria when he developed ...

Clue 7

Other scientists developed vaccines against diseases such as typhoid, diphtheria and tuberculosis, building on ...

Clue 8

Other scientists discovered the bacteria causing individual diseases using the methods developed by ...

I discovered that vaccinating people with cowpox stopped them from getting smallpox. This was the first successful vaccination.
Jenner
Pasteur
WHO DESERVES TO BE PART OF THE STATUE?
Other scientists
Ehrlich
Koch
Fleming, Florey and Chain

6.2 Fighting disease and infection – the present and the future

So now you know what happened in the past – but how does this help us understand what's happening in today's battles against disease and infection? What has all this work on Jenner, Pasteur and DNA got to do with you? Or, to put it another way, how can history help us understand what's happening today?

What do we learn from history?

One answer to this question is that knowing and understanding history helps us understand why things are happening today and places them 'in perspective'. This means that we understand whether something is really important or different, or whether it's only slightly different from what's gone before – in other words, what's really worth getting excited about!

It also means that we have a sense of how quickly things are changing nowadays and, therefore, why it's difficult to get everything right straightaway.

So, here are some of the issues that are around in February 2009, when I wrote this page and the next one.

Issue 1: The value of vaccinations

When I was growing up in the 1950s, measles was common. It was a serious illness. Occasionally, children died from measles. It also caused other problems. My mother had measles when she was three, back in 1928, and lost the hearing in one ear as a result. Seventy years later she lost the hearing in her other ear (for a different reason) and so spent her last ten years completely deaf. That outbreak of measles when she was aged three caused her a lot of misery.

Another disease in the 1950s was polio. I remember vividly hearing on the news that Jeff Hall, a Birmingham City footballer, had died of polio. Can you imagine what kind of story that would be today if a Premier League footballer died of a disease like polio?

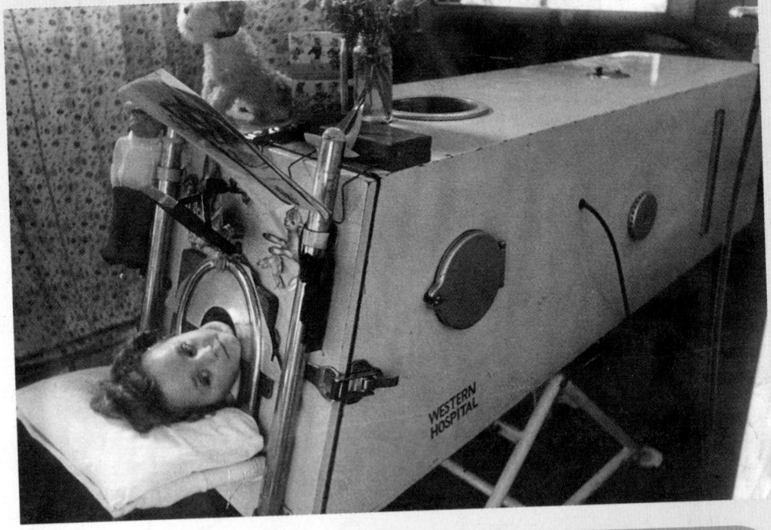

▲ This iron lung kept polio victims breathing.

Polio was eventually conquered later in the 1950s, when American research scientist Jonas Salk developed a vaccine that protected people from the disease. This was also the time when vaccines swiftly put an end to epidemics of measles, German measles and whooping cough. However, recently there has been a rapid increase in the number of measles cases in Britain. People have stopped using the vaccine for fear – now disproved by research – that the vaccine led to other medical problems.

Perspective

Is it unusual for helpful medical ideas to meet opposition? Why does this happen?

How might knowledge of the development of vaccination against smallpox in the 1800s affect attitudes to vaccinations today?

Issue 2: **Medical advances: inherited illnesses**

Scientists working on human DNA discovered how to identify whether a person's genes carry the risk of suffering from breast cancer. This means that in the future it may be possible to screen people for this gene and reduce the chances of people getting breast cancer. However, at the moment it could mean choosing which embryos develop into babies and which do not. The same kind of research is being applied to many other genetically inherited illnesses for which there is no cure, but may in the future be avoidable. By the time you read this, there will have been many similar stories about other diseases.

Perspective

What does this tell us about the pace of change in medicine?

Think back to what you have learned about attitudes to medical changes. What different kinds of reactions do you expect to such research?

Issue 3: **Medical problems that take us by surprise**

Problem drugs – thalidomide

Between 1959 and 1962, a new drug called thalidomide was given to women to reduce morning sickness during pregnancy. However, this drug had not been fully tested and led to children being born with severely deformed limbs. Thalidomide was then banned, but around 10,000 children worldwide had already been affected. Since then, research on thalidomide has continued and in a different form has been shown to help people with blood cancer and leprosy. The impact of thalidomide led to much more thorough testing of drugs before use.

Superbugs

'Superbugs' is the name given to infection-causing bacteria (such as MRSA) which have developed the ability to resist science's efforts to kill them, either with antiseptics or antibiotics. Most alarming have been the cases where superbugs have infected people in hospital, leading to some deaths. Major efforts to get rid of the superbugs have been pursued, although this is proving far more difficult than many people expected. However, a doctor writing in *The Times* in 2009 said 'the threat posed by a stay in your local hospital is nothing like as bad as the recent hype suggests. An otherwise healthy patient admitted for a planned operation in a decent NHS hospital would have to be on the ward for around 15 years to stand a more than evens chance of succumbing to MRSA.'

CJD

CJD is a rare and fatal brain disease, first identified in young people in 1996. The most likely explanation linked CJD to eating beef from cattle that had been infected with a disease known as BSE. The sudden appearance of CJD was alarming, but even more frightening was the fact that no one knew how many people had been infected.

Perspective

How have people in the past reacted to new and unexpected illnesses?

Are our responses to unexpected health problems any different from those of people in the past?

Is it unrealistic to expect science to solve all medical problems immediately?

Issue 4: Differing life expectancies and the work of the World Health Organization

This book has been almost entirely concerned with medicine in Britain and Europe. One of its key questions has been 'Why do we live so much longer nowadays?' But not everyone does live longer than in the past. Look at these statistics from 2007.

Country	Male life expectancy	Female life expectancy	Infant mortality – deaths per 1000 births	Adult rate of HIV infection
United Kingdom	76.1	81.1	5.1	0.2%
USA	75.0	80.8	6.4	0.6%
China	70.9	74.5	23.1	0.1%
Israel	77.3	81.7	6.9	0.1%
Kenya	49.8	48.1	59.3	6.7%
Liberia	38.0	41.4	155.8	5.9%
Nigeria	46.5	47.7	97.1	5.4%
Rwanda	46.3	48.4	89.6	5.1%
South Africa	43.3	42.2	60.7	21.5%
Zimbabwe	40.4	38.2	51.7	24.6%

The World Health Organization

The World Health Organization (WHO) was set up in 1948 by the United Nations. Its goal is to help all people throughout the world to reach the highest possible level of health. This involves tackling the differences you have seen in the table above, attempting to increase life expectancy in less economically developed countries through public health schemes.

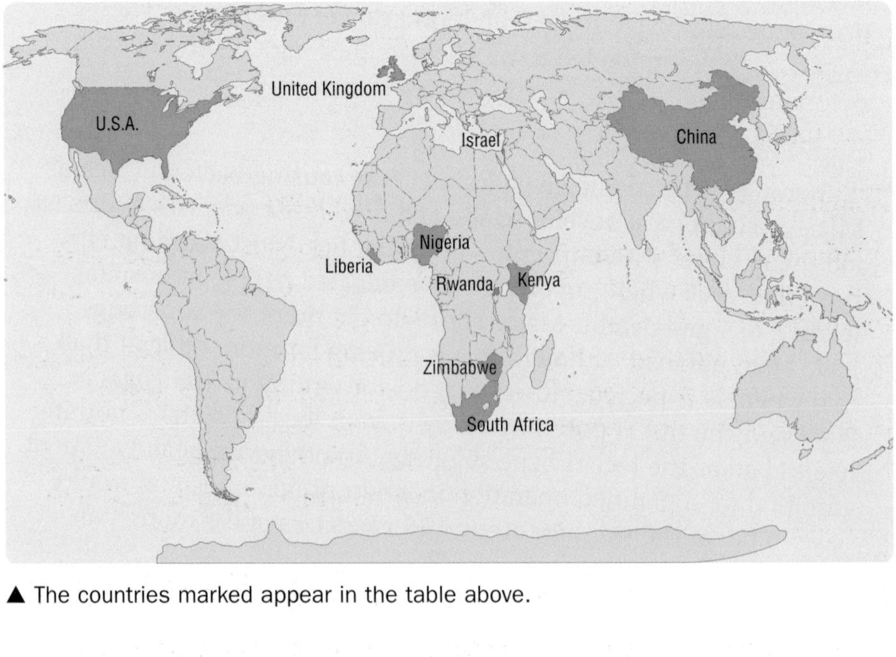

▲ The countries marked appear in the table above.

The WHO's greatest success has been the wiping out of smallpox. Although smallpox had been wiped out in Europe by the use of vaccination, it was still a major killer in other parts of the world in the 1960s. In 1967, the WHO began its campaign and by 1980 was able to declare that smallpox had been wiped out across the world. This had cost huge sums of money – £313 million over ten years – to pay for vaccines, treatments and to inspect individual countries, but many more times that cost has been saved.

WHO and the fight against HIV/AIDS

In 1987, the WHO launched a campaign to fight HIV/AIDS. HIV/AIDS destroys the body's immunity to other diseases, leaving people much more vulnerable to infections and other diseases, such as cancer. HIV/AIDS was only first identified in the early 1980s, but by 2007, 33.2 million people worldwide were living with HIV. In that one year, 2.5 million people became newly infected and 2.1 million died as a result of AIDS, including 330,000 children. The rapid spread of HIV/AIDS is partly due to modern travel, which is much cheaper, faster and more common than just 50 years ago.

Two thirds of HIV infections are in sub-Saharan Africa. New research suggests that part of the reason for the rapid spread in Africa may be linked to the fact that the Black Death of the 1300s did not affect Africa. People in Europe acquired some resistance to the Black Death and this also helps protect them against HIV/AIDS. Without this resistance, Africans are more vulnerable to HIV/AIDS.

The WHO's efforts focus on education to help people avoid HIV/AIDS because, although treatments can slow down the development of the symptoms, there is, as yet, no cure. Education focuses on helping people understand that HIV/AIDS is most easily passed on by drug users sharing needles or by unprotected sex. Transfusions of infected blood have also led to the spread of HIV/AIDS.

Information

AIDS – Acquired Immune Deficiency Syndrome

HIV – Human Immunodeficiency Virus

Perspective

How does your knowledge of the history of medicine help you understand:

- **a** why there are such differences in the statistics in the table opposite
- **b** what may be needed to improve the statistics in less economically developed countries?

Issue 5: How useful are alternative therapies?

Millions of people spend a huge amount of money on alternative therapies such as those shown below. However, there are many arguments about the usefulness of such treatments. Many patients say that particular therapies have helped them; scientists say there is no scientific proof that they work.

Three kinds of alternative therapies

Acupuncture

Acupuncture has been used in China for 4000 years. It involves inserting fine needles at pressure points on the body to release blocked energy. It has been used as an anaesthetic in operations.

Homeopathy

Homeopathy was founded in the 1700s by a German doctor, Samuel Hahnemann. It involves the patient taking a very weak amount of a substance which would produce symptoms similar to those the patient has. It is said to encourage the body to heal itself.

Herbal remedies

Many health shops sell 'herbal remedies' made from plants and animal substances which have been used in medicine for centuries. Examples include honey (which has been used against infection since Ancient Egypt) and valerian, a herb which helps people to sleep.

Perspective

Why have people supported or opposed unusual treatments in the past?

Does the fact that a medical method has been used for a long time mean it must work?

When have different ideas about causes and treatments existed side by side in the same society?

Disease and infection: A summary

Now you have completed the story of how people have understood and treated diseases across the centuries. This timeline shows you the key developments – and how treatments were linked to ideas about what caused diseases.

Activity

1 On pages 6–7 you began a graph recording the pattern of developments in disease and infection. Use this timeline to check and complete your graph.

The timeline below is not to chronological scale.

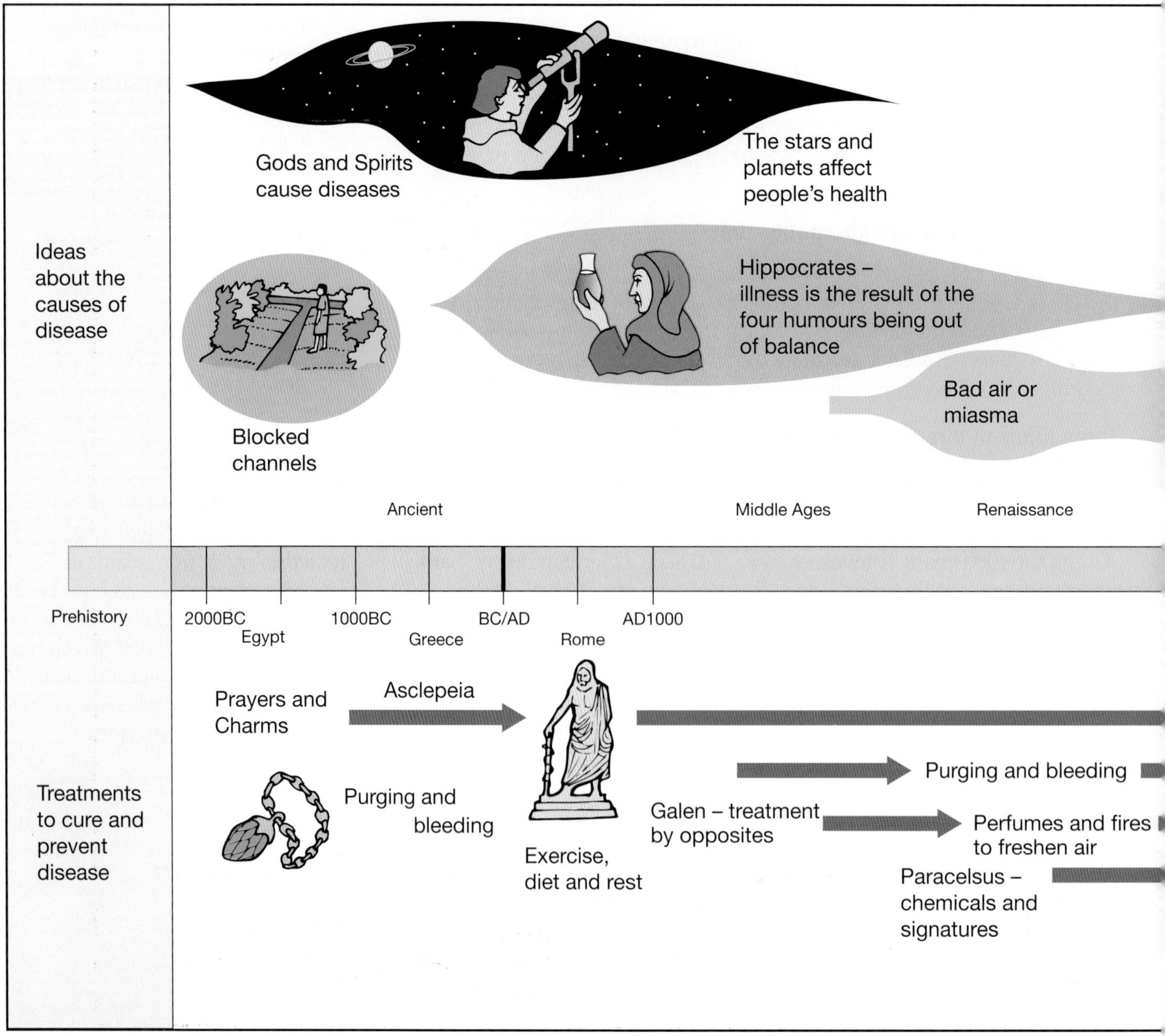

Activity

2 Work in a group of three. You are going to have up to three minutes to tell the story of disease and infection. Spend twenty minutes preparing your story. If your teacher gives you more preparation time, think about how to enliven the story with visuals and props. The story must include the answers to the following questions:

a How would you describe the pattern of continuity and change over time? Think about when there was long-lasting continuity and when there was rapid change.

b When was the pace of change fastest – and why was it fastest then?

c Which were the most important theories about what caused disease?

d How did those theories affect the way illnesses were treated?

e How does the pace of change and the nature of developments now compare with the past?

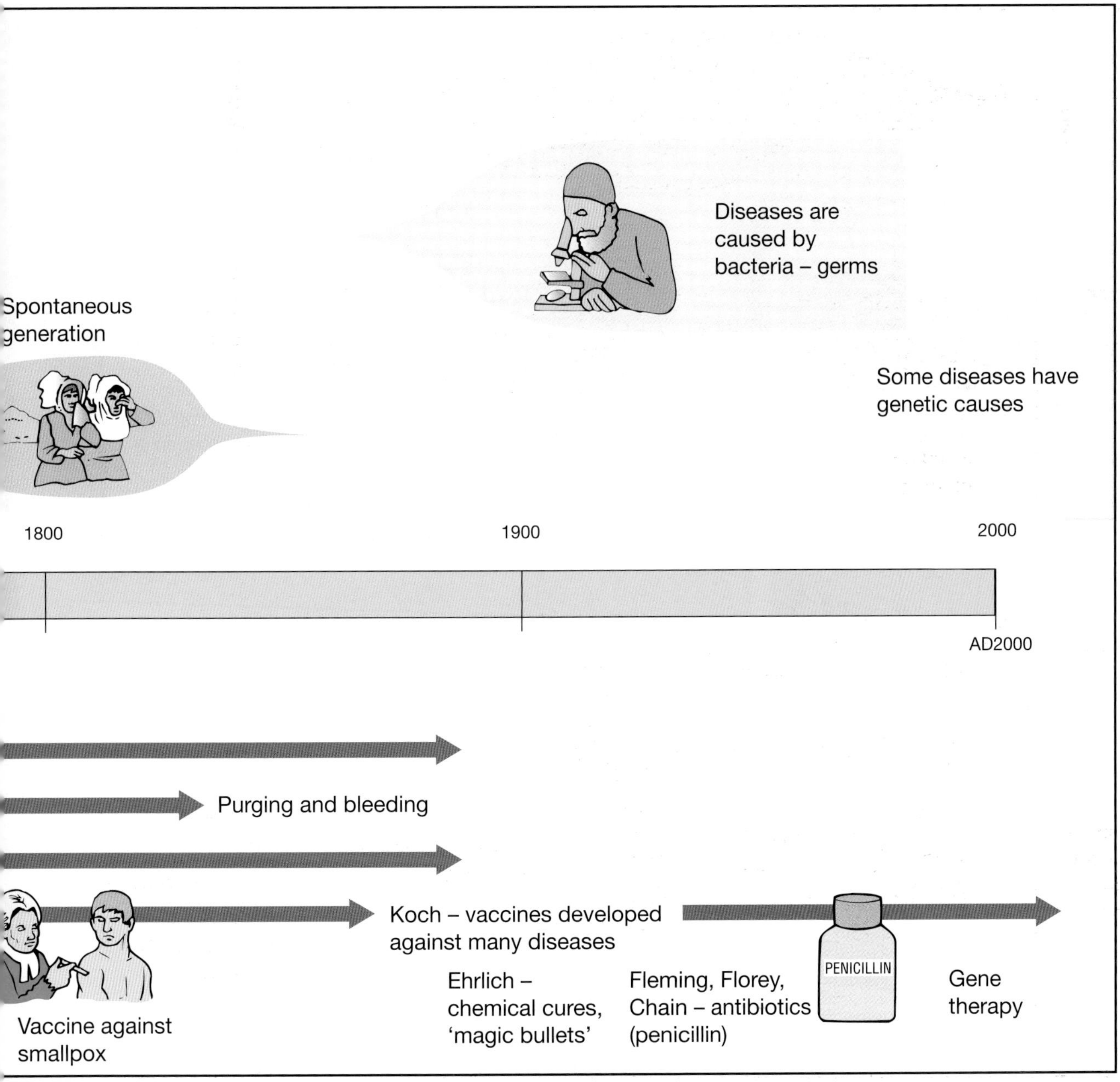

Meet the Examiner: How to answer Section A overview questions

SECTION A

You **must** answer this question.

Total marks for this question: 26 marks

Disease and Infection

1 Study **Sources A, B and C** in the Sources Booklet and then answer **all** parts of Question 1 which follow. In your answers you should refer to the sources by their letters.

(a) What does **Source A** suggest about ideas about how to treat diseases in the Middle Ages? Explain your answer using **Source A** and **your knowledge**. *(4 marks)*

(b) What different idea about how to treat diseases is suggested by **Source B**? Explain your answer using **Sources A and B** and **your knowledge**. *(6 marks)*

(c) Why were there different ideas about how to treat diseases at these times? Explain your answer using **Sources A and B** and **your knowledge**. *(8 marks)*

(d) Study **Source C**.
Ideas about how to treat diseases have changed at different times for different reasons. Why was this?
Explain your answer using **Sources A, B and C** and **your knowledge**. *(8 marks)*

Source A

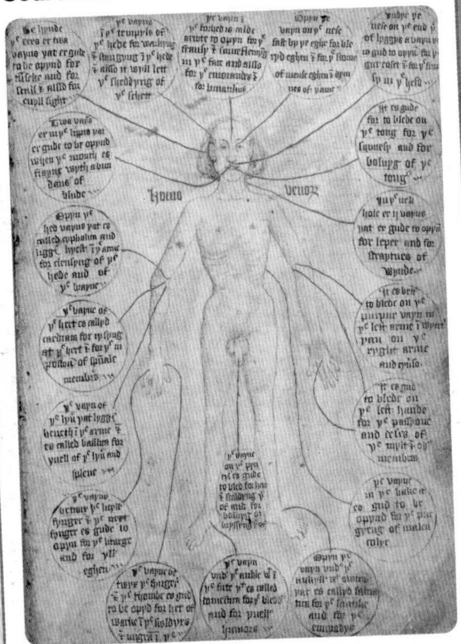

A bleeding chart used by surgeons in the Middle Ages. It identified the parts of the body from which patients could be bled.

Source B

'Joseph Meister, aged 9 years, had been bitten by a dog which had gone mad. The death of this child appearing to be inevitable I decided to try upon Joseph the method which I had found constantly successful with dogs. Young Meister was inoculated under the skin with half a syringeful of the spinal cord of a rabbit which had died of rabies. In the following days fresh inoculations were made. Joseph Meister has escaped the rabies which would have been caused by the bites.'

From 'A Lecture on the prevention of rabies' by Louis Pasteur, 1885

Source C

'We had an enormous number of wounded with infections, terrible burn cases among the crews of armoured cars. The usual medicines had absolutely no effect. The last thing I tried was penicillin. The first man was a young man called Newton. He had been in bed for six months with fractures of both legs. His sheets were soaked with pus. Normally he would have died in a short time. I gave three injections of penicillin a day and studied the effects under a microscope. The thing seemed like a miracle. In ten days' time the leg was cured and in a month's time the young fellow was back on his feet. I had enough penicillin for ten cases. Nine were complete cures.'

A description of the first use of penicillin in the 1940s

Activity

Answer questions 1(a)–(c), using the advice on pages 48–49 and 103–104 to help you.

This final question in Section A is an **overview question.** This means that you have to think about how and why treatments changed in **the whole history of medicine!** It is up to you to choose the periods and topics you write about.

'at different times' – the question asks you to write about more than one period of history

(d) Study **Source C**.
Ideas about treating diseases have improved at different times for different reasons. Why was this?
Explain your answer using **Sources A, B and C** and **your knowledge**. *(8 marks)*

'for different reasons' – the question asks you to discuss a range of factors

What kind of answer will win most marks?

Here are four kinds of answer. What order would you put them in – lowest marks first?

i a detailed description of how one change came about, e.g. how antibiotics developed because of the combined impact of war, governments, individuals and chance

ii a description of the impact of one factor on ideas about treatments, e.g. individual scientists such as Pasteur in Source B make discoveries

iii answers that discuss the effects of several factors in more than one period of time (e.g. science, individuals, chance, war) and come to an overall assessment of which factor or factors has done most to change ideas over time, for example that scientific discoveries (most importantly Pasteur's germ theory) had the most impact because they finally identified how to treat diseases effectively and led to other discoveries

iv a list of the effects of several factors, each with their own separate example, e.g. war played an important part in developing antibiotics (Source C), individuals made discoveries (Source B), science helped others, e.g. Koch identifies bacteria causing diseases.

Planning your answer

This question is worth 8 marks (2 minutes per marks equals about 15 minutes) so it is important to take a moment to plan your answer. This will produce a more thought-out answer than if you start writing off the top of your head. Remember there are **two** different aspects of the question to write about.

1 Take one minute to jot down – in single words or phrases – the main ideas about how to treat diseases in each of these periods:

a Ancient Greece to the Middle Ages
b the 1800s
c after 1900

Remember – you can use the sources **and** your own knowledge to help you.

2 Take one minute to jot down the factors that led to the changes – and which were most important. Think about:

Government
Religion and superstition
Chance
War
Science and technology
Individuals

Did the factors link together to create changes? Which factor(s) were most important?

3 Read the question again. You have about 15 minutes to write your answer to this question.

a Make a brief plan identifying the changes and reasons you are going to write about.

b Read the section headed 'What kind of answer will win most marks?', review your plan then draft your answer.

c Swap your draft with another student and work together to improve both drafts.

4 Remember to use the sources **and** your own knowledge. You will lose marks if you do not do both. Use the sources and your own knowledge to:

- explain how the treatments shown in the sources came about
- identify some other examples of treatments for disease at other times and why they came about.

Section 7: Public health after 1800 – when did it finally improve, and why?

7.1 How bad was public health in the early 1800s?

The Industrial Revolution was a time of huge change, transforming people's lives, mostly for the better. But its immediate effects were terrible with people living and working in worse conditions than they had in the Middle Ages. So how bad was life in the early 1800s – and when did it get better and why?

Source 1

▲ This shows the differences in average age at death among different groups of people in 1840. Chadwick collected these statistics for his report. Liverpool was chosen as an example of a large, rapidly growing town. Rutland was chosen as a country area.

Source 2

Death rates in cholera epidemics in Britain

1831–1832	26,101 deaths
1848–1849	53,293 deaths
1853–1854	20,079 deaths
1865	14,378 deaths

Source 3

A traveller's description of Leeds, reported in *The Morning Chronicle*, 1848: (Scavengers were employed to take away refuse and empty the privies.)

'The east and north-east districts of Leeds are, perhaps, the worst, a perfect wilderness of foulness.

'Conceive acre on acre of little streets, run up without attention to plan or health, acre on acre of closely-built and thickly-peopled ground, without a paving stone on the surface, or an inch of sewer beneath, deep trodden-churned sloughs of mud forming the only thoroughfares, privies often ruinous, all most horribly foul. Conceive streets and courts and yards which a scavenger never appears to have entered since King John's time and which gives the idea of a town built on a slimy bog. Conceive such a surface drenched with the liquid slops which each family flings out daily and nightly. Pigs seem to be the natural inhabitants, more common in some parts of Leeds than dogs and cats.'

Source 4

THE WATER THAT JOHN DRINKS.

▲ 'The Water that John drinks', a cartoon from *Punch* magazine, October 1849.

Activities

1. List the details in Sources 1–4 that show that public health conditions were very poor.
2. Which evidence do you think is the strongest argument against going back in time to live in the first half of the 1800s?
3. Why were conditions so bad? List as many reasons as you can find on the page opposite. (You will find out more on later pages.)

Source 5

◀ *Coalbrookdale at Night*, painted by Philippe Jacques de Loutherbourg in 1801. Coalbrookdale in Shropshire was the home of the iron industry. The great orange light comes from the fires in the furnaces where the iron was made. Artists flocked to paint scenes like this, which had never existed before. They also painted pictures of large textile factories, another new arrival in the landscape. However, for the people working in these industries the scenes were not so picturesque. Ten- or twelve-hour working days were common in hot and dirty conditions, surrounded by dangerous machinery.

Source 6

▲ *Over London by Rail*, an engraving of London housing by Gustave Doré in 1872. Houses in the towns were crammed together in the centre because people had to walk to work until the later 1800s. As towns grew fast between 1750 and 1850 there were no laws forcing local councils to provide sewers, fresh water or toilets in homes. Water came from pipes in the streets.

Source 7

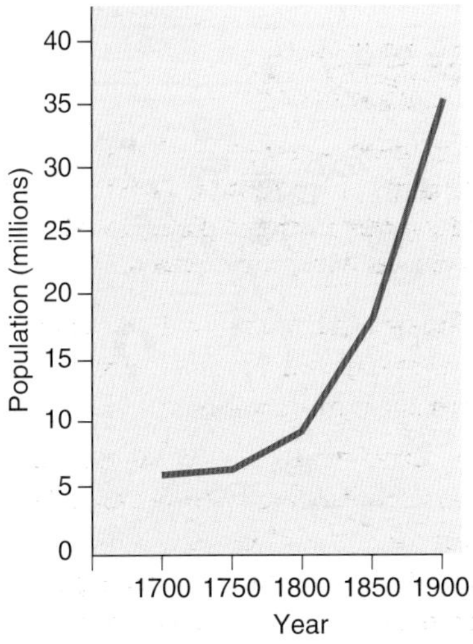

▲ The growth of the population of England and Wales, 1700–1900.

7.2 Why wasn't anything done to protect people's health in the early 1800s?

What is an iceberg doing in a history book? It's here to warn you always to look beyond the obvious explanation. Don't just look at the top of the iceberg but investigate the hidden dangers (explanations) beneath the surface. For this question it's easy to assume that the only reasons why public health was poor were vested interests – the selfish reasons of the rich who refused to pay for improvements. But what are the other reasons on the iceberg, hidden below the surface of the water?

Source 1

From 'Report on the Condition of the Town of Leeds' by James Smith, 1844:

'A proposal was made for the complete sewerage of the streets. I was present for nearly six hours of this debate. The chief theme of the speakers in opposition related to saving the pockets of the ratepayers and had very little regard to the sanitary results.'

Source 2

Extracts from a letter in *The Times*, 1 August 1854:

'We prefer to take our chance with cholera than be bullied into health …'

'There is nothing a man hates so much as being cleaned against his will, having his floors swept, his walls whitewashed, his pet dung heaps cleared away.'

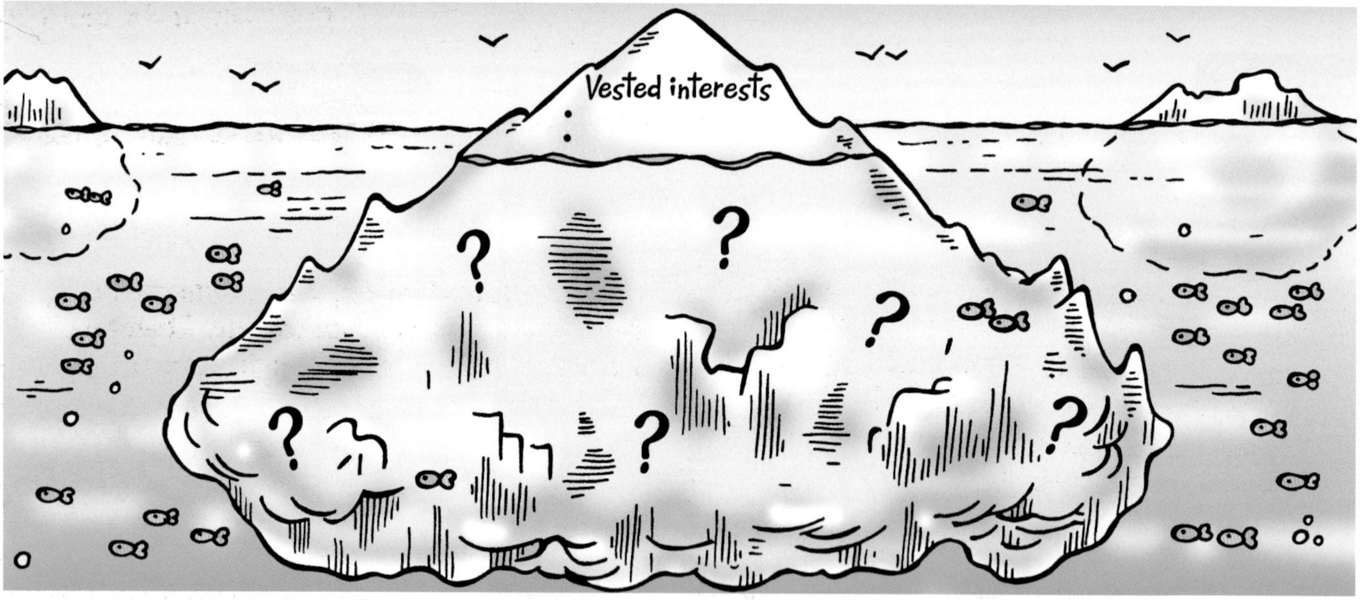

Activities

Complete your own copy of this iceberg illustration to explain fully why public health was so poor.

1. Read Sources 1 and 2. What exactly were the vested interests that were against improving public health? Add short notes to the bullet points at the top of the iceberg to summarise them.
2. What should go in the rest of the iceberg? Use the clues on the page opposite to write a series of short headings summing up the other reasons. Use the factors from page 9 to help you.
3. Now think about which reasons were most important. Review the reasons on your own iceberg drawing. How would you re-draw it to show which reasons were most important?
4. What was needed most to improve public health? Make three suggestions before you turn over and find out what happened.

Clue A

Pasteur's germ theory was not published and accepted by scientists and doctors until the 1860s. Pasteur's discovery of the value of boiling milk (pasteurisation) did not become common until the 1880s because many people believed that boiling killed the goodness.

Clue B

Towns had grown very fast. Landlords made profits from renting out houses so wanted them built quickly.

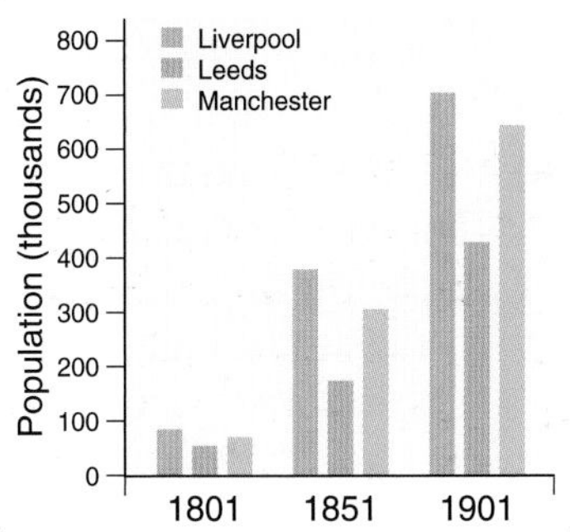

Clue C

Railways were not built to take people in and out of town centres in large numbers until the 1850s and later. Workers therefore had to live close to their places of work.

Clue D

There was a strong belief that people should help themselves to live better, healthier and more comfortable lives. People objected to local and national governments 'interfering' in their lives. The protests against compulsory smallpox vaccinations, which you read about in Section 5, are a good example.

Clue E

Governments were still not expected to play a major part in improving the living and working conditions of the people. There were no pensions or help for the sick and unemployed from governments. The first income tax was collected in 1798 and stayed low in the 1800s.

Clue F

Doctors were not paid by the government so had to charge fees to their patients. Therefore the poor could not afford to go to a doctor.

Clue G

Fresh food was difficult to get in many towns because it had to be brought in by horse and cart and was expensive. Food was often adulterated – mixed with other things (chalk in bread, sand in sugar, sawdust in flour) – by shopkeepers to increase its weight and so make more money from sales.

Clue H

Working conditions were at least as bad as home conditions. Workers in mines, workshops and factories had long hours and only very short breaks. Their toilet and washing facilities were very poor, with many people sharing one privy and only a pipe to wash at. Many people also fell ill from the work itself, swallowing coal and textile dust, which caused lung diseases.

Meet the Examiner: What was the most important factor in the improvement of public health?

exam BUSTERS

You have already been introduced to factors questions on pages 76–77. This tug-of-war activity gives you another technique to use when preparing for factors questions. Follow the activity instructions and then tackle the question below. Look back to pages 76–77 for more help with this kind of question.

Examine that Question

1 (a) Choose **one** of the factors below that affected the development of public health in the nineteenth century.

- Government
- Role of individuals

Describe the effect of that factor in improving public health in the nineteenth century. *(4 marks)*

(b) Which of these factors contributed most to improving public health in the nineteenth century? Explain your answer. *(8 marks)*

Activities

Step 1: Collect the evidence
On pages 149–157, you will find out how and why public health improved in the nineteenth century. Your first task is to collect evidence about the effects of each factor. Use the cards on page 148 to help you build up your evidence.

Step 2: Choose the teams
Use your evidence to choose the teams. We have started the teams by adding one name and one event to the team tabards – but which people and events are also in these teams?

Step 3: Look at the team members
Not everyone on a team has as big an impact on the result as everyone else – so which of the team members do you think were most important in the development of public health? Give the ones that you think were most important a double-strength pull.

Step 4: Debate the result
Decide which team you think has won the tug-of-war and write a speech explaining your choice and the evidence for your choice. Make sure you include at least one point that shows the weakness in the opposition argument.

Now debate the result with your class. Debates are very helpful for revision because you have to know the topic well enough to talk about it. If ideas and information stay in your mind it can be a bit of a jumble, but a debate forces you to sort it out clearly – talking about a topic gets you more than halfway to writing about it effectively in an examination.

Step 5: Consider science and technology
One other factor had a powerful influence on public health in the 1800s – science and technology. Use your cards from page 148 to select the science and technology team and decide which members had a double-strength pull. Then compare science and technology with the other factors – which is the overall winner?

Smarter Revision: Using card sorts to evaluate the role played by different factors

exam BUSTERS

1 Make your own set of the cards below. As you read Pages 149–157 you will find evidence of the roles that some of the factors played in improving public health. Make notes on the relevant factor card explaining its contributions.

INDIVIDUALS	GOVERNMENT	WAR	SCIENCE AND TECHNOLOGY	CHANCE

2 When you finish making notes, organise the cards into a shape that shows how important you think each factor is. You can use one of the shapes below or use your own design. Remember that some factors did not contribute at all.

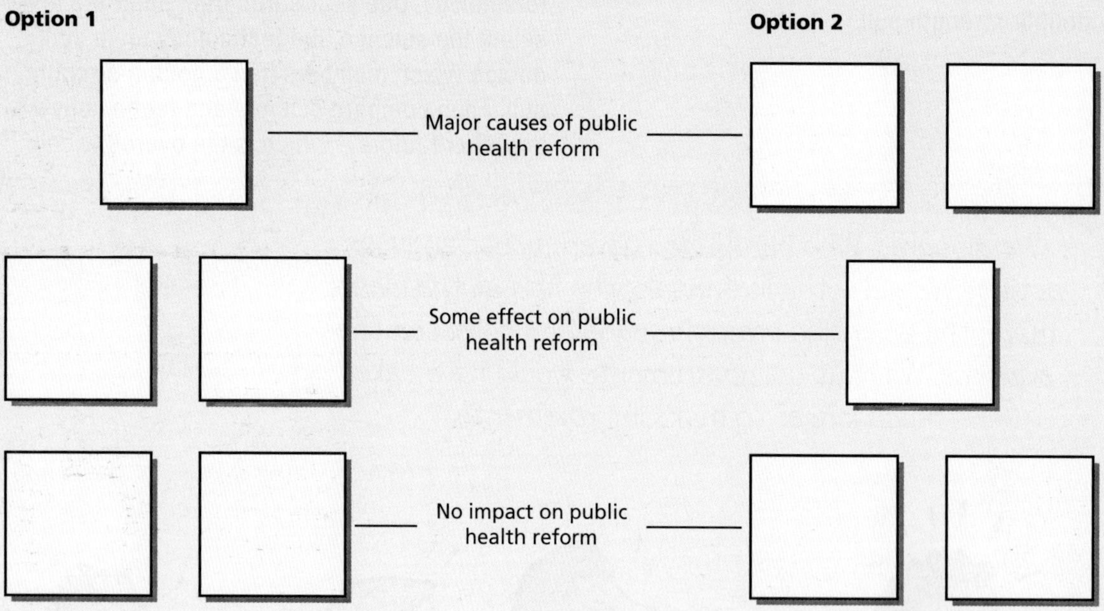

Why are card sorts useful?

Using the cards to collect evidence and then organising them into a pattern is really useful.

- **It helps you to select what to include in your answer.** In part (a) of the question on page 146 you have to describe the impact of a factor. You will probably not have time to write about every effect the factor had, but the information on the cards summarises the key points – so you can select the most important effects to write about.
- **It helps you plan a clear line of argument.** It is a lot easier to write a good answer to part (b) if you have a line of argument clear in your head before you start to write. The card sort helps you organise your argument about which factor or factors had the greatest effect. Students who are successful in the exam spend time thinking about their approach to the question before they start to write.

7.3 The story of public health in the 1800s

Activity

Use pages 149–157 to collect evidence for your factor cards on the opposite page. We have helped to begin with by highlighting the factors and we have included short activities to help identify key points.

Edwin Chadwick (1800–1890)

Chadwick was a civil servant who worked for the *Poor Law Commission* in the 1830s and 1840s. In 1848, he became a member of the National Board of Health. His main weakness was that he did not know how to get other people on his side. He was argumentative, arrogant and rude as well as extremely hard-working.

The work of Edwin Chadwick

In 1842, Chadwick published his 'Report on the Sanitary Conditions of the Labouring Population'. His evidence proved that:

1. The poor live in dirty, overcrowded conditions.
2. This causes a huge amount of illness.

3. Many people are too sick to work and so become poorer still.

4. Therefore other people have to pay higher taxes to help the poor.

His solution was for the government to reform public health. He said:

We can cut taxes and save money in the long run by:

1. improving drainage and sewers

2. removing refuse from streets and houses

3. providing clean water supplies

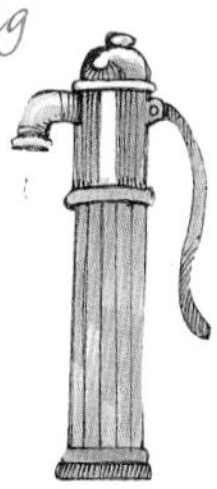

4. appointing medical officers in each area to check these reforms.

The impact of cholera

There was a lot of opposition to Chadwick's report. Many local tax-payers did not want to pay for improvements even though it meant lower taxes in the long run. The government was not happy either. It knew that local councils did not want the national government interfering in local matters. Then came another outbreak of cholera.

As cholera spread across Europe in 1847, fear grew in Britain of many thousands of deaths to come. Therefore, the government finally followed Chadwick's recommendations and passed the Public Health Act in the hope this would reduce the impact of cholera.

The Public Health /

The major points in

1 A national Board

2 In towns where tl government could public health impı sewerage and app

3 Local councils wer health improveme (called rates) to pa support of local rat

:ils were allowed to ıt Medical Officers of ı and local boards of to oversee public health.

GOVERNMENT

;, the 1848 Act was not compulsory. aged change but it did not force councils to ınges. Only 103 towns set up local boards of lany more did not and the National Board of et up to oversee reforms, was abolished in r only six years.

How important a part did Chadwick really play in public health reform?

Chadwick's positive impact

- Hard-work produced a mass of evidence supporting public health reform.
- 1842 Report influenced the government and persuaded people that reform was needed.
- His report's recommendations were the basis for the 1848 Public Health Act.

Chadwick's negative impact

- 1842 Report did not lead to immediate reform. The Public Health Act came in 1848.
- The 1848 Act did not force councils to reform public health.
- His personality antagonised people and did not win support for his cause.
- His influence faded in the 1850s.

What role did William Farr play?

INDIVIDUALS

Chadwick was not the only civil servant who built up evidence of the links between poverty, dirt and ill-health. After 1837 all births, deaths and marriages had to be registered and William Farr used this information to build an accurate picture of where the death rate was highest and what people died of. This proved the link between high death-rate and unhealthy living conditions. His statistics shamed some towns into improving local public health conditions. Therefore, Farr's evidence also put pressure on local and national government to make changes.

Activities

1 Why was the Public Health Act passed in 1848?
2 What were the limitations of the 1848 Public Health Act?
3 What was Chadwick's major contribution to public health reform?
4 Look back to page 57, Source 10. Do you think this Act had anything in common with King Edward III's orders?

The work of John Snow

INDIVIDUALS | SCIENCE AND TECHNOLOGY | CHANCE

Snow was a pioneer in surgery as well as public health, improving medical methods and using detailed evidence to challenge old theories. In 1849, he published a book saying that cholera spread through water, not in 'bad air', but his suggestion was mocked by many doctors. In 1854, another cholera outbreak gave him the chance to prove his theory that people caught cholera from water they used for washing and drinking.

Cholera killed over 500 people around Broad Street, near Snow's surgery, in just ten days. This led Snow to map out the deaths in detail and write a report detailing his evidence, called 'On the Mode of Communication of Cholera'.

Snow's evidence was so strong that the handle of the Broad Street water pump was taken away, stopping people getting water from the pump. There were no more deaths. It was later discovered that a cesspool, only a metre away from the pump, was leaking into the drinking water.

Snow had proved that clean water was essential for preventing the spread of cholera, but even this did not lead to a new Public Health Act enforcing change. Many scientists still clung to the 'bad air' theory (Pasteur had not yet published his germ theory).

▲ John Snow was born in Yorkshire in 1813, the son of a farm labourer. Aged 14 he was apprenticed to a surgeon and eventually became a fully qualified doctor.

Source 1

From Snow's 'On the Mode of Communication of Cholera', 1854:

'On proceeding to the spot, I found that nearly all of the deaths had taken place within a short distance of the Broad Street water pump. There were only ten deaths in houses situated decidedly nearer to another street pump. In five of these cases, the families of the deceased persons informed me that they always used the pump in Broad Street as they preferred the water to that of the pump that was nearer.

'There is a brewery in Broad Street. Perceiving that no brewer's men were registered as having died of cholera, I called on Mr Huggins, the owner. He informed that there were about 70 workmen employed in the brewery and that only two of them had been indisposed by cholera and then not seriously. The men are allowed to drink beer, and Mr Huggins believed that they do not drink water at all and never obtained water from the Broad Street pump.'

Activities

5 What was important about Snow's discovery?

6 Why do you think Source 2 was published?

Source 2

▲ This cartoon is called 'Death's Dispensary'. It was published in 1860.

Source 3

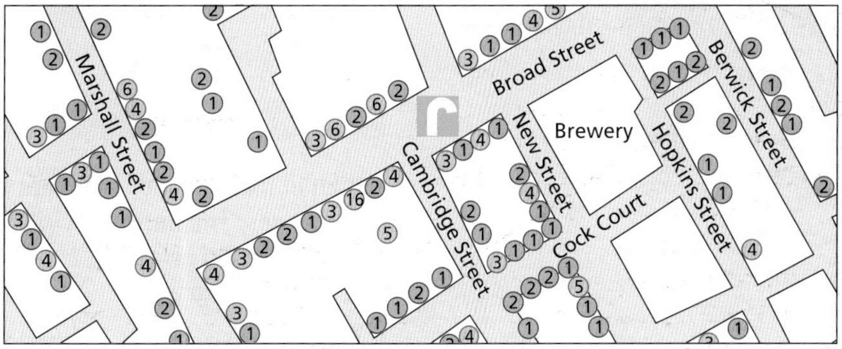

Pump
1 or 2 deaths from cholera
3 or more deaths from cholera

▲ A copy of part of Snow's map detailing deaths in the Broad Street area.

1852 – 'A Court for King Cholera'

Source 4

▼ A cartoon called 'A Court for King Cholera'. A court was an enclosed area of housing, often with little daylight and heavily over-populated. The cartoon was published in 1852 in *Punch* magazine, which commented on many political and social issues of the time. This was four years after the 1848 Public Health Act was passed.

Overcrowded and unhygienic lodging houses

Large pile of rubbish left in the street with a woman collecting from the rubbish

The street is overcrowded

Activities

A lot of thought and time went into creating cartoons like those on these two pages. The cartoonist was aiming to get across a message. Each detail of the cartoon gives you a clue about this message. We have picked out some details for you.

1 What do you think the cartoonist's message was in Source 4?
2 Why did he choose this title?
3 Which other details did the cartoonist include to get his message across?
4 Now analyse Source 5 in the same way, identifying the cartoonist's message and the details that he used to bring out his message.

1858 – The 'Great Stink'

The summer of 1858 was hot, very hot. There was no rain to fill the rivers and river levels fell, especially the Thames in London. As a result, the smell from the river grew worse and worse and was quickly called 'The Great Stink'. One of the very worst places was at the Houses of Parliament which are right on the river bank.

Source 5

▲ This cartoon was published in *The Times*, 18 June 1858.

Why was there no compulsory public health reform in the 1850s?

The 'Great Stink' of 1858 added to the evidence that more public reform was needed. In London itself, an effective, modern sewer system was built but there was no new Public Health Act to enforce improvements throughout the country.

Source 6

A letter in *The Times*, 1 August 1854:

'The Board of Health has fallen. We prefer to take our chance with cholera than be bullied into health. Everywhere the board's inspectors were bullying, insulting and expensive. They entered houses and factories insisting on changes revolting to the habits or pride of the masters and occupants. There is nothing a man hates so much as being cleaned against his will, having his floors swept, his walls whitewashed, his pet dung heaps cleared away, all at the command of a sort of sanitary bumbailiff. Mr. Chadwick set to work everywhere, washing and splashing, and Master John Bull was scrubbed and rubbed till the tears came to his eyes and his fists clenched themselves with worry and pain.'

Activity

5 Why were there no more public health reforms in the 1850s?

So why was conservatism finally defeated?

1: Octavia Hill and housing reformers

INDIVIDUALS

Governments were reluctant to pass laws forcing improvements in public health but there were individuals who showed what could be done. One campaigner was Octavia Hill who started teaching poor children when she was only 14 and was appalled by their homes. She bought three slum houses in 1865 and cleaned them up to show how to provide healthy homes for working people and stop overcrowding. Over time, she took over 2000 houses, improving them to a much higher standard of cleanliness. This idea led to similar schemes elsewhere and she went on to campaign for laws which would force local councils to improve housing. Her influence helped to persuade the government to pass the 1875 Artisans' Dwelling Act, giving councils the power to knock down slums on health grounds.

▲ Octavia Hill (1838–1912) who worked hard to improve housing for working class people.

2: The impact of Pasteur and scientific theory

INDIVIDUALS

SCIENCE AND TECHNOLOGY

In 1861, Pasteur published his germ theory. In 1864, he conducted a series of public experiments that convinced most scientists that diseases were caused by bacteria (germs) (see page 123). This finally provided the clear proof that was needed of the link between dirt and disease and showed that Chadwick, Farr and Snow had all been correct in their arguments.

Faced with this scientific proof, people were more willing to pay taxes to cover the costs of public health reforms – fresh water supplies, good sewers, public toilets – and more local towns began to make these reforms.

▲ By providing scientific proof that diseases were caused by bacteria, Pasteur encouraged people to pay for public health reforms.

3: Government and political reform

For years, governments had been unwilling to make public health reform compulsory. The only voters in general elections were wealthy landowners and the well-off middle classes, the very people who would have to pay more if public health reforms became compulsory. Governments did not want to offend these men (they were all men – no women could vote) and risk losing their votes in an election.

All this changed in 1867 when working men in towns were given the right to vote for the first time. Suddenly the numbers of voters had doubled. It increased again in 1884 when many working men in country areas got the vote. Politics had changed dramatically even though all women and some men still could not vote.

If politicians wanted to win elections they had to promise laws to win the votes of working men, not just the wealthy and middle classes.

The result: The Great Clean-up of the 1870s and 1880s

All the changes you have read about led up to a series of new laws in the 1870s and 1880s, all designed to improve the lives of ordinary people. The most important was the 1875 Public Health Act.

The Public Health Act of 1875

This Act said:

Local councils forced to provide clean water, public toilets and proper drains and sewers.

Councils forced to appoint a Medical Officer of Health and sanitary inspectors to inspect public health facilities.

Other laws were passed that:

- improved the standards of housing
- stopped the pollution of rivers (from which people got water)
- shortened working hours in factories for women and children
- made it illegal to add ingredients that made food unhealthy
- made education compulsory.

Activity

Why was the 1875 Public Health Act a major improvement on the 1848 Act?

How did technology make the Great Clean-up possible?

INDIVIDUALS

SCIENCE AND TECHNOLOGY

GOVERNMENT

Passing a law saying public health reform was compulsory was only the beginning. After that came the hard engineering work, building the new systems. This used engineering knowledge that had not been available a hundred years earlier but there had been great improvements in technology during the Industrial Revolution and the building of the railways (e.g. machinery powered by steam engines, methods of building pipelines and embankments). This knowledge was essential to make the laws effective.

▲ Until the 1860s cities had open sewers like this one in London. This photograph, taken in 1900, shows how long it took for local councils to get rid of the many, many miles of open sewers.

▲ Public health reform involved huge engineering projects to build sewers and water pipes under city streets. This photograph shows sewers being built.

◀ An invention that also made a difference was the flushing lavatory. Instead of privies needing to be emptied by hand and spade (and left rotting for days or weeks) the flushing system sent the waste instantly down into the sewer network. Of course, at first, such lavatories were only available to the rich but it was the beginning of a very important change.

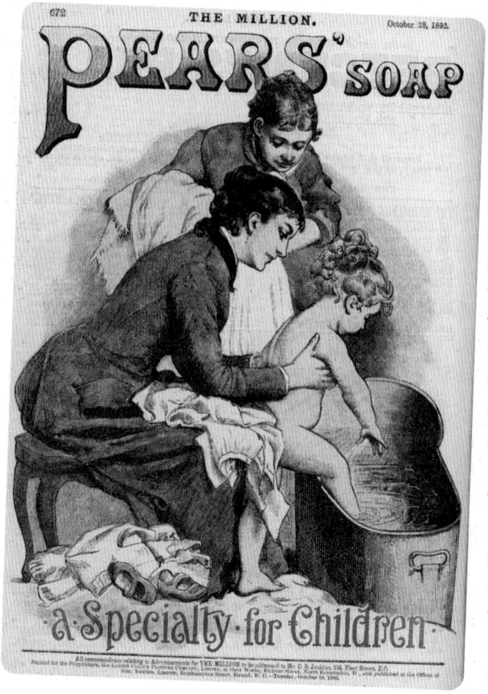

◀ And there was soap! Today a bar of soap is a very ordinary thing but it was much rarer in the mid-1800s partly because it was taxed and so was too expensive for many people to buy. In 1853 the tax was taken off soap so many more people could afford it and so washing did more to kill germs, even if people did not know it then.

Joseph Bazalgette (1819–1891)

Bazalgette was the engineer who designed and built London's sewer system after the Great Stink of 1858. He spent his early career in the railway industry, gaining experience of large engineering projects. After 1858 he planned and organised the building of London's sewer system, the same system that is still used today. This system included:

- 83 miles of main sewers, built underground from brick
- 1100 miles of sewers for each street and connecting to the main sewers
- a series of major pumping stations to drive the flow of sewage along the pipes.

The core of the work was completed by 1865 but it was such a huge project it took another ten years to complete. Fortunately Bazalgette looked ahead and forecast the growth of population so made sure the system had a much higher capacity than was needed in the 1860s.

Exporting cholera

These public health improvements certainly put an end to outbreaks of cholera in Britain, but it was still a huge danger worldwide. This cartoon was published in 1883 in an American magazine when cholera was sweeping Europe. What can you learn from the details?

▲ American cartoon of 1883 called 'The Kind of "Assisted Emigrant" We Can Not Afford to Admit'. The ship is British.

7.4 Why did public health improve further in the twentieth century?

We guided you through the story of nineteenth-century public health. Now you have to plan your own investigation using pages 158–163 so that you can answer the examination question below.

1 (a) Choose one of the factors below that affected the development of public health in the twentieth century.
- Government
- War

Describe the effect of that factor in improving public health in the twentieth century. *(4 marks)*

(b) Which of these factors contributed most to improving public health in the twentieth century? Explain your answer. *(8 marks)*

How much had public health really improved?

By 1900, life expectancy was starting to rise. It had reached 46 for men and 50 for women. Towns were becoming cleaner. Public health facilities were beginning to improve. But the key words so far are 'starting to' and 'beginning to'. Many people still suffered major health problems, partly because of dirt but even more because of poverty. The government gave no help to the sick, unemployed and elderly. Those who could not get help from friends and relatives or charities had to give up homes and go into a workhouse, run by the local council.

Sources 1 and 2 show the kind of statistics that led to demands for more reforms. Also influential were reports by Charles Booth and Seebohm Rowntree that demonstrated the extent of poverty and highlighted the links between poverty and ill-health.

Source 1

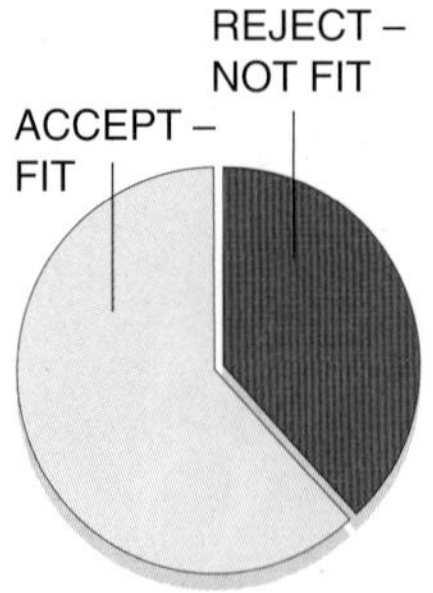

▲ During the Boer War (1899–1902) 38 per cent of recruits were rejected because they were not fit enough for the army because of health problems.

Source 2

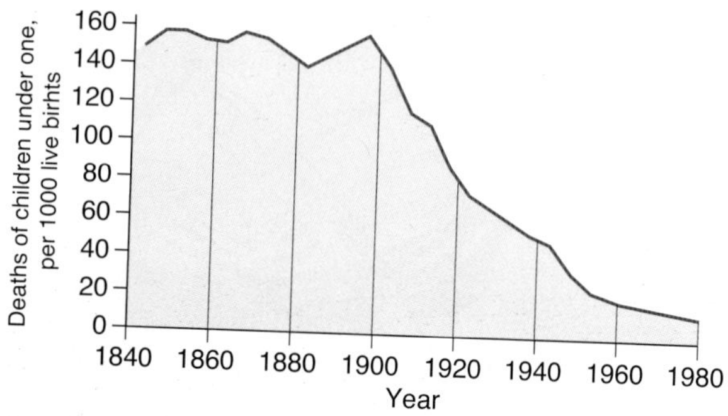

▲ The death rate of children under one year old 1840–1980

Seebohm Rowntree (1871–1954) ***Poverty: a Study of Town Life***

Rowntree investigated poverty and living conditions in York where his family had been in business for many years. In 1901, he published *Poverty: a Study of Town Life*, providing detailed evidence that more than a quarter of the people in York were living in poverty even though they were in work, and that poverty was having a serious impact on their health. This led him to increase his own workers' wages and to continue his research, charting changes in conditions. In 1941, he published a new report, 'Progress and Poverty', which showed a 50 per cent reduction in poverty since 1901 and that poverty in the 1930s was mostly the result of unemployment rather than low wages.

Activities

1. What do Sources 1 and 2 suggest about how much public health had improved by 1900?
2. Why was the research by Booth and Rowntree important?
3. Why was so much emphasis placed on helping mothers and children by reformers?

Charles Booth (1840–1916)

Life and Labour of the London Poor

Booth was a Liverpool businessman, a friend of Octavia Hill and others trying to improve living conditions for the poor. He was well aware of the effects of poverty on health among the Liverpool poor but thought that campaigners were exaggerating when they said that 25 per cent of Londoners lived in poverty. In 1886, Booth set about collecting the detailed, accurate evidence that would prove or disprove that figure.

He financed research into poverty in the East End of London and spent weeks living in the area, renting rooms in a common lodging house. The result was an extremely detailed description of living conditions and poverty, with coloured maps identifying the extent of poverty in each street of east London. He discovered that 35 per cent of people were living in poverty – far more than had been claimed.

Appalled by these results, Booth continued building up evidence of poverty and ill-health. He argued that government had to take responsibility for caring for people in poverty. One of his suggestions was an old-age pension.

The impact of the Liberal government 1906–1914

In 1906, a new Liberal government was elected with a landslide majority of votes. Many people expected this government to make major reforms to improve everyday life. These reforms may seem ordinary today but a hundred years ago they were revolutionary.

1902 – Compulsory training for midwives.

1906 – Meals provided free for schoolchildren in need.

1907 – All births had to be notified to the local Medical Officer of Health. A health visitor visited each mother to make sure she knew how to protect her baby's health.

1907 – Medical checks to be carried out on children in schools.

1908 – Old-age pensions paid to people over 70 who did not have enough money to live on.

1909 – Back-to-back housing banned. New regulations enforced higher standards of house building.

1911 – National Insurance Act provided help for the sick (see page 160).

1912 – Clinics held in schools to give children free medical treatment.

Source 3

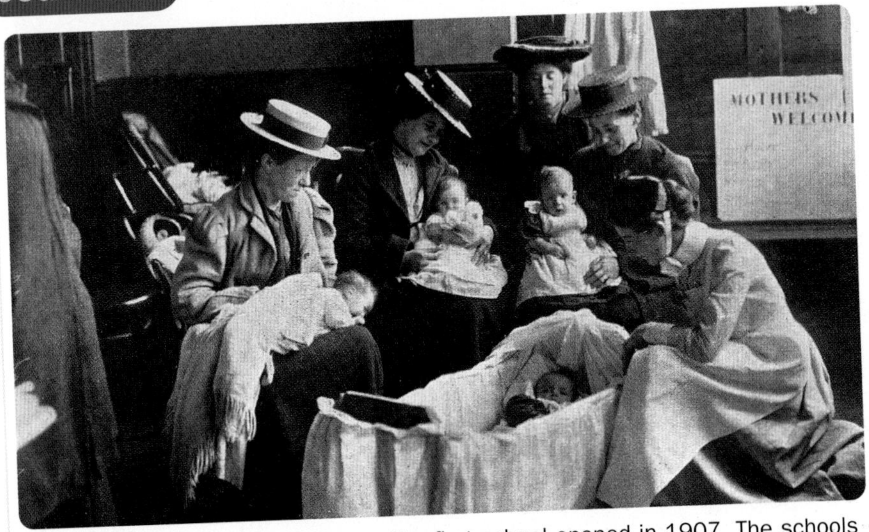

▲ Women at a school for mothers. The first school opened in 1907. The schools taught:

- the importance of hygiene and the danger of diarrhoea for infants
- how flies spread disease from privies and rubbish in streets
- that breast-feeding was better than bottle-feeding
- that good mothering was a duty to be performed for King and Country!

▲ David Lloyd George (1863–1945) was one of the most inspirational politicians in British history. He was a brilliant, persuasive speaker, determined to improve the lives of ordinary people and was a friend of Rowntree. He became a Liberal MP in 1890 and was Chancellor of the Exchequer in the Liberal government which introduced the reforms (above). He insisted on raising taxes on the well-off to pay for old-age pensions and the National Insurance Act of 1911 (see page 160). He became Prime Minister in 1916 during World War One.

A big step forward – the 1911 National Insurance Act

One of the greatest changes introduced by Lloyd George and the Liberal government was the National Insurance Act of 1911. The aim was to give workers medical help and sick pay if they could not work through illness. Until then, workers who fell ill had a choice – carry on working or get no pay, which meant they had no chance of affording medical help.

As Source 1 shows, the National Insurance scheme required the worker, his employer and the government to pay into a sickness fund. It was a major step forward but many people were left out of the scheme. It only included people in work, not their families. Most women and all children were excluded. So were the unemployed and elderly and anyone who had a long-lasting illness.

Source 4

The 1911 National Insurance Act said that workers, employers and the government must all pay money into a sickness fund.

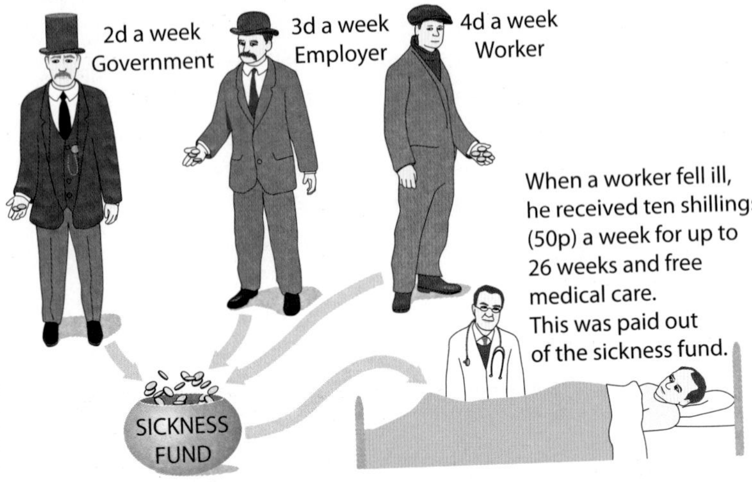

▲ How the National Insurance scheme worked

Developments in the 1930s

In 1919, after the end of World War One, a new Housing Act became law. Lloyd George had promised 'Homes fit for Heroes' for the returning soldiers and this Act said that local councils had to provide good homes for working people to rent. A quarter of a million new homes were built. In the 1930s, many old, unhealthy slum houses were cleared and another 700,000 new houses were built.

However, in other ways medical care was harder to find. In the 1930s, unemployment rose to over 3 million, leaving all those unemployed outside the National Insurance Scheme. Even people in jobs could not afford to keep up their payments and so could not get free medical help (see Source 6). The system set up in 1911 was failing. The most worrying evidence came from towns where unemployment was high. In some towns the number of deaths among children under the age of one was rising again, as you can see in Source 7.

Source 5

The Times, 2 January 1905, commenting on plans to provide free school meals for the poorest children:

'We have already reduced personal responsibility by taking away from parents the duty of educating their children. This is now used as an argument for taking away from them the duty of feeding their children. From that it is an easy step to paying for their proper housing. The proposed measure (free school meals) would go far to drain the remaining independence of the parents.'

Source 6

From an interview with Kathleen Davys, one of a Birmingham family of thirteen children growing up in the 1920s and 1930s. The local doctor charged sixpence for each visit:

'Headaches, we had vinegar and brown paper; for whooping cough we had camphorated oil rubbed on our chests or goose fat. For mumps we had stockings round our throats and measles we had tea stewed in the teapot by the fire – all different kinds of home cures. They thought they were better than going to the doctor's. Well they couldn't afford the doctor.'

Source 7

Town	1928	1931	1933
Wigan	93	103	110
Liverpool	94	94	98
St Helens	98	88	116
Bath	47	39	52
Brighton	50	54	47
Oxford	38	44	32

▲ The changing death rate per 1000 children aged less than one year in a variety of towns

The impact of World War Two

World War Two had a major impact on people's attitudes. It wasn't just the armed forces who were risking their lives. It was the first war in which all people felt they were 'in it together'. Many people at home died during bombing raids. The feeling grew that everyone should have access to good health care, not just the wealthy. In addition:

- Many children were evacuated from towns to the countryside and to better-off homes. Middle-class families were shocked at the condition of some of the children who were dirty, unhealthy and under-nourished.
- After all the sacrifices of the war, people wanted a better future. Better health care was an important part of this.
- During the war many people did get free health care to keep them fit for the war effort.

Activities

1 Why was the 1911 National Insurance Act such an important step forward?
2 a Why was *The Times* opposed to free school meals for the poor (Source 5)?
  b Which past developments were opposed in the same way?
3 Which problems remained in the 1930s?
4 Why was the Beveridge Report greeted so enthusiastically?

The Beveridge Report, 1942

The national coalition government asked a leading civil servant, Sir William Beveridge, to write a report on what should be done to improve people's lives. Beveridge (1879–1963) had played a key part in organising the 1911 National Insurance scheme so had a great deal of experience of the problems and which solutions were needed. He used this great experience in his report which recommended:

- setting up a National Health Service, free to everyone and paid for from taxes. Doctors, nurses and other medical workers would become government employees instead of charging the sick to create their wages.
- everyone in work would pay National Insurance out of their wages. This would pay benefits (sick-pay, old-age pensions, unemployment pay, etc.) to everyone whether they were working or not.

The Beveridge Report was greeted with enthusiasm by many people. People queued outside shops to buy their own copy and 600,000 copies were sold.

Source 8A

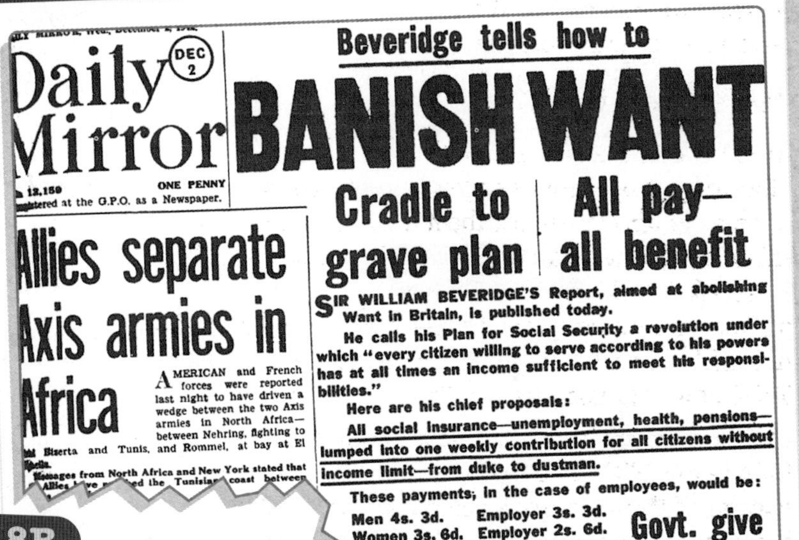

Daily Mirror DEC 2

12,159 ONE PENNY

Registered at the G.P.O. as a Newspaper.

Beveridge tells how to

BANISH WANT

Cradle to grave plan | All pay—all benefit

SIR WILLIAM BEVERIDGE'S Report, aimed at abolishing Want in Britain, is published today.

He calls his Plan for Social Security a revolution under which "every citizen willing to serve according to his powers has at all times an income sufficient to meet his responsibilities."

Here are his chief proposals:

All social insurance—unemployment, health, pensions—lumped into one weekly contribution for all citizens without income limit—from duke to dustman.

These payments, in the case of employees, would be:

Men 4s. 3d. Employer 3s. 3d.
Women 3s. 6d. Employer 2s. 6d.

Cradle to the grave benefits for all, including:

Free medical, dental, eyesight and hospital treatment;

Children's allowances of 8s. a week each, after the first child.

Increases in unemployment benefit (40s. for a couple) and abolition of the means test; industrial pension in place of workmen's compensation.

A charter for housewives, including marriage grant up to £10; maternity grant of £4 (and 36s. for 13 weeks for a paid worker); widow's benefit; separation and divorce provision; free domestic help in time of sickness.

Old age pensions rising to 40s. for a married couple on retirement.

Funeral grants up to £20.

... scheme ... a new Ministry ... Security

Allies separate Axis armies in Africa

AMERICAN and French forces were reported last night to have driven a wedge between the two Axis armies in North Africa—between Nehring, fighting to ... Bizerta and Tunis, and Rommel, at bay at El Agheila.

Messages from North Africa and New York stated that ... Allies have ... the Tunisian coast between ...

Govt. give hint of post-war planning

CHOOSING the eve of the publication of Sir William Beveridge's long-awaited report on Social Security, the Government yesterday gave the country its first indication of their own plans for post-war Britain.

These include the continuance of rationing for some time and control of industry (some industries being taken over as public corporations); the development of agriculture, forestry and public utilities like electricity.

The Government also announced the immediate setting up of a new Ministry of Town and Country Planning, and the rejection of the Scott and Uthwatt Committees' proposals for placing main responsibility for planning in the hands of a permanent commission ...

Source 8B

▲ **A** The front page and **B** a cartoon from the *Daily Mirror* for 2 December 1942, reporting the publication of the Beveridge Report.

The creation of the National Health Service

Despite the general enthusiasm for Beveridge's report and the idea of creating a National Health Service, there was powerful opposition. The most important opposition came from the doctors themselves, but their opposition ended when Aneurin Bevan, the Minister of Health, agreed that doctors could continue to treat patients privately and charge them fees as well as working for the NHS.

▲ Aneurin 'Nye' Bevan (1897–1960), Minister for Health in the Labour government which introduced the NHS.

Bevan was the son of a Welsh coal miner and himself started work underground aged 13. His background and work for the miners' union gave him deep experience of the problems of poverty and sickness and inspired him to become MP for Ebbw Vale in 1929. Like Lloyd George, he was an inspiring speaker, an idealist who was determined to make life better for working people. His speeches in favour of the NHS won support while he compromised on details to put an end to opposition from some doctors.

Source 9

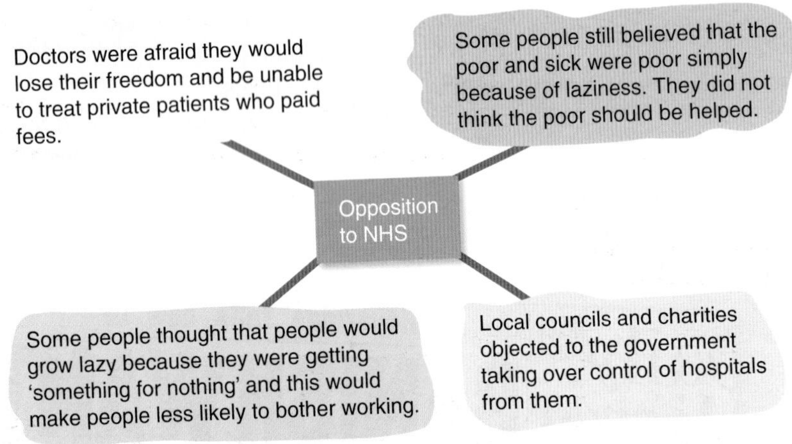

Source 10

Aneurin Bevan, Minister for Health, introducing the National Health Service to Parliament in 1946:

'Medical treatment should be made available to rich and poor alike in accordance with medical need and no other criteria. Worry about money in a time of sickness is a serious hindrance to recovery, apart from its unnecessary cruelty.'

Source 14

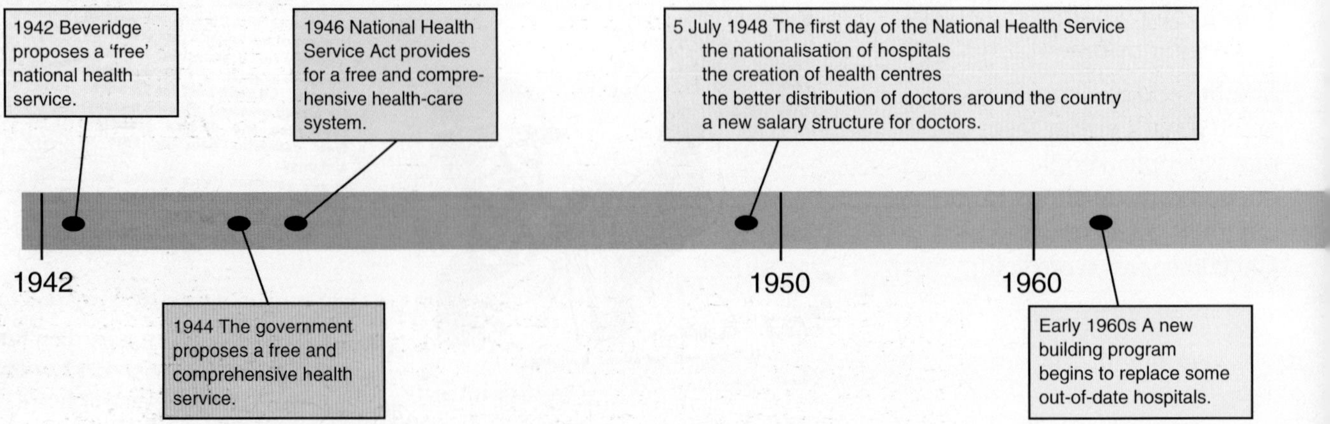

Source 11

In July 1948 the NHS was introduced. Now everyone could get free treatment. Until 1948 about 8 million people had never seen a doctor because they could not afford to do so. Source 13 shows the range of services provided by the NHS. Many hospitals were rebuilt. Doctors and nurses got new, improved equipment. The NHS played an important part in increasing people's life expectancy, particularly helping to reduce the numbers of women dying during, or shortly after, childbirth.

Source 12

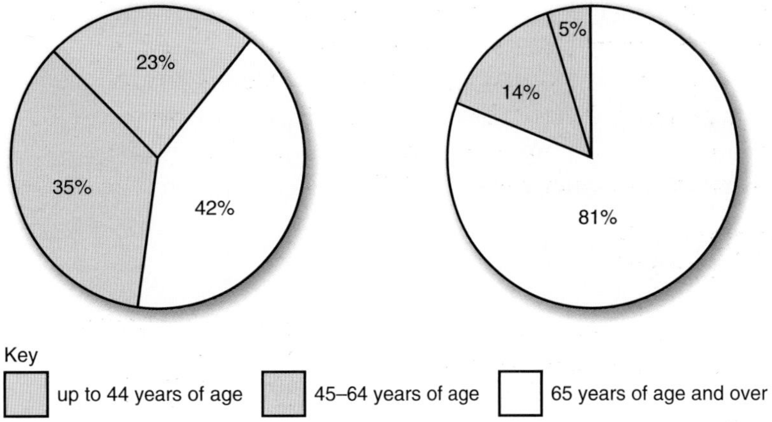

▲ These charts show how the age of death changed between 1919 and 1992.

Source 13

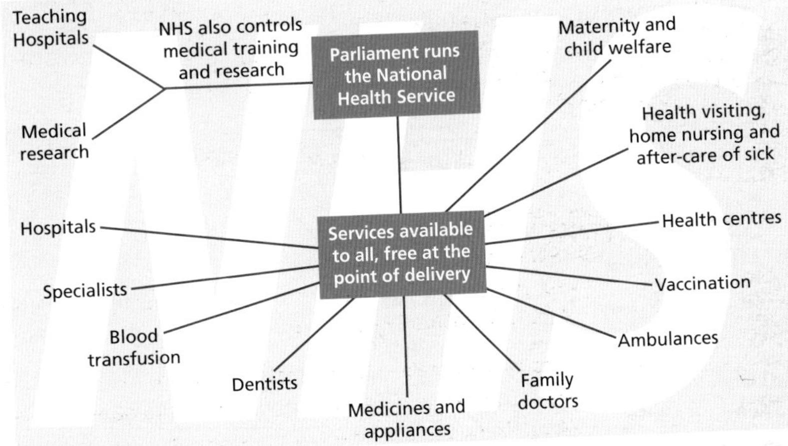

▲ Diagram showing the services provided by the NHS in 1948. Since then charges have been introduced for some items such as dentistry and prescription charges.

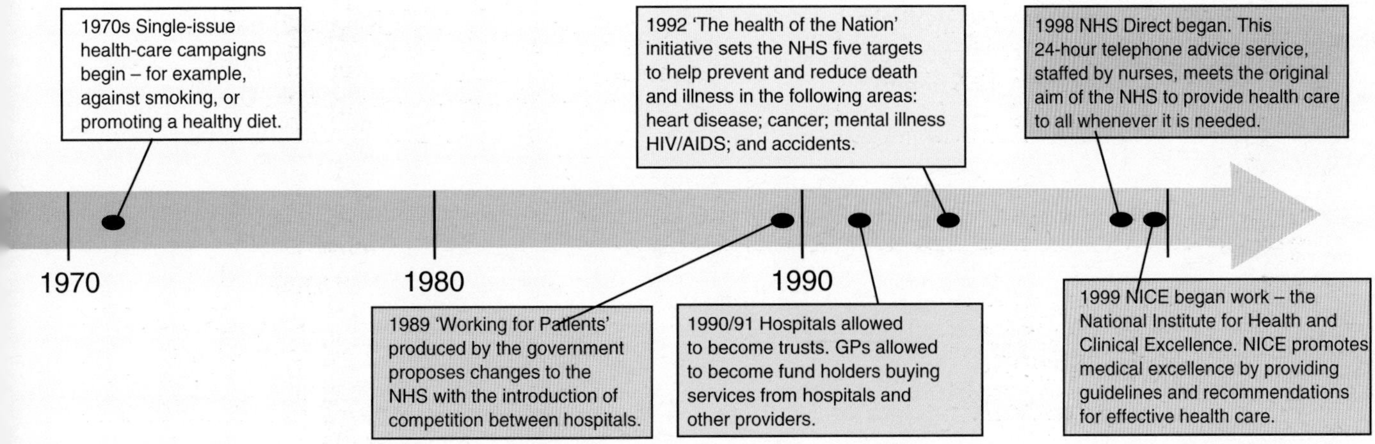

Public health: A summary

Now you have completed the story of public health across the centuries. This timeline shows you the key developments. Your task is to tell the story – accurately and interestingly.

Activity

1 On pages 6–7 you began a graph recording the pattern of developments in public health. Use this timeline to check and complete your graph.

The timeline below is not to chronological scale.

Public health developments

Hygiene left to individuals

Roman aqueducts, baths, sewers

Destruction of Roman system

Local laws in towns – poorly enforced

1665 plague – use of quarantine, cleaning, closing inns and theatres

Ancient | Middle Ages | Renaissance

Prehistory | Eygpt | Greece | Rome

Reasons for developments

Romans: Healthier armies, healthier traders and workers. Large cities needed good public health

Kings led armies – health not their responsibility. Plagues forced brief improvements

Activities

2 Work in a group of three. You are going to have up to three minutes to tell the story of public health. Spend twenty minutes preparing your story. If your teacher gives you more preparation time think about how to enliven the story with visuals and props.

Your story must include answers to the following questions:

a How would you describe the pattern of continuity and change over time? Think about when there was long-lasting continuity and when there was rapid change.

b Why did governments fail to make public health reforms for so long?

c When was the pace of change fastest – and why was it fastest then?

d Which two public health developments do you think were most important – and why?

e How important do you think public health reforms have been in improving life expectancy? (See the graph on pages 4–5.)

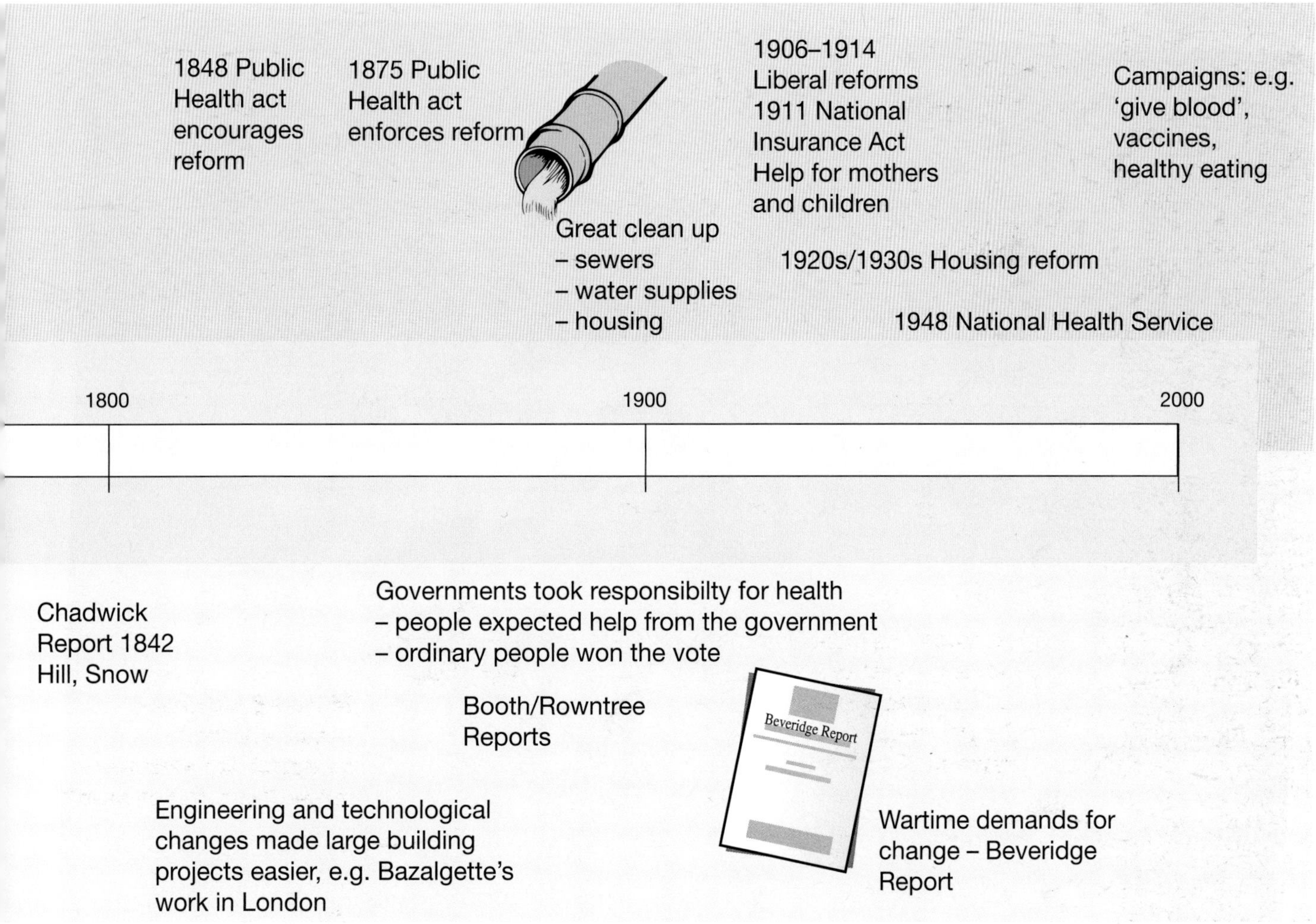

8.1 Why has there been such a revolution in surgery, and why was there opposition at first?

Now for surgery – still a gruesome experience in the early 1800s but, like public health, about to be changed dramatically. Your task is to find out why surgical problems were overcome and why some people opposed discoveries that made operations so much safer and easier for their fellow human beings.

Source 1

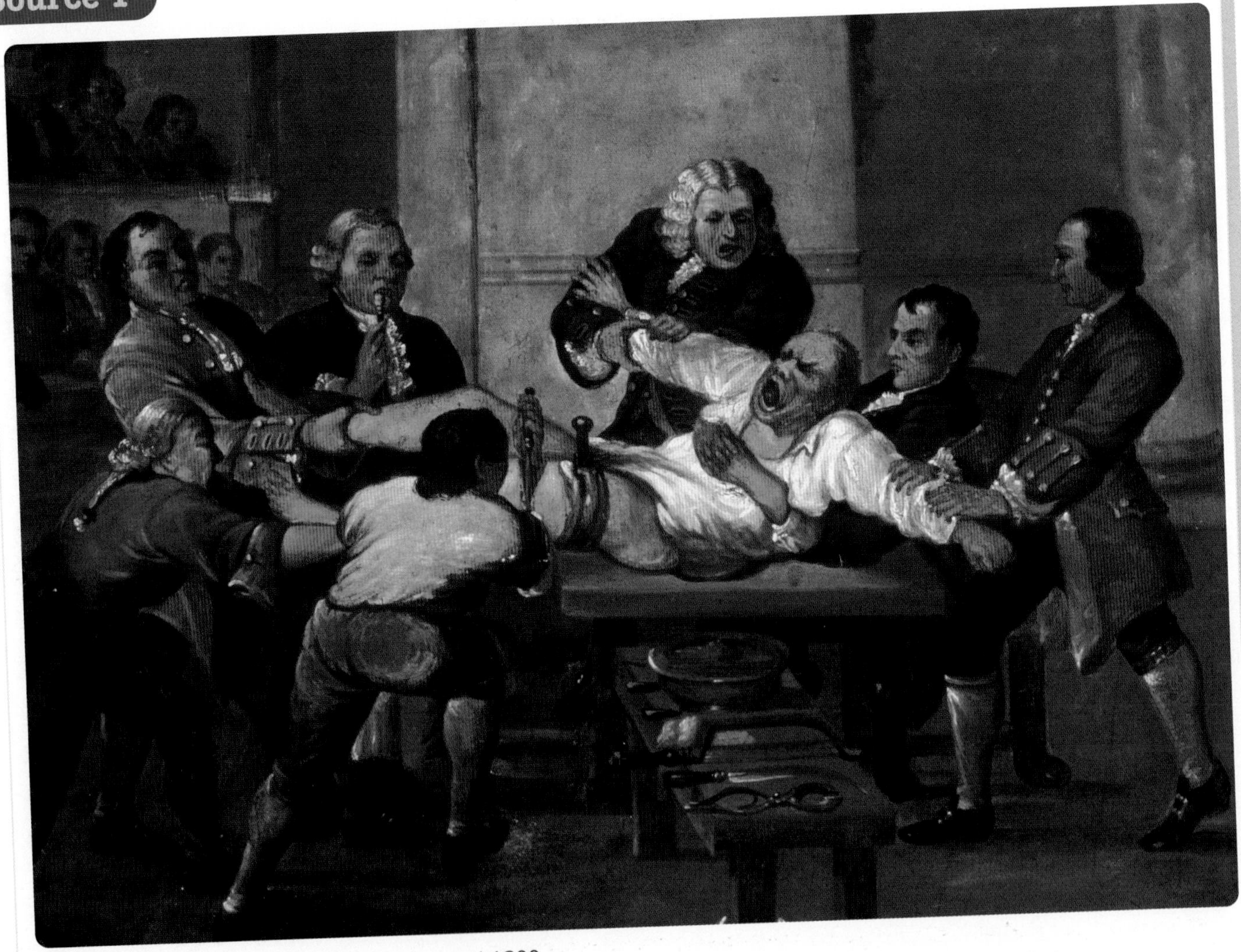

▲ A painting of an operation dating from around 1800.

Activities

1 Study Sources 1–4. Which three main dangers faced patients during operations at the beginning of the nineteenth century?
2 If Paré had time-travelled from the 1500s, what would he have seen in these operations that was similar to or different from his own time?

Source 2

The novelist Fanny Burney's account of her mastectomy operation in 1811:

'... when the dreadful steel was plunged into the breast – cutting through veins, arteries, flesh, nerves – I began a scream that lasted during the whole time of the incision – I almost marvel that it does not ring in my ears still! So excruciating was the agony. When the wound was made, and the instrument was withdrawn, the pain seemed undiminished, for the air that suddenly rushed into those delicate parts felt like a mass of small but sharp and forked poignards [daggers], that were tearing at the edges of the wound.'

Source 3

An account by Professor James Syme of amputating a leg at the hip joint. Syme was a surgeon working in Edinburgh in the early 1800s:

'I introduced a narrow knife about a foot long ... I cut along the bone. Finally I passed the knife around the head of the bone, cutting the remaining portion of the ligament, and this completed the operation, which certainly did not occupy at the most one minute. [My assistant] relaxed [the tourniquet so] that we might estimate the size and number of the bleeding vessels. It seemed at first sight as if the vessels which supplied so many jets of arterial blood could never be closed ... a single instant was sufficient to convince us that the patient's safety required all our [speed], and in the course of a few minutes haemorrhage was effectively stopped by the application of twelve ligatures.'

Source 4

Surgery in St Thomas's Hospital London in 1871, recalled by John Leeson, a medical student at the hospital:

'Ovariotomy was becoming common and one of our surgeons was keen on it. His mortality was round about 80 per cent. I used to dread seeing a notice of the operation, as I knew that in a few days the patient would probably be lying on the post-mortem table.

'I remember the house-surgeon in the operating theatre with his threaded needles dangling from the front flap of his coat. One of our surgeons lectured on anatomy in an old frock-coat buttoned up to the chin. I see him now, pawing the dissection as he lectured on it. When the coat was past even this work he took it up to the operating theatre. An operation was a dirty job and an outworn old coat was a suitable garment! I see it now, faded with age, stained with blood and spotted with pus.'

Activities

1 Look carefully at the timeline below.
   a What is the significance of the colour-coding?
   b What progress was made by 1916 in solving the three main surgical problems?
2 How do you think people at the time reacted to these surgical developments? Think about reactions to the work of Harvey and Jenner, for example.

The revolution in surgery

1845 Horace Wells used nitrous oxide as an anaesthetic.

1846 William Morton, an American dentist, used ether as an anaesthetic when removing teeth. It was also used during operations to remove tumours.

1847 Ignaz Semmelweiss called for doctors to wash their hands before entering the maternity wards in the General Hospital in Vienna.

James Simpson experimented with chloroform and established that it is an effective anaesthetic without some of the drawbacks of ether.

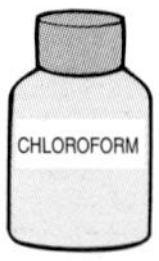

1853 Queen Victoria was given chloroform for the birth of her son Prince Leopold, by Dr John Snow, who was the leading anaesthetist of the time.

1861 Louis Pasteur published his germ theory.

1867 After reading Pasteur's germ theory, Joseph Lister, a Scottish surgeon, experimented with carbolic acid spray to produce the first antiseptic.

1878 Robert Koch, a bacteriologist, discovered the bacterium which caused septicaemia (blood poisoning). This boosted Lister's antiseptic ideas and was the start of aseptic surgery where operations were carried out in germ–free environments.

1880 Lister used sterilised catgut for internal stitches.

1889 William Halstead, an American surgeon, introduced the wearing of sterilised rubber gloves and surgical masks to further prevent infection.

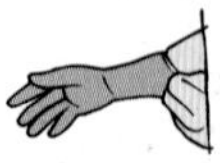

1901 Karl Landsteiner discovered the three types of blood groups which meant that safe and effective blood transfusions could be carried out.

1916 Sodium citrate was added to blood to prevent it clotting. This also meant that blood could be stored for several weeks.

Smarter Revision: Freeze-framed photos

exam BUSTERS

On page 37 we looked at how you can use a camera to help you remember the key features of a period or the work of an individual. You can also use this technique to explore change and continuity across a period. These students have produced freeze frames that sum up how surgery changed during the nineteenth century. They have collected or made their own props. These 'before and after' shots show the key changes that took place.

Activities

1. Can you spot the key changes that took place in surgery during the nineteenth century? On your own copy label the bottom photo to show what has changed.
2. Can you think of any changes or continuities that the students have missed? You may want to try to produce a better freeze frame.
3. Choose a different area of medicine; for example, public health or treatments. Produce two photos that show change and continuity across a period of your choice.

▼ BEFORE (Surgery at the start of the nineteenth century)

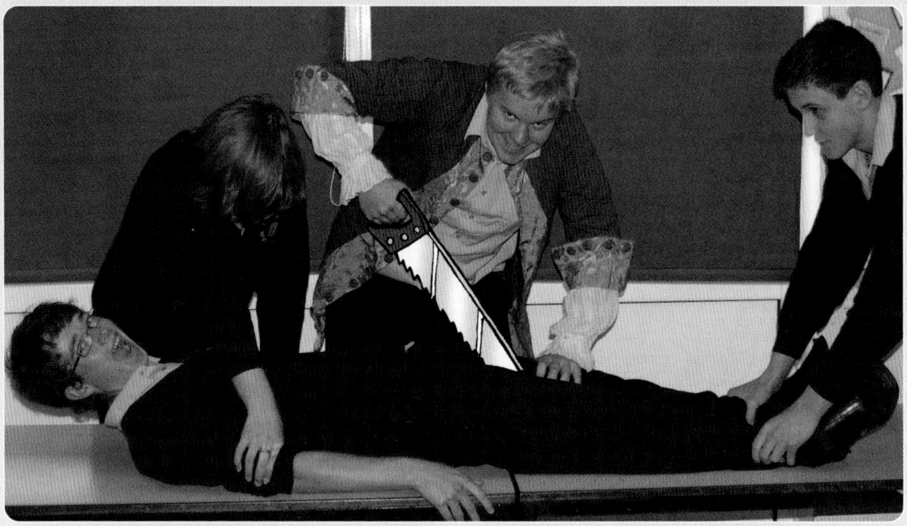

SAFETY WARNING

This activity was undertaken under the close supervision of the class teacher. In no circumstances use items such as a saw without close supervision and taking great care.

▼ AFTER (Surgery at the end of the nineteenth century)

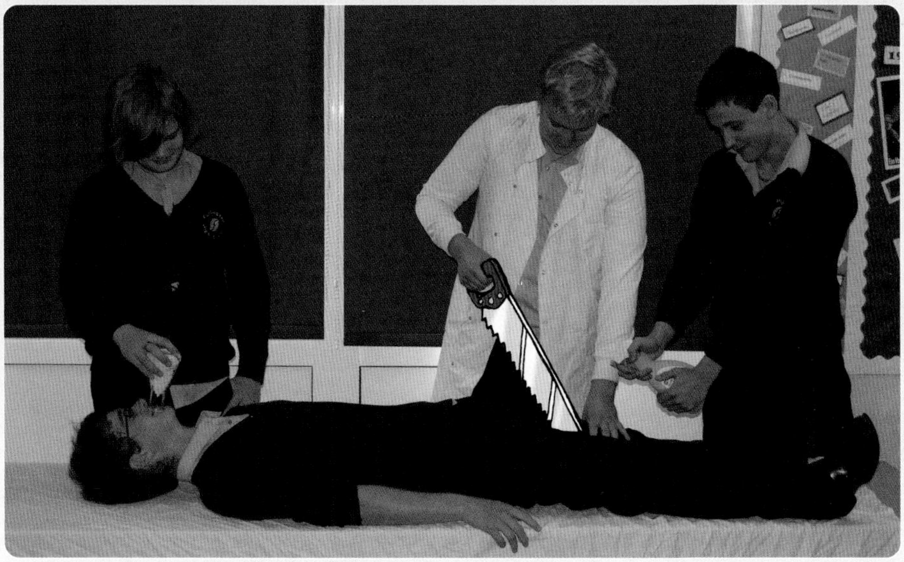

How were the first effective anaesthetics discovered?

The idea of time-travel can be quite attractive – until you go back before the 1850s. Before that you had to face up to pain, from having a tooth out to an amputation, without an effective anaesthetic. Many people having surgery simply died from the shock of the pain. Many more refused operations for fear of the pain. Therefore, the development of effective anaesthetics saved many thousands of lives. How did this great discovery happen – and why did many people oppose pain-free surgery?

Speed – the solution to pain in the early 1800s

Surgery in 1800 was little different from 2000 years earlier when the Roman author Celsus wrote: 'A surgeon should be filled with pity so that he wishes to cure the patient yet is not moved by his cries. He does everything just as if the cries of pain cause him no emotion.'

There were still no effective anaesthetics in the early 1800s. The patient was held down or tied down by the surgeon's assistants while the surgeon operated as quickly as possible. At the Battle of Borodino in 1812 Napoleon's surgeon, Dubois, amputated 200 limbs in 24 hours.

Because speed was the only way of reducing pain, surgeons were used to operating as speedily as possible. They prided themselves on their speed. Speed was one of the signs of a good surgeon. However, the development of effective anaesthetics from the 1840s onwards meant that speed was no longer so important and was a huge change for surgeons to get used to.

The pathway to effective anaesthetics

Step 1 'Laughing gas' (nitrous oxide)

Anaesthetics developed partly because of improved knowledge of chemistry. Scientists were finding that certain chemicals could have an effect on the human body. In 1799 Sir Humphry Davy discovered that 'laughing gas' (properly called nitrous oxide) reduced the sensation of pain. He suggested that it might be used in surgical operations and by dentists.

BUT

1 It did not make patients completely unconscious so was not a complete answer to the problem of pain.

2 An American dentist, Horace Wells, became convinced of the value of laughing gas after inhaling it at a fair. However, when he used it in a public demonstration his patient was in agony. This killed confidence in laughing gas as an anaesthetic.

Activities

1 Why was speed so essential to surgery in the early 1800s?
2 Take each of the three steps in turn. Why was each one a step forward?
3 How many reason for opposition can you find to put in the 'opposition basket'?
4 How did each of these factors help the development of anaesthetics?
   a science and technology
   b chance
   c individuals

Information

The dangers of speed!

Some surgeons became famous for their speed, although speed could also cause problems. Robert Liston, a famous London surgeon, once amputated a leg in two-and-a-half minutes but worked so fast that he accidentally cut off his patient's testicles as well. During another high-speed operation Liston amputated the fingers of his assistant and slashed the coat of a spectator who, fearing that he had been stabbed, dropped dead with fright. Both the assistant and the patient then died of infection caught during the operation or in the hospital ward.

Step 2 Ether

Source 1 describes the first successful operation using ether. A year later, in 1847, ether was used by J. R. Liston in London to anaesthetise a patient during a leg amputation.

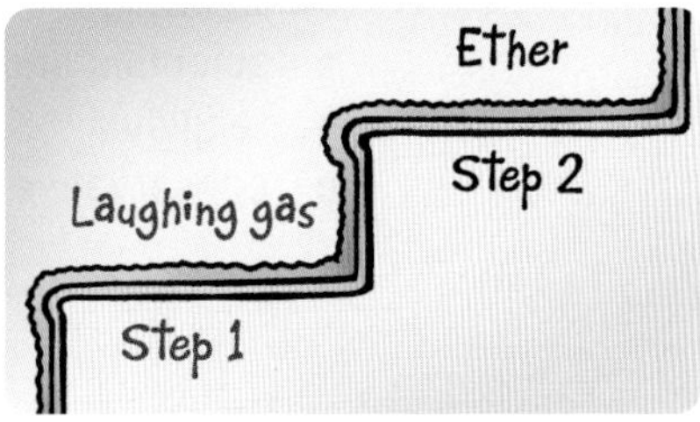

BUT

Ether had severe drawbacks as an anaesthetic. It irritated the eyes and lungs, causing coughing and sickness. It could catch fire if close to a flame and had a vile, clinging smell that took ages to go away. Finally, ether came in a large, heavy bottle that was difficult to carry around.

Source 1

An account of an operation to remove a neck tumour using ether as an anaesthetic by John Collins Warren, senior surgeon at Massachusetts General Hospital in the USA, in 1846:

'The patient was arranged for the operation in a sitting posture, and everything was made ready … The patient was then made to inhale a fluid from a tube with a glass globe. After four or five minutes he appeared to be asleep, and was thought by Dr Morton to be in a condition for the operation. I made an incision between two or three inches long in the direction of the tumour, and to my great surprise without any starting, crying, or other indication of pain.'

Step 3 Chloroform

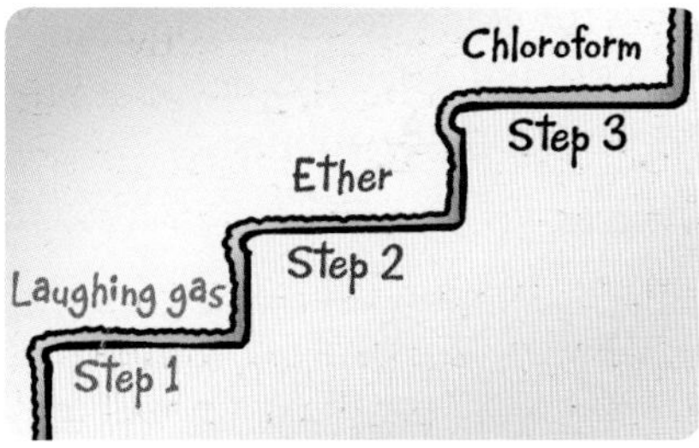

James Simpson was Professor of Midwifery at Edinburgh University. He had used ether but was searching for a better anaesthetic. One evening in 1847 he and several colleagues sat around a table experimenting with different chemicals to see what anaesthetic effects they had. Simpson wrote later, 'I poured some of the Chloroform fluid into tumblers in front of my assistants, Dr Keith and Dr Duncan, and myself. Before sitting down to supper we all inhaled the fluid, and were all "under the table" in a minute or two, to my wife's consternation and alarm.' Simpson realised that in chloroform he had discovered a very effective anaesthetic. Within days he started using it to help women in childbirth and in other operations. He wrote articles about his discovery and other surgeons started to use it in their operations.

Chloroform was the most effective anaesthetic yet discovered, but that didn't mean it was problem-free, as Source 3 shows.

Source 2

◄ Simpson and friends recovering from the effects of chloroform. A drawing made in 1857.

Source 3

Written by Margaret Matthewson of Shetland. In 1877 she went to Edinburgh for a shoulder operation. The surgeon, needing more time, gave her an extra large dose of chloroform. Afterwards she took 70 minutes to regain consciousness.

'I was conscious of no more until I awoke in a bed in a strange ward. My first thought was "My arm! Is it off or not?" I at once sat up to feel for it. I found it bandaged to my waist and breathed a sigh of thankfulness.

'I felt very sick and kept on vomiting … at intervals for several hours … I doubt it will be sometime ere I get over this horrid chloroform taste and its effects.'

Why was there opposition to chloroform?

Do you remember opposition to earlier medical developments?

- In 1800, Jenner's use of vaccination had been strongly criticised.
- In the 1600s, many doctors had refused to accept Harvey's theory of the circulation of the blood because it challenged Galen's ideas.
- In the Middle Ages, the Church had discouraged the whole idea of enquiry and new thinking.

So it is not surprising that even anaesthetics met opposition when first tried.

Activity

1 Look at the reasons for opposition to the use of chloroform below. Which reasons fit into each of these categories?
   a scientific and medical
   b religious
   c conservative attitudes

Reason 1

Chloroform was a new and untested gas. No one knew for sure if there would be long-term side effects on the bodies or minds of patients. They did not know what dose to give to different patients.

Reason 2

In 1848 Hannah Greener died while being given chloroform during an operation to remove her toenail. This first death from the use of chloroform scared surgeons and gave opponents of anaesthetics powerful evidence of their danger.

Reason 3

Anaesthetics did not necessarily make surgery safer. With a patient asleep, doctors attempted more complex operations, thus carrying infections deeper into the body and causing more loss of blood. The number of people dying from surgery may have increased after the discovery of anaesthetics. In the 1870s some surgeons stopped using chloroform as they were concerned about the high death rate (1 in 2500 operations) and returned to using ether mixed with nitrous oxide.

Reason 4

Letter to the medical journal *The Lancet* in 1849:

'The infliction [of pain] has been invented by the Almighty God. Pain may even be considered a blessing of the Gospel, and being blessed admits to being made either well or ill.'

Reason 5

Some people were particularly opposed to the idea of easing the pain of childbirth – believing that this would be unnatural. Letter to the medical journal *The Lancet* in 1853:

'It is a most unnatural practice. The pain and sorrow of labour exert a most powerful and useful influence upon the religious and moral character of women and upon all their future relations in life.'

Reason 6

A quotation from Army Chief of Medical Staff, 1854:

'... the smart use of the knife is a powerful stimulant and it is much better to hear a man bawl lustily than to see him sink silently into the grave.'

Why was opposition to chloroform overcome?

The debate over using anaesthetics continued, with anaesthetics gradually winning wider acceptance. James Simpson played a leading role. He used chloroform regularly and showed other doctors how it could be used safely. He also presented a powerful case for the use of chloroform as an anaesthetic, bringing Ambroise Paré to his defence.

The final breakthrough came when Queen Victoria accepted the use of chloroform during the delivery of her eighth child in 1857. She publicly praised 'that blessed chloroform'. The support of the queen meant opposition to anaesthetics was doomed.

However, this does not mean that all problems were now solved, as you saw in Reason 3 opposite. The 1870s is known as the 'Black period' in surgery because of the increased death rate but over time the use of anaesthetics improved. Other chemicals were used which relaxed muscles as well as simply putting patients to sleep. New chemicals also had fewer side-effects than chloroform. Local anaesthetics were developed as well as general anaesthetics. This took time – but Simpson's use of chloroform had been the key turning point.

Source 1

James Simpson speaking to a meeting of doctors in Edinburgh in 1847:

'Before the sixteenth century surgeons had no way of stemming the flow of blood after amputation of a limb other than by scorching with a red hot iron or boiling pitch. The great suggestion of Ambroise Paré, to shut up the bleeding vessels by tying them, was a vast improvement. It saved the sufferings of the patient while adding to their safety. But the practice was new, and like all innovations in medical practice, it was at first and for long, bitterly decried … attacked … suppressed.

'We look back with sorrow on the opponents of Paré. Our successors in years to come will look back with similar feelings. They will marvel at the idea of humane men confessing that they prefer operating on their patients in a waking instead of an anaesthetic state, and that the fearful agonies that they inflict should be endured quietly. All pain is destructive and even fatal in its effects.'

Source 2

Activities

2 List the reasons why anaesthetics became commonly used.

3 Which of these reasons do you think were most important?

4 **a** When do you think Source 2 was published?

b What does Source 2 suggest about attitudes to surgery at that time? Use the source and your knowledge to answer the question.

Source 3

▲ James Simpson

Why was there opposition to antiseptics?

Infection – the biggest danger in surgery

The idea of operations without anaesthetics is dramatic and horrible. Such operations did kill patients because the shock of the incision could kill. However, many more patients survived the operation but then died from something much less dramatic – infection. Doctors had used liquids such as wine and vinegar to keep wounds clean for centuries but, before Pasteur's germ theory, no-one knew what was causing infection in open wounds. That was why surgeons did things that seem obviously dangerous today. They reused bandages, spreading gangrene and skin infections from patient to patient. They did not wash their hands before an operation, nor did they sterilise their equipment, and some operated wearing old pus-stained clothes. This was how they had carried out operations for years. It was what they were used to.

A false start – the 'crazy' ideas of Ignaz Semmelweiss

The notice in Source 1 was placed by Dr Semmelweiss at the entrance to the maternity ward in the General Hospital in Vienna in 1847. It was so unusual that other doctors called him a crank and a fanatic and said that he was mentally unstable. Semmelweiss put up the notice because he was worried by the deaths of healthy women after childbirth. Most doctors regarded this as inevitable but Semmelweiss realised that women whose babies were delivered by midwives were much less likely to die from infection than women whose babies were delivered by medical students. He believed the reason was that medical students came straight to the delivery rooms from dissecting dead bodies. If they simply washed their hands, he thought, they would reduce the risk of infection to women. Semmelweiss pursued his crusade with great passion, calling doctors who did not wash their hands 'murderers'. Unfortunately he had little support and no-one built on his ideas.

Joseph Lister and the wonders of carbolic acid

Source 2

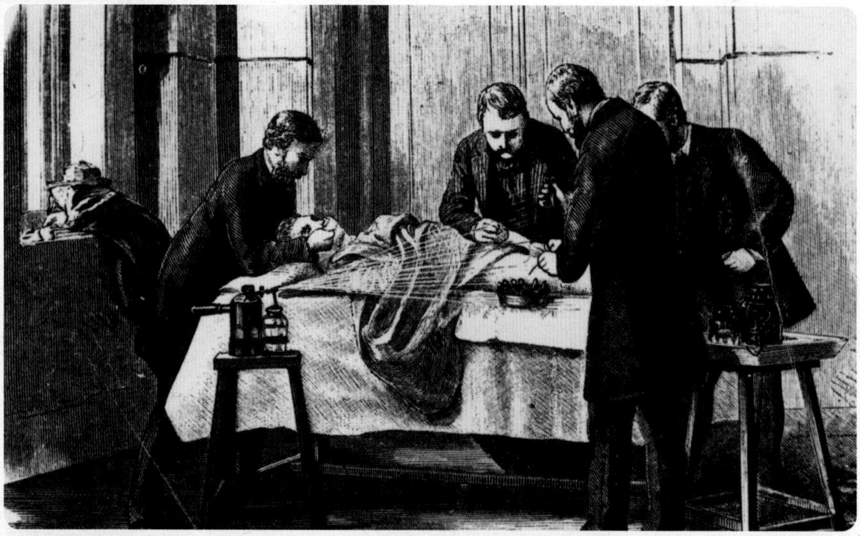

▲ An operation taking place while a carbolic spray disinfects the area. One assistant is using chloroform to anaesthetise the patient, another is mopping up blood with a sponge.

Activities

1 a What was Semmelweiss's method of stopping infection spreading?
  b Why was he ignored by other doctors?
  c Which medical discovery of the 1860s would have helped Semmelweiss convince others?
2 What was Lister's solution to the problem of infection?
3 How did Lister come to try his solution for tackling infection?
4 How many reasons for opposition can you find to put in the 'opposition basket'?

Source 1

From today, 15 May 1847, any doctor or student coming from the postmortem room must, before entering the maternity wards, wash his hands thoroughly in the basin of chlorinated water placed at the entrance. This order applies to everyone, without exception.

Where did his idea of **stopping infection** come from?

Joseph Lister's use of carbolic acid to prevent infection was as important a turning point as Simpson's use of chloroform. Lister was one of the outstanding surgeons of the nineteenth century. He had researched gangrene and infection, and had a keen interest in the application of science to medicine. That was why he knew all about Pasteur's work on germ theory, which helped to spark the idea for his own discovery.

▲ This meeting and conversation never happened but this drawing shows you how their ideas were linked.

Where did the idea of using **carbolic** come from?

The answer is sewage, as Lister described (see Source 3). He experimented with using carbolic in treating people who had compound fractures where the bone breaks through the skin. Infection often developed in these open wounds. Lister applied carbolic acid to the wound and used bandages soaked in carbolic. He found that the wounds healed and did not develop gangrene.

Source 3

Lister's description of how the idea of using carbolic developed:

'In 1864 I was struck by an account of the remarkable effects of using carbolic acid upon the sewage of Carlisle. It prevented all odour from the lands covered by the sewage and destroyed the parasites that usually infest cattle feeding on such land. The idea of using carbolic acid for the treatment of open fractures naturally occurred to me.'

Source 4

Joseph Lister, *On the New Method of Treating Compound Fracture*, 1867:

'James, aged 11 years, was admitted to the Glasgow Infirmary on August 2, 1865, with compound fracture of the left leg caused by the wheel of an empty cart passing over the limb a little below the middle. The wound, an inch and a half long and three quarters of an inch broad, was over the line of the fracture.

'A piece of lint dipped in carbolic acid was laid on the wound, and splints padded with cotton wool were applied. It was left undisturbed for four days and, when examined, it showed no sign of suppuration. For the next four days the wound was dressed with lint soaked with a solution of water and carbolic acid and olive oil which further prevented irritation to the skin. No pus was present, there seemed no danger of infection, and at the end of six weeks I found the bones united, and I discarded the splints. The sore was entirely healed.'

Source 5

From Lister's own record of amputations:

	Total amputations	Died	Percentage who died
1864–1866 (without antiseptics)	35	16	45.7
1867–1870 (with antiseptics)	40	6	15.0

Activity

5 Before you turn the page, using all you have found out about opposition to medical developments, list possible reasons why surgeons might oppose Lister's use of carbolic spray during operations.

Why was Lister's use of carbolic acid opposed?

In 1867 Lister published his results, showing the value of using carbolic acid. He also worked at improving his method:

Improvement 1
Handwashing with carbolic before operations to avoid infections getting into wounds.

Improvement 2
A carbolic spray to kill germs in the air around the operating table.

Improvement 3
An antiseptic ligature to tie up blood vessels and prevent blood loss.

Activities

1 Look at the reasons for opposition to the use of carbolic acid below. Which reasons fit into each of these categories?
   a Scientific
   b Conservative attitudes
   c Lister himself
2 How did the work of Koch help persuade doctors to follow Lister's ideas?

Reason 1

Lister's carbolic spray, which soaked the operating theatre, seemed very extreme. It cracked the surgeon's skin and made everything smell. The new precautions caused extra work, and made operations more expensive and less pleasant for the surgeons. One doctor wrote:

'The whole scene of an operation was covered in carbolic spray which dispersed its globules into every nook and cranny of the wound. Our faces and coat-sleeves often dripped with it. It was a relief to us all when the spray was abandoned. It was costly and cumbersome and often broke down.'

Reason 2

Despite anaesthetics, surgeons were still convinced that speed was essential in an operation – often because of the problem of bleeding. It seemed that Lister's antiseptic methods just slowed operations down.

Reason 3

When some surgeons did try copying Lister's methods they did not achieve the same results. This was usually because they were less systematic, but that didn't stop them criticising Lister. Others argued that antiseptics actually prevented the body's own defence mechanisms from operating effectively.

Reason 4

Pasteur's ideas had spread very slowly. Even trained surgeons found it difficult to accept that there were tiny micro-organisms all around which could cause disease.

One surgeon regularly joked with his assistants that they should shut the door of the operating theatre in case one of Mr Lister's microbes flew in.

Reason 5

For many centuries surgeons had lived with the idea that many of their patients would die. When Lister said he achieved good results, their first reaction was disbelief. For many the next reaction was to feel defensive, that Lister was criticising them for letting patients down.

Reason 6

Lister was not a showman like Pasteur. He did not give impressive public displays. Indeed, he appeared to be cold, arrogant and aloof and was sometimes critical of other surgeons. Many surgeons regarded him as a fanatic.

Reason 7

Lister was always changing his techniques. He did this because he wanted to find a substance that would work equally as well as carbolic spray, but without the corrosion that it caused. His critics simply said he was changing his methods because they did not work.

How did Lister help to change surgery?

Despite opposition, Lister's methods marked a turning point in surgery. In 1877 he moved to London to train young surgeons. Then came a link to another great name in medical history. In 1878 Robert Koch discovered the bacterium which caused septicaemia (blood poisoning). This gave a great boost to Lister's ideas.

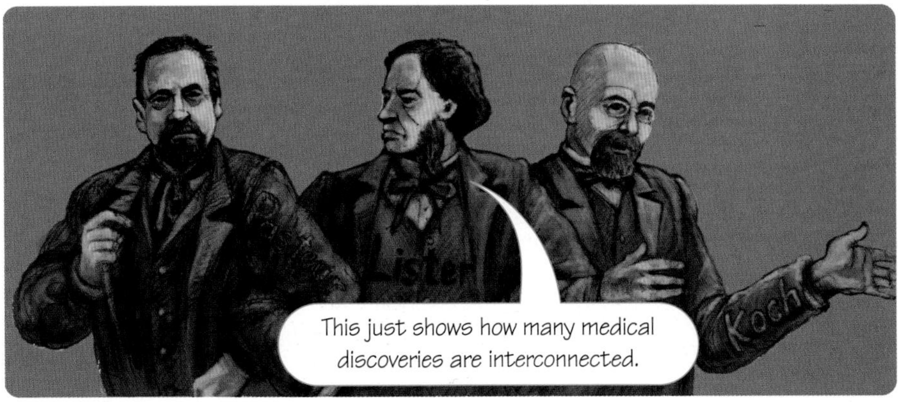

▲ In 1892 Lister and Pasteur were together given an award at the Sorbonne University in Paris for their contribution to the fight against disease. Koch learned from both of them, and also spurred them on to new discoveries.

Aseptic surgery

By the late 1890s Lister's antiseptic methods (which killed germs on the wound) developed into aseptic surgery, which meant removing all possible germs from the operating theatre. To ensure absolute cleanliness:

- Operating theatres and hospitals were rigorously cleaned.
- From 1887 all instruments were steam-sterilised.
- Surgeons abandoned operating in their ordinary clothes and wore surgical gowns and face masks.
- In 1894, sterilised rubber gloves were used for the first time. For, however well surgeons' hands were scrubbed, they could still hold bacteria in the folds of skin and under the nails.

Activities

3 How did conditions in operating theatres change after the 1880s to reduce infections?

4 How did a love story help to make operations safer?

More ambitious operations

With two of the basic problems of surgery now solved, surgeons attempted more ambitious operations.

- The first successful operation to remove an infected appendix came in the 1880s.
- The first heart operation was carried out in 1896 when surgeons repaired a heart damaged by a stab wound.

Simpson and Lister had made a major contribution. Their achievements helped make such operations possible.

William Halsted – a medical love story that made operations safer

In 1889 Caroline Hampton, an operating theatre nurse in America, developed a skin infection from the chemicals used to disinfect hands before operations. She showed her hands to the chief surgeon, William Halsted, and he arranged for the Goodyear Rubber Company to make a pair of thin rubber gloves to protect Caroline's hands. Within a year the nurse and the surgeon were married – and Halsted spread the idea of wearing rubber gloves during operations. He went on to become one of America's most famous surgeons, responsible for many new developments.

8.2 Why has surgery improved so much since 1900?

By 1900 doctors had gone a long way to solving the problems of pain and infection, two of the three major problems facing surgeons. The major problem remaining was bleeding – how to stop heavy blood loss. This problem was solved in the early 1900s, and many other surgical developments followed. This enquiry returns to the factor hunt and considers why surgery has changed so dramatically.

Why has surgery changed so dramatically?

Which team should win this tug-of-war? The Science and Technology team or the War team? Your task is to use the information on pages 180–183 to decide which developments in surgery belong on which team and who is pulling harder.

But before you start – think back over the history of surgery. Which factor has had the bigger impact on surgery in the past?

Activities

Step 1: Choose the teams
On pages 180–183 you can find out about eight developments in surgery since 1900. Each one could be on the War team or the Science and Technology team. Your first job is to decide which team each development is on.

Step 2: Look at the team members
Not everyone on a team is as skilled or as heavy as everyone else – so which of the developments do you think were most important in the development of surgery? Give the ones that you think were most important a double-strength pull.

Step 3: Look for other factors
Were war and science and technology the only factors helping the development of surgery since 1900? Did you spot any more?

Step 4: Debate the result
Decide which team you think has won the tug-of-war and write a speech explaining your choice and the evidence for your choice. Make sure you include at least one point that shows the weakness in the opposition argument. Now debate the result with your class.

Developments in surgery since 1900

Information

Development 1: X-rays

A German scientist, Wilhelm Röntgen, was carrying out experiments in 1895 when he realised that rays of light in a covered tube were lighting up a far wall. They could pass through black paper, wood and flesh. He did not know what they were so he called them X-rays. Within months of Röntgen publishing his discovery, the first X-ray machines were being used in hospitals to identify diseases and broken bones.

World War One had a major impact on the common use of X-rays. Surgeons needed to locate bullets and shrapnel lodged deep within wounded men and X-rays provided the answer. Governments ordered the making of many more X-ray machines and they were installed in all major hospitals on the Western Front.

In France, the scientist Marie Curie (see below) persuaded the government to pay for mobile X-ray machines that could be transported round the battlefronts. These became known among grateful soldiers as 'petite curies' – little Curies.

▲ A portable X-ray machine, a 'petite curie', from World War One.

Information

Development 2: Marie Curie and radiation therapy

Radiation therapy (or radiotherapy as it is also called) developed closely from Röntgen's discovery of X-rays through the work of the Polish scientist Marie Curie, together with her French husband, Pierre. In the process of researching the use of X-rays, they noticed that the skin on their hands was being burned by the material they were handling. They investigated this further and this led to the discovery of radium, which has been used ever since to diagnose cancers and in radiotherapy to treat cancers, often reducing the need for surgery. Their research was the beginning of the modern treatment of cancers. As the research continued, it became so complex that they built up a team of research scientists to share ideas. Marie Curie is the only woman to have won two Nobel Prizes, for her work on X-rays and on radium.

▲ Marie Curie (1867–1934), photographed with her daughter, Irene, in 1920. Marie Curie died of leukaemia, contracted from the radioactive material she handled as an essential part of her work.

Information

Development 3: Fighting infection and disease

Lister had begun the fight against infection, but wartime wounds caused problems that needed new solutions. Many wounds were very deep and bullets carried fragments of clothing carrying bacteria deep inside the body. This caused very deep infections. Gradually, through practice and trying out new methods on thousands of cases, surgeons learned to cut away the infected tissue and protect the body with a saline solution. However, it was the development of penicillin in World War Two (see page 127) that provided the real breakthrough in fighting infection successfully.

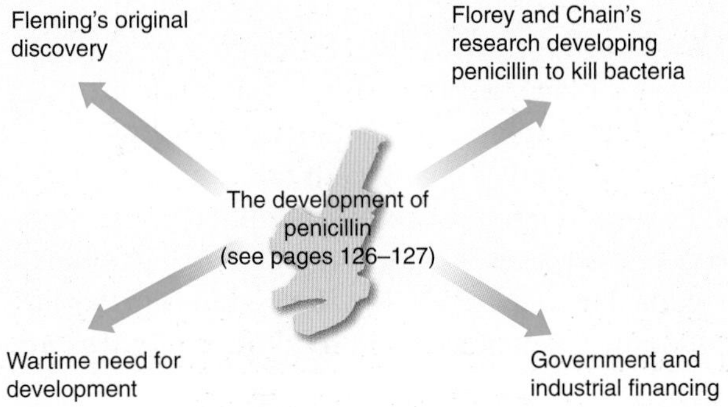

▲ Only war led to the mass production of penicillin shown here.

Information

Development 4: Blood transfusions

Blood transfusions were often attempted in the 1800s. Sometimes they worked. Mostly they did not. Nobody knew why. Then in 1901, Karl Landsteiner discovered the existence of blood groups. After this, blood transfusions became possible, provided the patient and the donor were in the same place. When doctors tried to store blood, it clotted and could not be used for transfusions.

The problem of storing blood was solved during World War One. There was a huge need for blood and many soldiers bled to death because there was no store of blood to use. Two breakthroughs solved this problem. Firstly, sodium citrate was added to blood to prevent it clotting. Later in the war, scientists discovered how to separate and store the crucial blood cells and keep them in bottles for future use. This made possible the huge blood banks that supply blood today.

▲ Attempts at blood transfusion had been made since Harvey had discovered the circulation of the blood. These sometimes involved trying to move blood from one animal to another or even, as you can see in this seventeenth century drawing, from a lamb to a man.

Information

Development 5: Plastic surgery

Plastic surgery had been carried out in India centuries earlier, but was always limited by pain and the danger of infection. The terrible injuries of both World Wars led to a rapid improvement in techniques, especially the use of skin grafts. In World War One, the injuries were mostly from bullet and shell damage. Surgeons carried out over 11,000 plastic surgery operations, increasing their experience and learning from each other. In World War Two, there were many more burns cases in tanks and aeroplanes. Archibald McIndoe alone carried out 4000 operations on burns cases.

▲ An aeroplane burns after crashing. One of the pilots survived, though he was badly injured.

Archibald McIndoe (1900–1960)

McIndoe was a New Zealander who studied at home and then in America before coming to England in 1930. His cousin Sir Harold Gillies, a pioneer plastic surgeon in World War One, encouraged McIndoe to work in plastic surgery. In 1938, he became Consultant in Plastic Surgery to the Royal Air Force and so was ready and well-placed to help the many airmen who suffered terrible burns during the Battle of Britain and throughout World War Two. He used skin grafts to reconstruct faces and hands seemingly destroyed by fire, and also helped his patients psychologically to deal with the great changes in their appearance and the horrors they had been through. He even helped some of his patients financially to start life again as civilians. His patients were devoted to him, setting up The Guinea Pig Club, open to all those he treated.

Information

Development 6: Transplant surgery

The first heart transplant was carried out in South Africa in 1967. Other organs had been transplanted before then (kidneys in 1954 and liver in 1963) and since then even more ambitious transplants have been carried out including the first marrow transplant in 1980, and first heart and lung transplant in 1982. All depend on high levels of technical skill and the scientific breakthroughs that make transplants possible. For example, before transplants could be successful, scientists had to first discover drugs to stop the body rejecting organs, and then 'tissue-typing' which (like blood groups) matches organs to suitable recipients.

Christiaan Barnard (1922–2001)

This South African heart surgeon became famous for carrying out the world's first heart transplant in 1967. In reality, Barnard did not work alone but headed a team of highly skilled and experienced doctors, nurses and scientists. The patient died after 18 days, but much had been learned and since then many successful heart transplants have been performed.

Information

Development 7: Improved anaesthetics

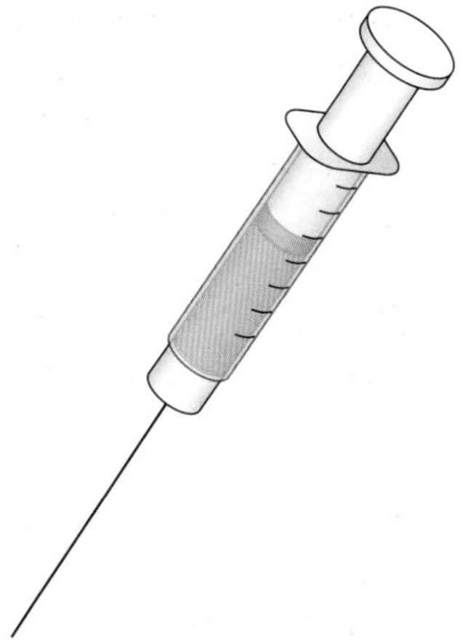

Anaesthetics in the later 1800s had to be inhaled through nose and mouth. This made it difficult to control the dosage. Surgeons had to err on the side of caution for fear of killing a patient, so still tended to operate as fast as they could. In the 1930s, Helmuth Wesse developed anaesthetics that could be injected into the blood stream, allowing more precise control of doses and, therefore, improving safety and enabling longer operations.

Nowadays, local anaesthetics are so effective that patients can even have major operations such as hip-replacements without going to sleep at all, as this description of a hip replacement shows – the patient stayed awake throughout!

'The two hour operation to replace the ball and socket of my left hip took place without a general anaesthetic. I had had a local anaesthetic in my lower back so I could feel nothing. I lay on my right side with a strap to stop me rolling over. Throughout the operation I was able to watch my heart rate on a machine near my head. There was a sheet between me and the surgeon but throughout the operation the surgeon told me what he was about to do next. For example, "Now I will saw through your femur" and I heard the electric saw cutting through me. I saw the nurses carry in my new ball and socket, and I felt my body being stretched when the consultant asked people to help with the traction. One advantage of not having a full anaesthetic was that I did not have the danger of an adverse reaction to the anaesthetic and I was able to recover much more quickly because the effects of anaesthetic can remain in one's system for weeks and even months.'

Information

Development 8: Keyhole and micro-surgery

Once upon a time, major surgery required surgeons to make large cuts into the body. Nowadays, such large incisions are avoided as often as possible and in some universities there are 'Departments of minimally-invasive surgery', meaning that surgeons cut into the body through a tiny hole – this is what they mean by 'keyhole surgery'. This has become possible because of a range of technological developments involving computers and miniaturisation. All the tools needed are inside an instrument called an endoscope controlled by the surgeon using miniature cameras, fibre-optic cables and computers.

Micro-surgery has also developed because of improvements in technology. Surgeons can now rejoin blood vessels and nerves, restoring the use of damaged limbs and can also re-attach severed limbs.

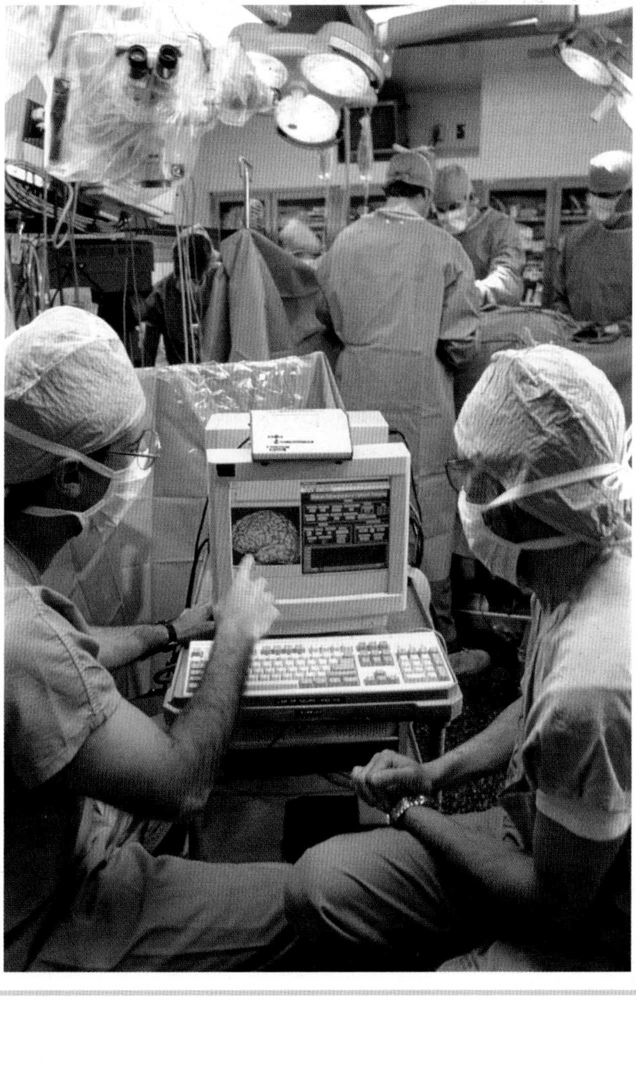

Surgeons using reflected light to measure changes in the brain during surgery, allowing them to distinguish between healthy and diseased tissue. ▶

Meet the Examiner: How to improve that answer!

By now you should feel like an expert on surgery and feel confident that you know how to approach the different types of exam questions. This 'Meet the Examiner' page is different. You will not get advice from the examiner … you are the examiner!

Activities

1 How would you advise students to tackle question 1(a)?
   a What are the key do's and don'ts on answering this kind of question? Use pages 76–77 to help you.
   b What should they include in their answer?
   You could record your advice on tape to help with revision.

2 Read the answer to question 1(b). The strengths of the answer have been highlighted. Advise the student on how to improve the answer.

1 (a) Choose **one** of the factors below that have affected the development of surgery in the twentieth century.

- War
- Science and Technology

Describe the effects of that factor on the development of surgery in the twentieth century. *(4 marks)*

(b) Which factor has contributed more to the development of surgery in the twentieth century? Explain your answer. *(8 marks)*

1(b) The First World War led to many improvements in surgery. During the war X-rays became widely used for the first time. They were used to find bullets deep in the body. The war also created a need for better ways to carry out blood transfusions. Before the war these were carried out with on the spot donors because doctors had no way of storing blood properly. During the First World War large amounts of blood were needed and this method was not practical. This led to new methods of storing blood being developed. Doctors discovered that tiny cells in the blood could be bottled, packed in ice and stored where needed.

The war also created a need to develop new methods to prevent infection during surgery. By trial and error, surgeons developed new techniques. They cut away infected tissue and soaked the wound with a saline solution. During the First World War surgeons were faced with hundreds of thousands of casualties. This meant that they had to learn fast and had the opportunity to practise new techniques. For example, surgeons developed new techniques for repairing broken bones. They also improved methods of grafting skin which led to the development of plastic surgery. The Second World War also led to improvements in surgery. During the twentieth century there have been big improvements in surgery. War was the key factor that led to change.

The student **explains** that the war provided the need for change.

The student **proves** that changes took place during the war – by briefly referring to the situation before the war.

The student **links** things that happened during the war to changes in surgery.

The student provides **specific examples** to support their points.

How to answer comparison questions – part 3

Comparing developments in different periods

1 (a) Choose **one** of the historical periods below.
- The nineteenth century
- The twentieth century

What were the main developments in surgery at that time? *(4 marks)*

(b) In which period was there the most improvement in surgery? Explain your answer. *(8 marks)*

Another type of comparison question asks you to compare developments in two historical periods. To answer these questions effectively, you need to think about the **significance** of developments, not just how many developments took place.

Look at the list of surgical developments below. There are six developments from the twentieth century compared to three from the nineteenth century. However, does this mean that developments in surgery in the twentieth century were more important than those in the nineteenth century?

1 You need to consider <u>how important</u> each change was. Imagine that you are putting each development on a set of scales – some will weigh more than others.

Develop your own weighting system to evaluate the changes that took place in each century. You could, for example, give developments that solved major, long-lasting problems a weighting of 4, and developments that simply built on past discoveries a weighting of 1. You could also develop a chart like this one.

Development	Weighting	Explanation

2 As well as evaluating specific developments, you can also **use your knowledge of the big picture of surgery**.
- Had the major problems in surgery begun to be solved by 1900?
- What was really new about developments in the twentieth century?

3 Now plan and write your answers to both parts of question 1 above.

1840s	1860s	1895	1900s	1914–1918	1939–1945	1950s	1970s	1980s
Simpson uses chloroform as anaesthetic	Lister uses carbolic acid as effective antiseptic	Discovery of X-rays	Discovery of blood groups and development of blood transfusion	Use of X-ray machines in wartime	McIndoe makes further improvments in plastic surgery	Improved antiseptics and use of penicillin to fight post-surgery infection	First heart transplant	Keyhole and micro-surgery

Surgery and anatomy: A summary

Now you have completed the story of surgery and anatomy across the centuries. This timeline shows you the key developments. Your task is to tell the story – accurately and interestingly!

Activity

1 On pages 6–7, you began a graph recording the pattern of developments in surgery and anatomy. Use this timeline to check and complete your graph.

The timeline below is not to chronological scale.

	Ancient World	Middle Ages	Renaissance	
How did they deal with PAIN? (anaesthetics)	 Herbal drinks e.g.opium, mandrake, hemlock, alcohol	Speed of surgery/tying or holding down the patient		
How did they deal with INFECTION? (anaesthetics)	Honey, vinegar, wine	Honey, wine → Vinegar →	Boiling oil for gunshot wounds Paré's oil instead of boiling oil	
How did they deal with blood loss?		Red hot cauteries closed wounds	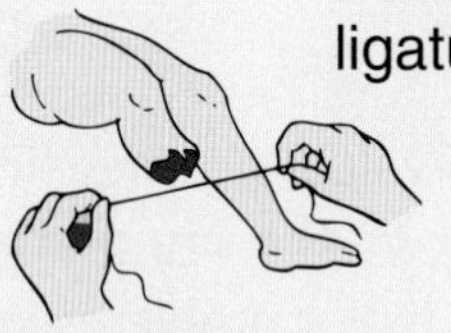 Paré's ligatures	
What did they know about anatomy?	Aristotle and importance of heart and brain Galen – dissect human bodies if possible Knowledge of major organs and bones 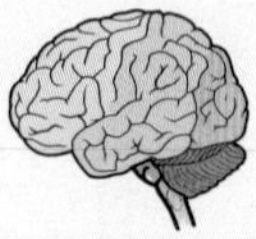		Vesalius published research Harvey – circulation of blood	
Types of surgery/ equipment	Setting broken bones Trephining Sewing cuts	 Bleeding Amputations	Setting broken bones trephining sewing cuts amputations bleeding	

Activity

2 Work in a group of three. You are going to have up to three minutes to tell the story of surgery and anatomy. Spend twenty minutes preparing your story. If your teacher gives you more preparation time, think about how to enliven the story with visuals and props. Your story must include answers to the following questions:

a How would you describe the pattern of continuity and change over time? Think about when there was long-lasting continuity and when there was rapid change.

b Why was there so little change in surgery for so many centuries?

c What were the most important changes in surgery and why did they happen when they did?

d How does the pace of change and the nature of developments now compare with the past?

	1800s	1900s and after
	Nitrous oxide Ether  Chloroform (Simpson)	Use of wide range of chemicals Development of local as well as general anaesthetics
	Semmelwiss – washing hands  Lister – carbolic acid/sprays	Use of steam sterilising, operating gowns, rubber gloves 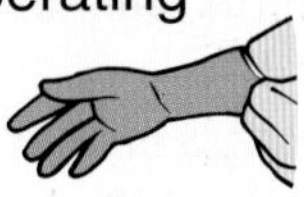 Development of antiseptic and aseptic surgery
	Ligatures more effective used in combination with antiseptics	Discovery of blood groups (Landsteiner) and transfusions Methods of storing blood supplies
	Increased focus on dissection and training doctors Increasingly detailed discoveries using better microscopes etc. 	Discovery of DNA
	Deeper, lengthier surgery e.g. removal of appendix Microscopes	Keyhole and microsurgery Plastic surgery Transplants X-rays  Radiotherapy

Section 9: Is Florence Nightingale the only woman in medicine worth remembering?

Women have almost disappeared from the last three sections. After centuries of trying to keep women out of medicine, men had succeeded by the early 1800s, but it was a short-lived success. By 1900, women were starting to play more important roles. One woman from this period is very famous – Florence Nightingale. Your task is to decide whether she is the only woman in medicine worth remembering.

How difficult was it for women to make an impact on medicine?

Until the 1700s, women had been able to qualify as surgeons and midwives, as well as playing the main role in everyday medicine as mothers and wisewomen. However, they were never allowed to become physicians as that required university training – and women were not allowed to go to university. In the 1800s, men even succeeded in preventing women from qualifying as surgeons and midwives, however good their practical skills.

Source 1

Some memorials put up to women healers:

Margaret Colfe. Having been above forty years a willing nurse, midwife, surgeon and, in part, physician to all both rich and poor, without expecting reward. (Lewisham, 1643)

Prudence Potter. Her life was spent in the industrious and successful practice of physic, surgery and midwifery. (Devon, 1689)

Dorothy Burton. Has excellent skill in surgery, sore eyes, aches etc and has done many famous good cures upon poor folks that were otherwise destitute of help. (1629)

Source 2

Thomas Huxley, a leading scientist, in 1851:

'In every excellent characteristic, whether mental or physical, the average woman is inferior to the average man.'

Activities

1 In a few words, sum up the attitudes to women in:
  a Source 1
  b Sources 2, 3 and 4.

2 Use pages 189–195 to complete the table below to explain why each of these women is worth remembering for her contribution to medicine.

	Impact – how many people were helped or hindered by their work?	Change – how did their work affect medicine or the sick or other women?	Longevity – how long did their impact last?
Florence Nightingale			
Elizabeth Blackwell and Elizabeth Garrett Anderson			
Mary Seacole			

Source 3

'An ideal woman' as described by the novelist W.M. Thackeray in the 1850s:

'An exquisite slave: a humble, flattering, tea-making, pianoforte-playing being who laughs at our jokes, however old they may be.'

Source 4

A statement by students (all male) at Middlesex Hospital, London, protesting against Elizabeth Garrett attending lectures in 1861:

'We consider that the mix of the sexes in the same class is likely to lead to results of an unpleasant nature. Lecturers are likely to feel some restraint through the presence of females in giving that explicit enunciation of some facts which is necessary. The presence of young females as spectators in the operating theatre is an outrage on our natural instincts and feelings.'

What were hospitals like in the early 1800s?

Source 5

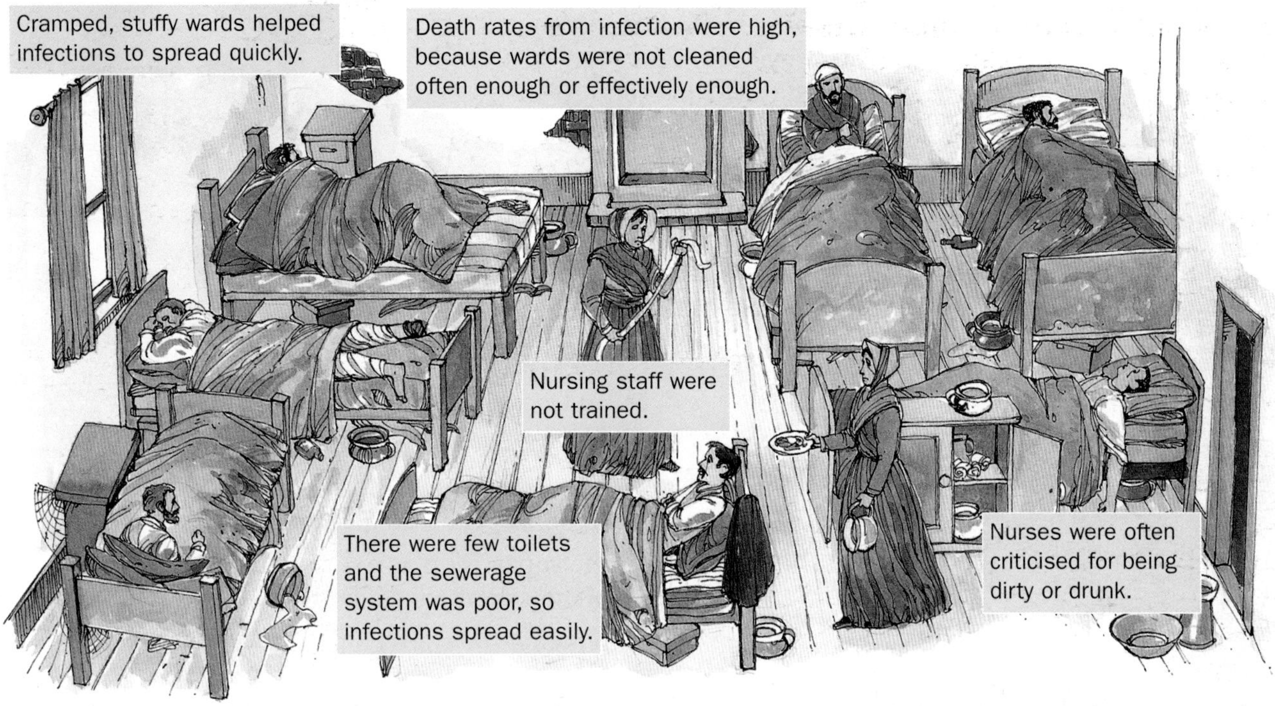

▲ Dangers to health in hospital wards in the early 1800s

This is what hospitals were like in the days before Pasteur, Lister – and Nightingale. For many people, hospitals were the places they went to die – if not from the disease they had when they went in, then from another disease they caught on the wards. Anyone who had the money paid for nurses and doctors to visit them at home. Even operations were carried out at home because home seemed a healthier place than a hospital ward.

Source 6

An extract from *Martin Chuzzlewit*, a novel by Charles Dickens, published in 1844. In this extract, the nurse, Betsy Prig, is handing her patient over to the care of another nurse, Sarah Gamp. Dickens wrote in his introduction to this novel that 'Mrs Betsy Prig is an accurate description of a hospital nurse':

'"How are we?" asked Mrs Gamp. Mrs Prig said, "He's as cross as two sticks. He wouldn't have washed if he'd had his own way."

"She put soap in my mouth," said the unfortunate patient, feebly.

"Couldn't you keep it shut then?" said Mrs Prig.

Mrs Prig seized the patient by the chin and began to scrape his unhappy head with the hair brush. The brush was the hardest possible instrument and his eye-lids were red with the pain.

Then Mrs Gamp and Mrs Prig put on his coat.

"I don't think it's quite right" said the poor invalid. "There's a bottle in my pocket. Why have you made me sit on a bottle?"

"Oh" cried Mrs Gamp, "he's got my gin bottle. I put it in his coat when it hung behind the door."'

Activities

3 Using Sources 5 and 6, make a list of the reforms that were needed to improve hospitals and nursing.

4 Which developments in Sections 6, 7 and 8 do you think may have helped to improve hospital wards?

5 Use what you learned on the opposite page. How difficult would it be for any woman to play a major part in changing conditions in hospitals?

Florence Nightingale (1820–1910)

Florence horrified her wealthy family by wanting to be a nurse. After many arguments she had her way, training in Germany before returning to Britain to work as a nurse, and eventually becoming Superintendent of Nurses in a London hospital. When the Crimean War broke out in 1854, she heard reports of the terrible conditions in the Crimea and so she talked to the Minister for War, Sidney Herbert, a family friend. He arranged for her to take 38 nurses to the Crimea.

In the Crimea

Arriving at the army hospital at Scutari, Florence was appalled by the dirty conditions. She concentrated on cleaning the hospital and patients. She wrote back to the British government:

- 25 November 1854

'It appears that in these [army] hospitals the washing of linen and of the men are considered a minor detail. No washing has been performed for the men or the beds – except by ourselves. When we came here, there was no soap or basins or towels in the wards. The consequences of all this are fever, cholera, gangrene, lice … Two or three hundred arm-slings, stump-pillows and other medical appliances are being weekly manufactured and given out by us. No arrangement seems to have been made to do this before.'

- 10 December 1854

'What we have achieved:

- a great deal more cleaning of wards – mops, scrubbing brushes given out by ourselves
- the supervision and stirring up of the whole organisation generally
- repair of the wards for 800 wounded.'

The death rate in the hospital fell from 40 per cent of wounded to 2 per cent. Florence and her nurses worked at the hospital rather than visiting the front line of fighting.

Source 1

◀ A painting from 1855, showing Florence Nightingale in Scutari Hospital. Newspapers began to call her 'the lady with the lamp' because it was claimed that she walked the wards at night making sure wounded soldiers were comfortable.

The impact of Florence Nightingale

Florence returned to Britain a national heroine and this helped her raise money to set up her first nursing school. She was not a hands-on nurse, but a great organiser convinced that her life's work was to improve conditions in hospitals and training of nurses for the good of the patients. Those skills and beliefs were visible in the Crimea where she concentrated on improving hygiene and cleanliness. She continued to focus on these aspects of care throughout her life. In 1859, she wrote her book *Notes on Nursing*, and in 1863 *Notes on Hospitals*. Both books were very influential all over the world, providing the basis for training nurses and hospital design.

One surprising thing about her was that she paid little attention to Pasteur's germ theory when it appeared in the decade *after* the Crimean War. Like Chadwick, she had been brought up in the early 1800s, when miasma (bad air) was the main theory about what caused disease. She continued to associate disease with dirt and this is why she concentrated on improving:

- sanitation in hospitals – clean water supplies, good drains and sewers, toilet facilities, total cleanliness
- good ventilation in hospitals to make sure patients got fresh, clean air to breathe
- food supplies, clothing and washing facilities for patients.

As a result, her nursing schools concentrated on training nurses in very practical skills. She did not let doctors teach nurses about germ theory because she felt that such ideas would simply get in the way of nurses' more important task – keeping patients and wards clean.

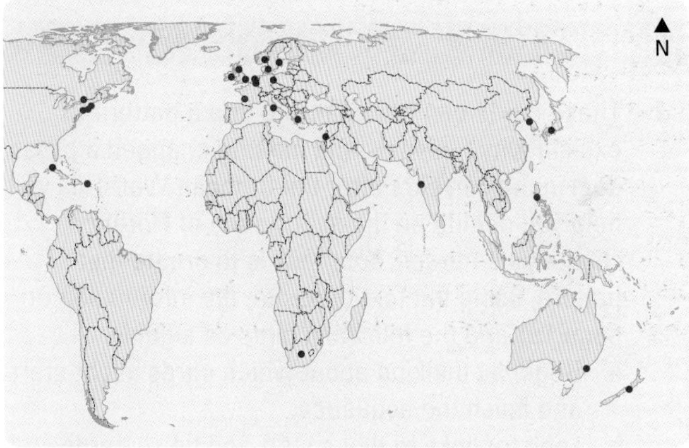

▲ The red dots on this map show the world-wide spread of nursing schools using Florence Nightingale's system of nurse education.

The impact of other factors on nursing and hospitals

Although Florence Nightingale's nurses were not taught about some of the major medical breakthroughs, these did affect their careers and the development of hospitals. The improvements in hospital buildings and sanitation could not have come about without improved engineering techniques and the new ideas about public health you read about in Section 8. Changes in surgery increased the numbers of complex operations and surgeons required better-trained nurses to assist them. Despite Nightingale's relegation of germ theory, it had a very significant impact on all aspects of medicine, including surgery, and in turn affected the ways that nurses carried out their work.

Activities

1. In what ways did Florence Nightingale change conditions in the Crimea?
2. What kinds of training did she provide for nurses at her schools?
3. Pencil in answers to your table from page 188, then complete the activity on page 192. Revise your ideas about Florence Nightingale's role in medicine.

What really changed hospitals and nursing?

Source 1

	1861	1921
Number of patients	About 65,000	228,500
Hospital beds per thousand people	3.2	6.1

▲ The number of patients and hospital beds, 1861 and 1921

Source 2

Problems in 1860	Solutions in 1920
Unhygienic surgery dressings	Aseptic surgery and dressings
Untrained nurses	Trained nurses
Cramped, stuffy wards	Spacious, light, well-ventilated wards
Poor sanitation and sewerage	Good sanitation, toilets
Lack of cleanliness	Cleanliness

▲ A summary of changes in hospitals between 1860 and 1920

Activities

1 These cards can be organised into a pattern to explain why hospitals and nursing changed a great deal in the 60 years after the Crimean War. This will help you decide on the importance of Florence Nightingale herself. Your task is to create that pattern, using the text opposite, the information on page 191 and the following hints as a guide:
- a Begin by thinking about which cards might start and finish the sequence.
- b Look for links to those start and finish cards.
- c Build up links – draw in lines on your own copy and annotate the lines, explaining why you have made the links.

2 Which of the developments on the cards do you think were most important in changing a) hospitals and b) nursing?

Florence Nightingale's work in the Crimea

The discovery that bacteria cause diseases

Increased public awareness of the need for clean hospitals and qualified nurses

Money raised for Nightingale fund

Mary Seacole's work in the Crimea

Developments in surgery such as anaesthetics and antiseptics

A wider range of operations and treatments carried out so the demand for good nurses increased

Better hospitals and better-qualified nurses

Improvements in engineering and public health

Florence Nightingale's books influenced training and the design of hospitals

Florence Nightingale set up training schools for nurses. These nurses showed their value, increasing respect for nurses and leading to more women becoming nurses.

Elizabeth Blackwell and Elizabeth Garrett Anderson

▲ Elizabeth Blackwell (1821–1910). Born in Bristol, she had to go to the USA to qualify as a doctor. She qualified in 1849 and later set up the New York Infirmary for Poor Women and Children, staffed completely by women. She also travelled back to Britain to encourage other women wanting to become doctors, including Elizabeth Garrett.

▲ Elizabeth Garrett Anderson (1836–1917), the first woman to qualify as a doctor in Britain. You can follow her story through the activity below.

Activities

In 1852, a new law required all doctors to belong to one of the Colleges of Surgeons, Physicians or Apothecaries. All were closed to women.

3 Boxes A–D tell the story of women's fight to become doctors. Boxes E–H explain the different ways in which men tried to block women's progress.

Match up the boxes in pairs, showing how men tried to push back each advance by women.

4 Complete your table from page 188.

Box A

During the 1860s, Elizabeth Garrett worked as a nurse and then attended lectures at the Middlesex Hospital.

Box B

Elizabeth Garrett passed all the exams to qualify as a doctor. The final step before she could work as a doctor was to become a member of one of the Colleges of Surgeons, Physicians or Apothecaries.

Box C

In 1874, six women, led by Sophia Jex-Blake, completed the medical course at Edinburgh University.

Box D

In 1876, a law was passed opening all medical qualifications to women.

Box E

The Colleges of Surgeons and Physicians refused to allow women members which, therefore, stopped Garrett working as a doctor. She had to take the College of Apothecaries to court before it accepted her as a member. After that it, too, changed its rules so that women could not become members.

Box F

Male students at the Middlesex Hospital protested that Elizabeth Garrett should not be allowed to attend lectures.

Box G

For the five years after 1876, the Royal College of Surgeons refused to allow anyone to take exams in midwifery as a way of preventing women from learning alongside men.

Box H

Edinburgh University said it could only give medical degrees to men. The women had to complete their degrees in Dublin or Switzerland.

Mary Seacole (1805–1881)

Born in Jamaica, the daughter of a local healer, Mary became a very knowledgeable healer and midwife. She gained more experience in Panama, where she showed people how to deal with an outbreak of cholera, isolating patients and cleaning out dirt. She also treated gunshot wounds. In 1854, she heard about the Crimean War and travelled to Britain to volunteer her services to the army, but nobody would see her. She then paid her own way to the Crimea.

In the Crimea

Mary set up her 'British Hotel', providing food and drinks to the soldiers. She also treated sickness and tended the wounded on the battlefield. Her bravery in helping the wounded while fighting continued to make her hugely popular and highly respected among the soldiers.

Source 1

An extract from Mary Seacole's own life story *The Wonderful Adventures of Mrs Seacole in Many Lands*, 1857. In this extract, Seacole describes a typical day for her during the Crimean War.

'I was generally up and busy by daybreak, sometimes earlier. By 7 o'clock the morning coffee would be ready. From that time until 9 o'clock, officers on duty in the neighbourhood, or passing by, would look in for breakfast. About half past nine my sick patients began to show themselves. In the following hour they came thickly, and sometimes it was past 12 noon before I had got through the duty. That over, there was the hospital to visit across the way.'

Source 2

This article was published in *The Times* in September 1855. It is written by William Howard Russell, who sent regular reports to the newspaper from the Crimea.

'In the hour of their illness, these men have found a kind and successful physician, a Mrs Seacole. She is from Kingston (Jamaica) and she doctors and cures all manner of men with extra-ordinary success. She is always in attendance near the battlefield to aid the wounded, and has earned many a poor fellow's blessing.'

Source 3

An extract from a letter written by Dr Reid to his family in 1855. Dr Reid was a surgeon serving in the British army during the war.

'Here I met a celebrated person. A coloured woman, Mrs Seacole. Out of the goodness of her heart and at her own expense she supplied hot tea to the poor sufferers while they waited to be lifted into the boats [that took them to the hospital]. She did not spare herself if she could do any good to the suffering soldiers. In rain and snow, day after day, she was at her post. With her stove and kettle, in any shelter she could find, she brewed tea for all who wanted it – and there were many.'

After the Crimean War

Both Florence Nightingale and Mary Seacole played important roles in the Crimea, but those roles and their impact after the war were very different. Mary returned to Britain without money. Once again her skills and experience were ignored and her fame was brief, apart from among the many soldiers she had helped who always remembered her with affection. Ex-soldiers and *The Times* newspaper tried to raise funds to help her, but this failed when the organising company went bankrupt. After publishing her memoirs, she was better-off, but still nobody in Britain tried to use or learn from her medical skills. It is only recently that her work has received the acclaim it deserved.

Source 4

An extract from a poem published about Mary Seacole in *Punch* magazine, 1856, after Mary returned to Britain:

'She gave her aid to all in need
To hungry, sick and cold
Open hand and heart, ready to give
Kind words, and acts, and gold
And now the good soul is "in a hole"
What soldier in all the land
To set her on her feet again
Won't give a helping hand?'

Source 5

From an article in *The Times*, 4 September 2000:

'It is now emerging that the "Lady with the Lamp" was not really the best-loved nurse of the Crimean War. That honour belongs to Mary Seacole. It was she whom soldiers considered the true "Mother of the Army". While Miss Nightingale worked at the official hospital far from the fighting, Mrs Seacole set up her own supply store and medical unit just five miles from the fighting. While Miss Nightingale dismayed wounded officers by walking past their beds without even a word, Mrs Seacole went into the war zone armed with bandages and medicines, to look after the wounded.'

meet the examiner

1 (a) Choose **one** of the individuals below:
- Florence Nightingale
- Mary Seacole

Describe her work. *(4 marks)*

(b) Which of these individuals contributed most to the development of nursing in the nineteenth century? Explain your answer. *(8 marks)*

Activities

1. In what ways did Mary Seacole help soldiers during the Crimean War?
2. 'The effects of Mary Seacole's work were short-lived.' Explain why you agree or disagree with this statement?
3. Complete your table from page 188.

Section 10: Conclusions

This final section helps you look back across your whole course and make sense of the overall pictures of the history of medicine and health. The activities will help you revise effectively. But first let's go back to the very first question we asked and returned to on page 116 – why do we live much healthier and longer lives than in the past?

10.1 What do we owe our lives to?

'History is not the story of strangers, aliens from another universe; it is the story of us had we been born a little earlier.'

This is a wonderful quotation. It reminds us that we aren't any different from people who lived many years ago – after all, they were our ancestors. Way back in time, in the 1800s, 1400s, the Roman Empire, there were people with our DNA, people who looked like us, had the same colour hair or eyes, the same way of walking, the same energy or laziness!

But what if you'd been born in their time?

You now know that there is one very important way in which we are different from our ancestors. On average we live much longer, healthier lives. Let's take the example of one real family – John and Margaret Pepys and their children from the 1600s. John was an ordinary working man, a tailor who worked in London. They had eleven children, born between 1627 and 1641, shown below at their time of death.

Why do we live so much longer nowadays?

Activities

On page 116 we introduced these cards to bring in the question of why we live much longer, healthier lives than people in earlier centuries such as the Pepys family. Now it's time to come up with an answer.

1. Create your own set of cards then fill in the bullet points by listing the most important developments in each topic.
2. Draw the pattern of cards below onto a large sheet of paper, then mark in links between the topics, such as how the work of Pasteur and Lister was linked. Jot down a few words explaining each link you draw.
3. Do you agree with this pattern, suggesting that the development of germ theory, followed closely by Public Health, is the most important reason why we live longer, healthier lives nowadays?

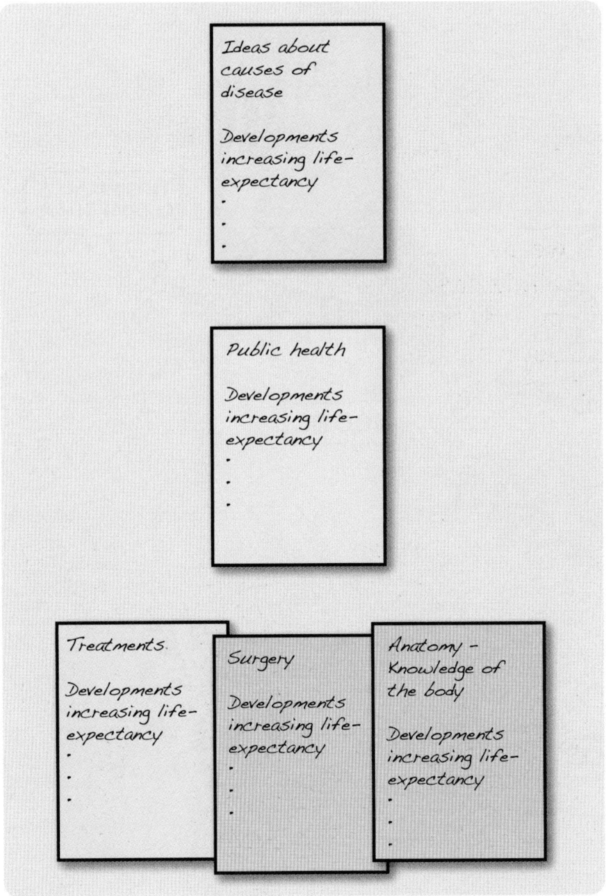

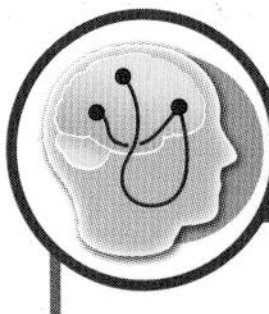

smarter revision reminder

In Section 1 we introduced you to a number of methods of building up the information you need to revise from. It was important to do this from the beginning so that you've done it steadily, in small chunks. Imagine if you were starting now from scratch on your revision notes! But you may have gaps or you may not have completed all the activities for the most recent periods of medical history – and you will need them to help with the activities on the next few pages! So make sure you are up to date with:

Living graphs summarising the development of major themes over time. See pages 6–7.

Memory maps recording the chief features of medicine in each period of history. See pages 14–15.

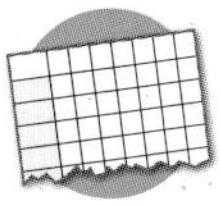

Factors charts recording the impact of factors that helped or hindered the development of medicine. See page 46.

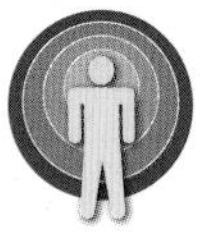

'Role of the individual' charts summarising the work of an individual and his or her impact. See page 27.

10.2 The road to Bacteria-ville – using road maps to revise key themes

Creating a road map is an excellent way of summarising developments across a long period of time. We have created this example for you as a guide. Can you use your living graphs to help complete road maps for other important themes?

Activities

1. This road map summarises the story of changing ideas about the causes of disease across time. Work with a partner or in a small group. You will have one minute to tell the story of this theme aloud to the rest of the class. Use the map to help you plan and tell the story.
2. Create your own road map for at least one of these themes across time:
   - a surgery
   - b public health
   - c treatments for disease.

   Think about how your map shows changes and continuities, pace of change, connections between topics, important people, reasons for change and continuity, ideas that got nowhere and any other parts of the story.

GODS AND SNEEZES SPREAD DISEASES
ONE PRAYER WILL STOP THE BLACK DEATH
RELIGION ROW
BACTERIA-VILLE
PEOPLE HERE SEEM TO LIVE A LOT LONGER
PASTEUR MANSION
KOCH HALL
SPONTANEOUS GENERATION VILLAS
I'M ALMOST THERE BUT I CAN'T GET IN YET
ROAD CLOSED UNTIL 1860
LANCET
I'VE TRIED ALL THE SIDE ROADS BUT I DON'T SEEM TO BE GETTING ANYWHERE
THIS COULD GET VERY TALL INDEED
BUT I BUILT IT UP AND MADE SURE ALL THESE PEOPLE CAME TO LIVE HERE
GALEN DRIVE
AD 1100
CHURCH SUPPORT ROAD
AD 200
DNA TOWERS
BLOOD STREET
PHLEGM STREET
AD 500
AD 1300
THOSE ANCIENT CHAPS WHO BUILT THIS ROAD GOT EVERYTHING RIGHT WHY WOULD YOU WANT TO LIVE ANYWHERE ELSE?

10.3 What was so special about each period of medical history?

Now it's time to think about each period of medical history – what made each period special and can you sum up each period by identifying its key features in just FIVE words or phrases? Dig out those memory maps and make sure you can remember the key developments in each period.

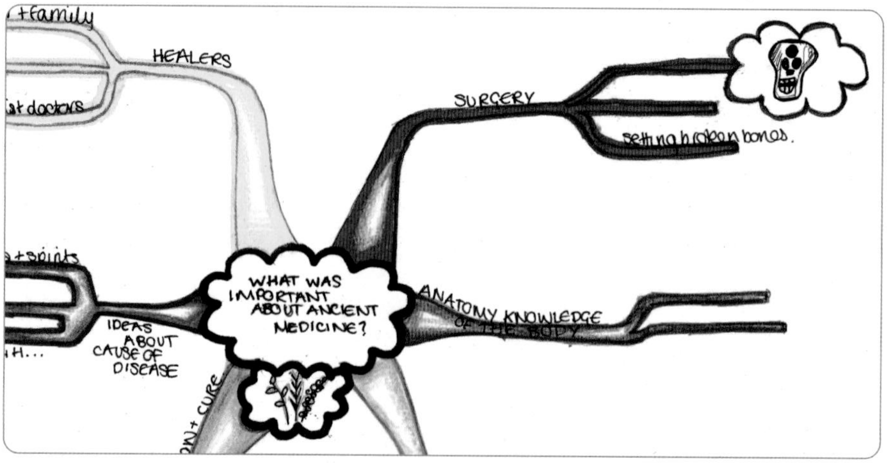

Activities

The period cards below and opposite sum up medical knowledge and methods in each period.

1 Create a new Word file or start a sheet of A4 paper for each of the five periods.

2 Put down the period name and the four headings below. Then note down the major features of medicine in the period under each heading, adding your own examples and details to support the outline on the cards.
- Understanding of the cause of disease
- Treatments
- Public health
- Surgery and anatomy

3 At the foot of each page, write:
  a the names of key individuals from this period
  b key features of life in the period that affected medicine.

4 Across the top of the page, write up to five single words, names or short phrases that sum up medicine in the period. To choose your words, names or phrases think about:
  a what makes this period different from others
  b whether this was a time of continuity or change (if change, how rapid was it?)
  c the overall significance of the period in the history of medicine.

5 Compare your five words, names or phrases with those chosen by the rest of the class. For each period pick out the best five words, names or phrases from the ideas put forward by the class.

Prehistoric and ancient medicine

1

Some important, long-lasting aspects of medicine began in the Prehistoric Period. These included the idea that gods and spirits caused diseases, simple surgery and the use of herbal remedies. While most people continued to pray to the gods to help them recover from illness, Egyptian and Greek specialist doctors believed that sickness had natural causes. Hippocrates developed the Theory of the Four Humours, which was further developed by Galen. Treatments included herbal remedies, prayer, bleeding and purging, and rest, exercise and diet. Most people had to look after their own health and hygiene but the Romans made a major effort to improve public health in military forts and towns by building aqueducts, sewers and public baths.

2

Medieval medicine

The destruction of the Roman Empire led to the collapse of Roman public health systems and the destruction of many books containing medical knowledge. However, everyday medicine for ordinary people continued unchanged, based on prayers and herbal remedies. In the 1200s universities were set up and physicians were trained, reading the works of Galen and Arab doctors such as Ibn Sina. Their methods were based on Greek and Roman ideas and so they believed that illness was caused when the humours were out of balance. Some attempts were made to clean up towns, especially after the Black Death in 1348. There were minor improvements in surgery as surgeons gained a lot of practice in war but, overall, new ideas were discouraged by the Christian Church.

3

Renaissance medicine

The Renaissance saw a battle between old and new ideas. There were some important new discoveries – Vesalius improved knowledge of anatomy, Harvey discovered that the blood circulates round the body and Paré improved surgical techniques. These discoveries (and the invention of the microscope) provided the basis for later developments but did not make people healthier. Many doctors were still hostile to new ideas and people still believed that God or bad air caused diseases. Governments still did not think it was their responsibility to improve public health. However, the idea of science being based on experiments and challenging old ideas was growing, providing the essential background for later breakthroughs.

4

Medicine in the 1800s

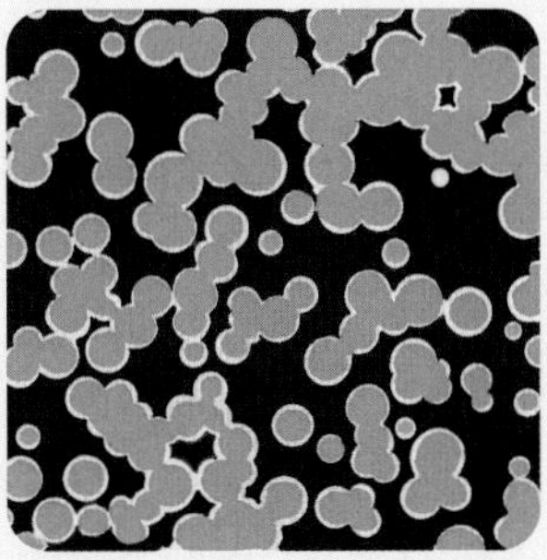

The major breakthroughs began. First came the use of vaccination against smallpox, which showed that opposition to new ideas was still strong but could be beaten. Epidemics of diseases such as cholera in the filthy, over-populated industrial towns forced governments to begin to improve public health. Then came Pasteur's germ theory, which at last explained the true cause of disease. From this came more vaccines to prevent diseases and major improvements in public health, which also benefited from improved engineering methods. Surgery was also revolutionised with the first effective anaesthetics and antiseptics. Hospitals became places to go to get well instead of places to go to die. By 1900 life expectancy was finally beginning to increase but there was still a huge gap between the health of rich and poor, and very high infant mortality.

5

Medicine since 1900

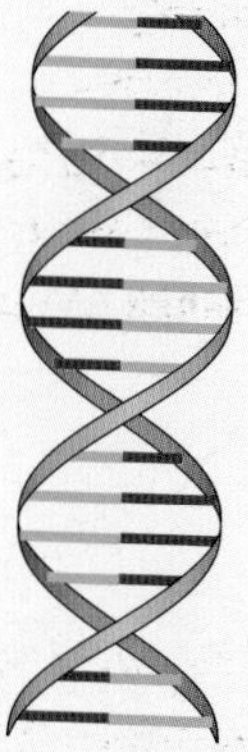

DNA

The 1900s continued the stories begun in the 1800s. Developments in science and technology continued to improve surgery and to help find the first chemical and antibiotic cures for illnesses and infections.

Wars also forced governments to invest more in these developments and to improve public health. They introduced better education, housing and public health provision, leading to the Beveridge Report in 1942 and the foundation of the National Health Service providing free medical care. In the 1950s scientists discovered the existence of DNA, the 'building bricks' of the human body, paving the way in the twenty-first century for the possibility of preventing inherited diseases – possibly an even bigger breakthrough than Pasteur's germ theory.

10.4 Which factors were most influential?

You have done a lot of work on factors – the reasons why medicine developed – or didn't – in each period. Now weigh up the overall impact of these factors and decide which factors were most important. This will not only help you revise but develop that very important skill – working as a team. It's amazing how a group of people working together can spark a whole host of good ideas that a person working by him or herself would have missed.

Activity

Your whole class is going to work as a team to reach a verdict on which factors were most important in helping and hindering the development of medicine.

Stage 1

Divide into pairs or small groups. Each group take one of the factors opposite and complete a 'washing line' (like the one partly completed below) for the factor. Use the details opposite to help your research.

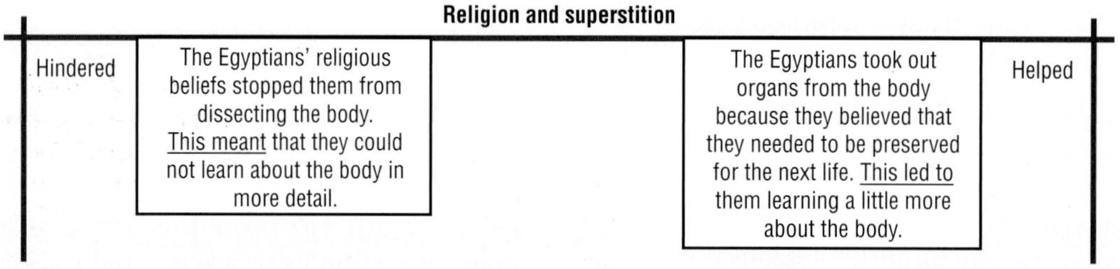

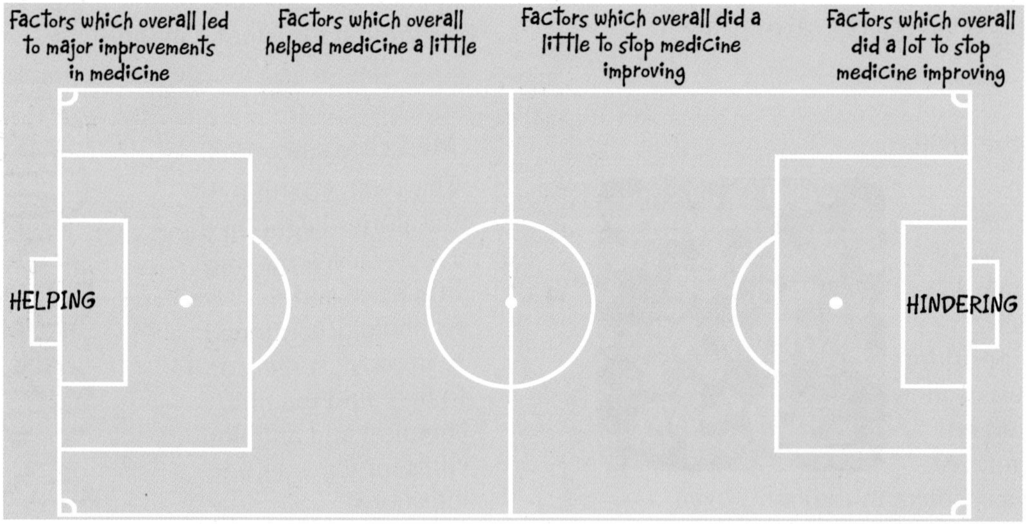

Stage 2

Decide where the factor should go on the pitch above. You need to weigh up the impact of the factor overall. Most of them will have examples at both ends of the 'washing line' so you have to think about their overall impact.

Stage 3

Repeat Stages 1 and 2 for one other factor. Then compare your conclusion about the factor with the group who researched the factor in Stage 1. Between your groups reach a final decision on where the factor goes on the pitch.

Stage 4

a Report back to the whole class on where your factor goes on the pitch. Your teacher will build up this plan on the board.

b Now debate which of the factors in the Helping penalty area did most to help medicine develop. Each group that researched these factors in Stage 1 has a minute to argue in its favour and 30 seconds to argue against its opponents. Then take a class vote on the winner.

c Repeat the debate for the factors in the other penalty area.

Get busy! What about the Romans and their Empire; Paré, Pasteur and Koch's rivalry; and blood transfusions? And the Boer War and World War Two, penicillin and plastic surgery, the NHS?
WAR
PORTABLE X-RAY MACHINE
Lots of gods, Egyptian hygiene, dissection, causes of Black Death, prayers to stop disease, Christianity and Islam, supporting Galen, challenging new ideas. Lots to do here.
SUPERSTITION AND RELIGION
KORAN
BIBLE
Pasteur said germs cause disease. So that means I can …
INDIVIDUAL GENIUS
GALEN
VESALIUS
JENNER
PASTEUR
KOCH
CURIE
NIGHTINGALE
The Romans and their army, kings and the Black Death, making vaccination compulsory, Public Health Acts, Liberal government reforms, funding research (or not!).
GOVERNMENT
BEVERIDGE REPORT
CHANCE
SURGERY BY PARÉ
Check up on Pasteur and chicken cholera and how Fleming discovered penicillin.
ATTITUDES
CONSERVATISM
THE CHURCH SAYS OLD IDEAS RULE!
ENQUIRY
NEW IDEAS ARE BEST ASK WILLIAM HARVEY
What about the people who bravely tried new ideas – Vesalius, Snow, Pasteur and all those people you listed who fought against those selfish vested interests?
Think about opposition to Harvey, Jenner, Simpson and Lister – and those good people who opposed public health reform. Long live vested interests!
SCIENCE AND TECHNOLOGY
Lots to research here – Greek philosophy, Roman engineering, printing, Renaissance inventions, Pasteur's industrial research, stopping the Great Stink, chemicals, X-rays and all kinds of modern developments.

10.5 Which individuals were most significant?

One of the key factors has been the work of individuals so let's complete these revision tasks by deciding on the greatest medical pioneer of them all. And make yourself a set of Top Trumps cards to help revision while you're awarding the gold, silver and bronze medals.

Role of the individual chart

Hippocrates

Hippocrates was born around 460BC and died around 370BC. He was a teacher and doctor on the island of Cos.

Activity

Below you can see some of the candidates for the awards ceremony at the Medical Olympics. Your task is to decide which of these medical pioneers get the medals. This is how you do it.

1 Work in a small group to create Top Trumps cards for key individuals in the history of medicine. Use your 'Role of the Individual' charts to help you.

a Decide which people to have in your list. Use the group below to set you thinking but look for some famous names who are missing.

b Decide what score each person gets for each of the criteria opposite and reach a decision about their overall score.

c Make your cards.

▲ GCSE students present the candidates for the 'Most Significant Individuals' award.

Use your criteria carefully!

What do the criteria on the Top Trumps card mean?

Originality – the highest marks go to people who did or thought something that nobody had ever done or thought of before. Lower marks for building on someone else's idea even if it was a great success.

Impact – how many people were helped or hindered by this individual's work? High marks for a worldwide impact, lower marks for a local impact.

Correctness – the highest marks go to ideas that were not only correct but people understood why they were correct. Good marks for correct ideas or methods when the individual knew it worked but didn't know how. And low marks for ideas that turned out to be wrong even if they lasted a long time!

Overall significance – use half marks if you wish – it might help separate all these star performers.

Longevity – how long did someone's impact last? The idea might be wrong but a wrong idea that lasted a long time was still very influential. What about a modern discovery that's not been around long? Do you think it will last? If so, then give it a high mark.

Activities

2 As a class compare your cards.
- **a** Did you choose the same people?
- **b** Did you give them the same scores?

3
- **a** Add up the class totals for each individual and see who is the winner.
- **b** Write short acceptance speeches for the top three, explaining why they won their medals.

Medical terms

ailment an illness that is not serious
amputation the removal of a limb by surgery
amulet a charm that the wearer believes gives protection from disease
anaesthetic a drug or drugs given to produce unconsciousness before and during surgery
anatomy the science of understanding the structure and make-up of the body
antibiotics a group of drugs used to treat infections caused by bacteria, e.g. penicillin
antisepsis the prevention of infection by stopping the growth of bacteria by the use of antiseptics
antiseptics chemicals used to destroy bacteria and prevent infection
apothecary a pharmacist or chemist
arteries blood vessels that carry blood away from the heart
arthritis the painful swelling of joints
Asclepion temple of the Greek god of healing Asclepius (or Askiepios)
astrology the study of the planets and how they might influence the lives of people

bacterium (pl. bacteria) see germ
bezoar stone a ball of indigestible material found in goats' stomachs
biochemist a scientist who studies the make-up of living things
Black Death a phrase used in the Middle Ages to describe bubonic plague. (The 'blackness' was caused by bleeding under the skin. Over 50 per cent of all cases were fatal)
bleed/bleeding the treatment of opening a vein or applying leeches to draw blood from the patient. Also means the loss of blood caused by damage to the blood vessels
buboes black swellings in armpits and groin that were symptoms of the Black Death

cauterise using a hot iron to burn body tissue. This seals a wound and stops bleeding
cell the basic unit of life that makes up the bodies of plants, animals and humans. Billions of cells are contained in the human body
cesspool/cesspit a place for collecting and storing sewage
charlatans people pretending to have a skill or knowledge that they don't really have
chemotherapy treatment of a disease such as cancer by the use of chemicals
chilblains painful swellings on feet and hands caused by exposure to cold and wet
chirurgery/chirurgeons surgery/surgeons
chloroform a liquid whose vapour acts as an anaesthetic and produces unconsciousness
chromosomes thread-like structures in the cells of the body that contain genetic information
consumption/consumptive fever tuberculosis which was observed as the wasting away of the body
contagion the passing of disease from one person to another
contaminated/contamination something that is infected
court an enclosed area of housing, often with little daylight and heavily over-populated
culture/culturing the growth of micro-organisms in the laboratory

diarrhoea a symptom of a disease; frequent, fluid bowel movements
dissection the cutting up and examination of a body
DNA Deoxyribonucleic acid, the molecule that genes are made of. See gene
dysentery a severe infection causing frequent, fluid bowel movements

effluvia/effluvial unpleasant smells from waste matter. Blamed for disease in the eighteenth and nineteenth centuries
embalm the treatment of a dead body to preserve it
endoscope an instrument used to view inside the body

faeces waste material from the stomach and digestive system

gangrene (gas gangrene) the infection of dead tissue causing, in the case of gas gangrene, foul smelling gas
gene part of a cell that determines how our bodies look and work. Genes are passed from parents to children
genetic engineering the investigation of genes and how they can be used to change how the body works
germ a micro-organism that causes disease
germ theory the theory that germs cause disease, often by infection through the air

Health Authority the people controlling NHS health care in the regions
herbal remedy a medicine made up from a mixture of plants, often containing beneficial ingredients
high-tech surgery surgery using the most modern techniques, including computers, new skills and new drugs
Hippocratic Oath the principles by which doctors work, for the best health of the patient and to do no harm, named after Hippocrates who wrote it
humours the Ancient Greeks believed the body contained four humours of liquids – blood, phlegm, black bile and yellow bile

immune protected against a disease
immunise the process of giving protection from disease through the body's own immune system
immunity protection against disease through the body's own defences or immune system
incision a cut made with a knife during surgery
infection the formation of disease causing germs or micro-organisms
infirmary a place where the sick are treated, a hospital
inoculation putting a low dose of a disease into the body to help it fight against a more serious attack of the disease

King's Evil see scrofula

laissez-faire belief that governments should not interfere in people's lives. It prevented public health schemes getting underway in the nineteenth century
leeches blood-sucking worms used to drain blood from a wound

leper someone suffering from leprosy, an infection that causes damage to the nerves and skin
ligament tough elastic tissue that holds joints of the body together
ligatures a thread used to tie a blood vessel during an operation
lunatic an old-fashioned word for someone who is insane

malady see ailment
maternity concerning motherhood and looking after children
medical officer a person appointed to look after the public health of an area
melancholy part of the theory of four humours, brought on by excess of gloominess
miasma smells from decomposing material that were believed to cause disease
microbe another name for a micro-organism
micro-organism a tiny single-celled living organism too small to be seen by the naked eye. Disease-causing micro-organisms are called bacteria

osteoarthritis see arthritis

papyrus early 'paper' made from the papyrus plant
patent remedy a medicine usually sold for a profit. In the nineteenth century patent medicines were often made from a mix of ingredients that had no medical benefits. They were also known as 'cure-alls'
penicillin the first antibiotic drug produced from the mould penicillium to treat infections
physic a medicine or the skill of healing
physician a doctor of medicine who trained at university
physiology the study of how the body works
plague a serious infectious disease spread to humans by fleas from rats and mice
pneumonia the inflammation of the lungs due to an infection
Poor Law Commission three commissioners who controlled the work of parishes which provided help for the poor. They were influential in public health reforms
poultice a warm dressing made of layers of fabric and moist paste
prognosis medical judgement about the probable course and result of a disease
public health refers to the well being of the whole community
pus a pale yellow or green fluid found where there is an infection in the body
putrid decomposing

quack a person who falsely claims to have medical ability or qualifications
quinine the drug treatment for malaria

radiotherapy treatment of a disease such as cancer by the use of radium
radium a metallic chemical element discovered by Marie Curie in 1898 (see radiotherapy)
remedy a drug or treatment that cures or controls the symptoms of a disease
rheumatism a term describing stiffness in muscles or joints
rickets a disease caused by a poor diet resulting in a misshapen skeleton

sanatorium a place where people who are chronically (very) ill can be cared for
scrofula sometimes known as the King's Evil. It is tuberculosis of a gland in the neck. At one time it was believed that being touched by the king could cure the disease
septicaemia blood poisoning caused by the spread of bacteria from an infected area
sinew a tendon or fibrous cord that joins a muscle to a bone
spontaneous generation the theory that decaying matter turns into germs
staphylococci bacteria found on the skin that can cause infection if the bacteria become trapped
sterilise to destroy all living micro-organisms from surfaces and surgical instruments, e.g. on a scalpel before an operation
stye a small pus-filled abscess near the eyelashes caused by infection
sulphonamide an antibacterial drug used to treat bronchitis and pneumonia
superbugs bacteria that have developed immunity to treatment by antibiotics or methods of destroying them by cleaning
supernatural something that cannot be given an ordinary explanation
superstition an unreasonable belief based on ignorance and sometimes fear
suppuration the formation and/or discharge of pus
suture the closing of a cut or wound by the use of stitches (sutures)
syphilis a sexually-transmitted disease that was common from the late fifteenth century until the introduction of penicillin

thalidomide a drug to help morning sickness that was withdrawn in 1961 after it was found to cause limb deformities in babies born to women who had taken it
therapy the treatment of either a physical or mental disease
transfusion the use of blood given by one person to another when a patient has suffered severe blood loss
trephining the drilling of a hole in the skull (also called trepanning)
tumour a swelling caused by cells reproducing at an increased rate/an abnormal growth of cells that may or may not be cancerous

ulcer an open sore on the skin
unpasteurised food or drink that has not been pasteurised. Pasteurisation is a process of heating that destroys harmful bacteria
uroscopy diagnosing illness by examining the patient's urine

vaccination the injection into the body of killed or weakened organisms to give the body resistance against disease
virus a tiny micro-organism, smaller than bacteria, responsible for infections such as colds, flu, polio and chicken pox

wise woman a person believed to be skilled in magic or local customs
witch/witchcraft a person who practises magic and is believed to have dealings with evil spirits
worms an infestation where worms live as parasites in the human body

Index